Environmental Management in The Colorado River Basin

A. B. Crawford and D. F. Peterson

Utah State University Press

Logan, Utah

ENVIRONMENTAL MANAGEMENT IN THE COLORADO RIVER BASIN

Environmental Management
in the
Colorado River Basin

Edited by

A. BERRY CRAWFORD
and
DEAN F. PETERSON

Published by
UTAH STATE UNIVERSITY PRESS
Logan, Utah
1974

© 1974 by Utah State University Press

Library of Congress Cataloging in Publication Data

Colorado River Basin, Environmental Management Conference,
  Salt Lake City, 1973
    Environmental management in the Colorado River Basin
    Sponsored by the Environmental Protection Agency and others.
    Includes bibliographies.
    1. Environmental protection—Colorado River watershed
—Congresses. 2. Water resources development—Colorado
River watershed—Congresses. 3. Colorado River
watershed—Economic conditions—Congresses. I. Crawford,
A. Berry, ed. II. Peterson, Dean F., ed.
III. United States. Environmental Protection Agency.
IV. Title.
TD171.3.C58764   1973   363.6   74-1212364
ISBN 0-87421-068-2

CONTENTS

Introduction

WORKSHOPS

RECREATION

RECREATION AND WORKSHOP SUMMARY

AGRICULTURE

Introduction

A. B. Crawford and D. F. Peterson*

The Colorado is probably the most utilized, controlled, and fought over river in the world. It flows through lands of incomparable beauty and includes nearly seven percent of the nation's contiguous land mass, including parts of seven states. From the time of early settlers to the present, the water of the Colorado River has been the key to development of the arid region.

At the present time, irrigated agriculture accounts for approximately ninety-seven percent of consumptive water use in the basin. Although the potential for additional irrigated agriculture is great and the demand for agricultural products will probably increase considerably in the years ahead, it is doubtful whether the basin's water-limited agriculture will expand beyond present levels. Two reasons stand out. The first is that few options still exist for increasing the amount of water in the basin and the efficiency of its use. The second is that agriculture must compete for the basin's water with growing urban populations and a developing energy production industry. If the basin's urban population increases 253 percent by the year 2000 (from 1.7 million in 1960 to 4.3 million) as anticipated, municipal water use will increase more than threefold. If the basin's vast store of energy resources are developed at levels and rates approximating even the most modest predictions, large amounts of water will be required. A million barrel per day oil shale industry would consume approximately 150,000 acre feet of water annually, and coal development in the Four Corners region is not expected to result in the consumption of lesser amounts.

*Co-Organizers of Conference, Respectively, Vice-President for Research and Associate Director of the Environment and Man Program, Utah State University, Logan, Utah

Because of the increased water use and the fact that the lower basin already is consuming Colorado River water in excess of its entitled amount, it is obvious that difficult planning and management decisions will have to be made in the near future. These decisions will affect not only the future of agriculture, energy production, and urban development in the basin, but also the quality of the basin's natural environment. Air quality in urban centers and areas adjacent to energy production facilities, salinity in the Colorado River, the effects of mining operations on scenic landforms and terrestrial and aquatic ecosystems—these are among the important environmental concerns that must be taken into account in future management decisions.

The chapters of this volume represent the proceedings of a two-day conference held in Salt Lake City on October 15-16, 1973. This conference, entitled "Environmental Management in the Colorado River Basin," explored the needs, conditions, and prospects for achieving a coordinated and basin-wide program of environmental management. The conference began with analyses by David Crandall and Gary Weatherford of problems confronting any basin-wide planning effort. Against the political and institutional perspectives provided by these first two speakers, Terry Davies and Peter House discussed the prospects of using environmental indices and the concept of carrying capacity in comprehensive planning.

Since aridity and the limited assimilative capacity of the basin's environmental media place rather severe constraints on the kinds and levels of development which the basin's resources are capable of supporting and sustaining, the concept of carrying capacity was selected as an organizing theme of the conference. Following the background papers referred to above, workshops were held on each of the following areas of development occurring in the basin: recreation, agriculture, energy development, transportation, and urbanization. Two position papers were written as a basis for discussion in each workshop. The position papers themselves were organized as answers to certain carrying capacity-related questions, viz.: At what levels will an area of development approach or exceed carrying capacity constraints? How does development in this area constrain or limit other kinds of development?

Following these individual workshops, a synthesis, "Carrying Capacity in the Colorado River Basin and the Allocation of Scarce

Resources among Competing Areas of Development," concluded the series. The position papers for this workshop were written by two interdisciplinary teams, one from Utah State University and the other from Colorado State University.

Three other papers are included in this volume. In one Cesar Sepulveda assesses the international implications of the problem of salinity; in another, John Busterud discusses the future of regional planning in the United States. The paper by Carl Braithwaite provides a glimpse of future directions in environmental legislation. And, finally, the selection by Wynne Thorne outlines research needs in relation to management problems in the Colorado River Basin.

CHAPTER I

Basin-Wide Planning and the Problem of Multiple Jurisdictions

Gary D. Weatherford*

THESIS: PLURALISM PRESENTLY IMPAIRS PLANNING

Let me give you the bad news first. The best-laid conceptions of environmental "carrying capacity" are no better than the institutions which must set and enforce the legal standards defining that capacity.

The institutional framework for effective, coordinated and comprehensive environmental management does not now exist in the Colorado River Basin. Such a framework for environmental management does not exist because dominant public institutions and private interest groups have had very little incentive to allow it to exist. The competition surrounding the natural resources of the Colorado River Basin persisted at a level too high to accommodate regional planning and management of the environment.

And if by some miracle an environmental super-agency were plopped down on the Basin tomorrow, or even next year, it could not govern. It might symbolize some noble aspirations and start the public conditioning necessary for the ultimate acceptance of some form of regional management, but it could not effectively regulate the forces that cause environmental impacts. It could not govern due to the diversity of values, interests and jurisdictions which now operate in the Basin.

Spirited pluralism is the order of the day and it cannot be blithely or quickly wished away, planned a way or re-organized away.

*Lawyer; Ferris, Weatherford and Brennan, San Diego, California

Now for the good news. The rampant pluralism evident in the Basin can yield to some meaningful levels of environmental management over time through the incremental evolution of a variety of planning approaches and institutions; but only if serious attention is given soon to improving the incentives for environmental planning. Such a progression of events probably ought not to be charted, or seriously influenced, however, until there is more disinterested and sustained study of the conditions and costs associated with institutional change in the Basin.

That, in brief, is the good and bad news I want to share with you this morning. Although I have past and present associations with institutions which have regulatory or research interests, respectively, in the Colorado River Basin, my comments are my own and are not offered as a position statement for any other person, group or institution.

CARRYING CAPACITY AS A BASIN-WIDE PLANNING CONCEPT[1]

This conference seems to be organized, for the most part, around the subject of environmental carrying capacity. The concept of carrying capacity is probably as good a vehicle as any to introduce some of the more evident prospects and problems of environmental management in the Colorado River Basin.

Generally, the "carrying capacity" of any given environment is not self-evident or self-enforced.[2] Mother Nature does not step out

---

[1]From a physical vantage point, the hydrological basin appears to be the most logical unit for environmental planning and assessment. I assume, without conclusive evidence, that environmental carrying capacity standards in general are best determined and implemented from a basin-wide perspective. This assumption ought to be seriously examined, however, as it may be politically necessary to commence environmental planning and management on a sub-basin scale.

[2]Justice William O. Douglas spoke eloquently of nature's need for human representation in his dissenting opinion in *Sierra Club* v. *Morton* 92 S. Ct. 1361, 1370 (1972):

Inanimate objects are sometimes parties in litigation. A ship has a legal personality. . . . So it should be as respects valleys, alpine meadows, rivers, lakes, estuaries, beaches, ridges, groves of trees, swampland, or even air that feels the destructive pressures of modern technology and modern life. The river for example, is the living symbol of all the life it sustains or nourishes—fish, aquatic insects, water ouzels, otter, fishes, deer, elk, bear, and all other animals, including man, who are dependent on it or who

from behind a tree and personally zap offenders, although she provides us with some memorable accountings of our mistakes from time to time.

"Carrying capacity," as I am using the term, is a management concept. It is not synonymous with the actual limits of nature. Rather, it is a construct reflecting human values and based on limited human perceptions of nature. It is a relative standard concerning the load limits of nature about which reasonable minds can and do differ. One person's minimum capacity is often another's maximum capacity. What to one observer is a residual margin for loading the environment may be a "red-alert" overloading of the environment according to another.

The relativity of judgment implicit in in the concept of carrying capacity highlights the important role that institutions must play in any environmental management strategy. Perhaps the most important question confronting us is not, *"What* are the most useful indices for determining the optimum parameters of carrying capacity?", but rather, *"Who* decides? Further, "How is the decision made?", "How is the decision implemented?" and "How is the decision enforced?" (I know you are not surprised that a lawyer believes the institutional facets of the problem are the most interesting and important!)

It is true, however, that carrying capacity standards for the environmental must be formulated, adopted and enforced by political and legal institutions. The threshhold between the exotic world of theoretical indices and the thicket of institutional decision-making must be crossed. It is often a painful crossing. When carrying capacity standards emerge, battered and bruised, from the political and legal process, often even their friends do not recognize them. Indeed, sometimes the standards never emerge at all—or only after a long period of confinement.

To illustrate the point, we need only observe the absence of numerical standards for total dissolved solids in the Colorado River. The Water Quality Act of 1965, as amended, provided a scheme for the formulation and enforcement of legal standards. Yet it has

---

enjoy it for its sight, its sound, or its life. The river as plaintiff speaks for the ecological unit of life that is part of it. Those people who have a meaningful relation to that body of water—whether it be a fisherman, a canoeist, a zoologist, or a logger—must be able to speak for the values which the river represents and which are threatened with destruction.

been clear to the Basin states and the EPA that the adoption of a numerical standard, such as 500 ppm, for the Colorado River would immediately give rise to a continuing state of non-compliance. Given such non-compliance, the EPA would have to take on all of the Basin states in a battle that would probably involve lengthy court tests.

The approach that has been taken instead is to fashion a remedial program that has some "development" overtones: (1) defer the adoption of standards,[3] (2) to seek a large-scale, federally-subsidized salinity control program,[4] and (3) try to reduce the salinity to a point where "realistic" standards can be met.

These responses to the salinity problem suggest that, interestingly enough, the institutional framework for decision-making may often be shaped by the subject matter that is being decided; that is, different types of subject matter call for different forms of decision-making.[5] "Development" decision-making, for example, appears to differ in many respects from "environmental" decision-making.

Environmental decisions increasingly tend to be made in a "regulatory" framework.[6] Decisions are made pursuant to legal standards that are designed to permit similar conditions to be regulated in a somewhat uniform manner. Water quality standards are an example. The application of legal standards in regulatory decision-making tends to create visible winners and losers. The competing interests in an environmental dispute cannot be compromised by

---

[3]See "Conclusions and Recommendations" of the Proceedings of the EPA Conference in the Matter of Pollution of the Interstate Waters of the Colorado River and its Tributaries—Colorado, New Mexico, Arizona, California, Nevada, Wyoming and Utah, Seventh Session Reconvened, April 26-27, 1972, Denver, Colorado, p. 169-173.

[4]See Sen. Bill 1807, 93 Cong., 1 Sess. (introduced May 14, 1973), a bill to authorize the Secretary of the Interior to execute a program of salinity control for the Colorado River. It calls for (1) the continuance and expedition of the "Colorado River Water Quality Improvement Program, February 1972"; (2) the construction of the La Verkin Springs, Paradox Valley and Grand Valley salinity control units; the creation of a Colorado River Basin Salinity Control Council; and the submission of biennial reports.

[5]See Dean Mann, "Political Incentives in U.S. Water Policy: The Changing Emphasis on Distributive and Regulatory Politics," paper given at the International Political Science Association, Ninth World Congress, Specialist Meetings on Environmental Public Policy, August 22, 1973, Montreal, Canada.

[6]See Theodore J. Lowi, "American Business Public Policy, Case Studies and Political Theory," World Politics, XVI (4) 677-715, 1964; also Mann, "Political Incentives in U.S. Water Policy."

simply putting together a bigger bundle of benefits. The contestants lobby and litigate against one another, and they engage in various forms of bargaining, but most often it takes a third party to resolve the conflict. Discord is part and parcel of this method of decision-making.

The major "developmental" decisions for the Colorado River Basin have not been made within a regulatory framework, but rather have been made within interstate political coalitions which have been organized to obtain federal funding and subsidy.[7] In this mode of decision-making conflicts between potential beneficiaries commonly have been resolved within the confines of the political coalition by "in-house" bargaining. Open conflict is not favored in this tradition of decision making.[8]

What I am suggesting here is that the subject matter of environmental carrying capacity presently falls more within a divisive "regulatory" mode of decision making than it does within a unifying "developmental" mode of decision making. Rest assured, then, that the entire institutional process of formulating, adopting and enforcing your environmental carrying capacity standards will involve vigorous bargaining.[9] The creation of a statutory scheme compelling an administrative agency to adopt carrying-capacity standards would be the result of legislative lobbying and debate. The adoption of carrying capacity standards by an agency will inevitably be preceded by bargaining. And, once the standards are adopted, another phase of bargaining—over enforcement—can always be expected. Throughout this process, from standard-setting to standard-enforcement, court litigation looms as an available mode of bargaining.

Since carrying capacity standards, in the last analysis, are no more effective than the institutions that formulate, adopt and enforce them, an understanding of the institutional complexion of the Colorado

---

[7]This phenomenon is exemplified by the legislative history of the Colorado River Storage Project Act of 1956.

[8]This is not to deny the occurrence of open conflict in the development history of the Colorado River Basin; witness the series of *Arizona v. California* lawsuits. Such protracted conflict represents a breakdown in the "distributive" mode of allocating resources. It is generally disfavored because it causes delays in the development and utilization of the particular resource involved.

[9]See Matthew Holden, Jr., *Pollution Control as a Bargaining Process: An Essay on Regulatory Decision-Making* (Ithaca, N.Y.: Cornell Univ. Water Resources Center, 1966.)

River Basin would seem to be a prerequisite for any serious proponent of refined environmental indices for the Basin.

THE MISLEADING FACTOR OF PUBLIC OWNERSHIP

From the vantage point of land ownership, the Colorado River Basin would appear to provide almost utopian possibilities for environmental planning. The 242,000 square miles of the basin are predominantly publicly owned and controlled. Federal ownership constitutes 56% of the land area, Indian ownership accounts for 16.5%, state ownership amounts to 8.5%, and private ownership constitutes only 19%.[10] (Looking at the federal land interests someone might even conclude that the Colorado River Basin has already been nationalized!)

What more could a planner ask for? No other river basin in the contiguous states provides such a public ownership base for planning. Why, then, hasn't the Colorado River Basin become an exemplar of rational environmental planning?

The answer is simple. The publicly owned resources of the basin are committed to fragmented objectives under an array of multiple-purpose programs. The politically and economically powerful beneficiaries of those programs currently have little incentive to support the growth of basin-wide environmental planning and management. The federal agencies which control the dominant share of the land, water, and air resources respond to the pluralism of the many local, state, and private groups which claim an interest in the natural resources of the basin.

Let's look briefly at some of the multiplicity of interests and values which impede basin-wide planning.

THE PROBLEM OF MULTIPLE JURISDICTIONS

Factor of Political Identity and Loyalty. The multiplicity of governmental jurisdictions represented in the Colorado River Basin is formidable: two nations, seven states, some thirty Indian tribes, about seventy counties and several municipalities.

---

[10]See Lower Colorado Region Comprehensive Framework Study (June 1971), Appendix VI, "Land Resources and Use," p. 49; Upper Colorado Region Comprehensive Framework Study (June 1971), Appendix VI, "Land Resources and Use," p. 14.

These political boundaries amount to more than a lifeless grid invisibly subdividing the region. They are repositories of social traditions, values, economic interests and political power. To a surprisingly marked degree people identify with political boundaries. Attempts to manipulate or circumvent these political boundaries under the guise of basin-wide planning will meet with resistance. Planners who overlook these political boundaries will imperil their plans.

The Important Role of the States. The multiplicity of states represents the single most powerful obstacle to basin-wide environmental planning.

Historically the seven basin states have tried to lay claim to as much of the natural resource base of the Colorado River Basin as possible on behalf of their citizens. And few issues have united the citizens within each of those states more than the issue of water resources and economic devlopment.[11]

The highest degree of interstate unity attained among these basin states has been developmental in orientation and essentially subregional in scope, reflected in the aggregation of states into upper and lower basins.

There have been a few instances of basin-wide unity among the states, but only where there has existed a mutuality of interest in the full utilization and development of the Colorado River.

Some twenty years after it was executed by the negotiators, the Colorado River Compact of 1922 was approved by the seventh basin state. Off and on since the late thirties the Committee of Fourteen, composed of two representatives from each basin state, has exerted some common influence on national water resources policy. The committee has recently come to life in questioning the new accord between the United States and Mexico concerning salinity control. Under the impetus of an EPA enforcement conference the seven basin states also reached agreement in 1972 on broad guidelines for solving the salinity problem.

---

[11]See Daniel J. Elazar. 1966. *American Federalism: A View from the States* (New York: Crowell, 1966). Elazar identifies "water resources" as the issue involving the greatest internal unity (vis-a-vis other states) in the states of Arizona, California and Colorado, but he notes that it is also the issue which generates the most conflict within those states. Economic development is the unity issue in New Mexico and Wyoming. *Supra*, at 16-17.

In the main, however, each basin state has operated either autonomously or through sub-regional coalitions. The upper basin states have succeeded to allot water by compact, rather than litigation, to establish on ongoing compact commission and to push the Colorado River Storage Project through Congress. But, again, the impetus for even this sub-regional showing of unity has been economic development and utilization, not environmental protection.

Conceptions of a basin-wide institution to coordinate planning and/or development have surfaced from time to time, but they have always been sacrificed before the altar of state autonomy.

The idea of a single interstate compact commission with authority to control and manage the Colorado River is older than the 1922 Colorado River Compact itself. There is evidence, for instance, that some of the compact commissioners had a permanent compact commission in mind when they first assembled for negotiations, but the political impracticality of such an expectation soon became apparent in the negotiations.[12]

Not even the planners of the New Deal could put the upper and lower basins together. Drainage basin committees were formed throughout the country to assist in the work of the National Resources Committee in the 1930's. True to form, the Colorado River was studied by two committees, one for the upper basin and one for the lower.

Perhaps the best illustration of the important position the basin states hold in any basin-wide planning scheme is found in the Water Resources Planning Act of 1965.

As you know, the planning act sets out a procedure for establishing river basin (and related land resources) commissions. Concurrence by one-half of the affected states is the normal requirement for establishing a basin commission under the act. As to the Upper Colorado River Basin, however, the act provides that "at least three of the four states of Colorado, New Mexico, Utah and Wyoming" would have to concur before a commission could be established.[13] Neither the upper nor the lower basin states have given birth to a commission under the Water Resources Planning Act.

---

[12]See Reuel Leslie Olson, *The Colorado River Compact* (Los Angeles, 1926), p. 25.

[13]Section 201(a), Title II, Water Resources Planning Act, 42 U.S.C. Sec. 1962b.

The planning which has occurred in the Colorado River Basin under the aegis of the planning act has further reflected the influence of the basin states. The Comprehensive Framework Studies, while very important, exemplify the political pluralism of the basin. Separate "regional" studies were done of the Upper Basin, Lower Basin and California.

The Role of the Urban Centers Located in Basin States But Outside the Basin. No analysis of the multiple jurisdictions affecting environmental management of the Colorado River Basin would be complete without an acknowledgement of the extra-territorial influence exerted by urban areas situated within the basin states but outside the basin itself. Phoenix and Tucson are the only sizeable domestic urban areas within the Basin. The influence of Los Angeles, Albuquerque, Denver, Salt Lake City and Las Vegas, respectively, has been manifest throughout the management history of the Colorado River Basin. This urban political power has filtered through federal elected politicians and various state and federal governmental units which have jurisdictional reach over the basin itself. State capitals, state engineer's offices, congressmen and the committees on which they sit, and various bureaus and agencies of the federal government have responded to the voting power of urban constituencies. The results can be seen in the exportation of water and power resources from the Basin to these urban centers.[14]

The Role of Federal Agencies and Programs. The mutiplicity problem is compounded by the staggering multiplicity of federal agencies and programs. The numerous federal agencies and programs operating in the basin were inventoried in the Comprehensive Framework Studies[15] and need little introduction to this audience. Suffice it to say they reflect a diversity of values and programs. Each of these federal agencies and bureaus has its mission as well as its constituency —its own set of private and public support groups.

Individual federal bureaus or agencies have assumed some leader-

---

[14]The recent action of the Los Angeles City Council in support of more stringent air pollution safeguards for one of its future sources of electric power, the Navajo Generating Station, may herald a growing public awareness that the enjoyment of resources exported from the Basin is paralleled by environmental degradation within the Basin.

[15]See Appendix III, Legal and Institutional Environments, Upper Colorado Region Comprehensive Framework Study (June 1971).

ship in coordinating interagency and federal-state planning efforts in the basin. But interagency rivalry and the absence of clear authority has prevented the development of a viable and sustained interagency planning effort.

Indian Tribes, Rural Towns and Counties. The multiplicity of rural political jurisdictions in the basin has and will increasingly present a challenge to environmental planning. Competition for economic development is a major thrust among rural Anglo and Indian populations in the basin. Coupled with this developmental philosophy, however, is a concern for the preservation of certain cultural and scenic values indigenous to the region.

One problem in the past has been that the inhabitants of the basin lack meaningful participation in much of the decision-making that affects their lives. With some exceptions, the rural Anglo and reservation Indian populations have tended to participate in only the latter stages of major decisions, acting without parity of information and without benefit of a full assessment of the social, economic or environmental impact of the proposed development.

If increased participation by these local interests in the management decisions is attained, of course, the multiplicity of interests in the basin will be heightened, not lessened. But that is as it should be. Those persons whose economic development has been deferred by virtue of being last in line, and whose living environment is directly affected by developmental forces penetrating the basin from the outside deserve to participate more fully in the environmental and developmental decision-making.

THE PROBLEM OF VESTED QUASI-PUBLIC AND PRIVATE INTERESTS

Quasi-public and private interests also impede movement toward basin-wide planning. Private rights have been created in most of the water, much of the mineral wealth, and some of the land and timber. The basin is laced with a multitude of patented and unpatented mining claims, mineral leases, water and power contracts, logging rights and grazing permits. Most of these private rights were created long before the era of heightened environmental consciousness. They are subject to being regulated or condemned in the public interest, but at a price. Even if the multiplicity of political jurisdictions were to be reduced, then, the multiplicity of private rights would have to be recognized as a factor in future planning. And in many instances these private rights are protected or asserted through public or quasi-public "districts" or private "associations" which can muster war chests to lobby and litigate when the need arises.

DEVELOPMENT PLANNING AS A SOURCE OF BASIN-WIDE UNITY

Although economic development has not yet provided enough incentive to homogenize the political forces of the basin, it may provide the basis for a basin-wide political coalition in the future.

Water is the key ingredient to the further exploitation of the basin's land and mineral resources. The big crunch between water supply and demand is already upon us from the vantage point of water quality; it will soon be graphic in terms of water quantity. Many variables, which have the potential of precipitating a water supply crisis, wait in the wings. An extended abnormally dry cycle, completion of the Central Arizona Project and other pending projects, satisfaction of federal and Indian reserved water rights, imposition of water quality standards requiring the maintenance of minimum flows, extensive oil shale development, widespread coal gasification, an aggravated energy crisis—any of these events could trigger an enforced reduction in water use.

Under those circumstances a basin-wide coalition of interests might arise in support of a mammoth water-importation project to augment the flow of the Colorado River.

In 1978 the ten-year moratorium on federal investigations of interregional water diversion schemes for the Colorado River Basin will expire. Irrespective of the enormous economic costs and potential environmental impacts involved, an attempt will probaly be made to gain Congressional authorization of a large-scale water importation project.[16]

Such a "physical solution" has enormous appeal in some quarters. It points to a way of avoiding tough management decisions that breed conflict, such as the further reduction of wasteful practices, the acquisition of vested water rights or the recognition of unpopular priorities.

---

[16]See, generally, Dean E. Mann, *Interbasin Water Transfers: A Political and Institutional Analysis* (Washington, D.C.: National Water Commission, 1972); also, Weatherford, "Legal Aspects of Interregional Water Diversion," 15 U.C.L.A. *Law Rev.* 1299 (1968).

It could also be represented as a project designed to meet the nation's obligations to Mexico and the American Indian.

Ironically, then, it may well be that the situations providing the most immediate incentives for a basin-wide management coalition are situations which could raise more environmental issues than they would answer. As anomalous as it might seem, the long-term interests of environmental planning and management in the region might be better served by perpetuation of fragmented decision-making than by a regional coalition or institution whose primary mission would be to solve water supply problems by augmentation rather than conservation.

Clearly the formal semblance of political unity is not the answer to the problem of multiple jurisdictions.

THE POSITIVE SIDE OF MULTIPLICITY

The present pluralism has some good qualities. There appears to be a growing public awareness, within and without the basin, that a range of significant values is at stake in the private and public decisions that are being made concerning the basin's natural resources. The very fact that conflicts over natural resource use are becoming more frequent and notorious reflects the fact that decision making is being subjected to more public scrutiny and review.

Environmental impact statements—while reflecting the disjointed nature of current environmental planning by failing for the most part to analyze either cumulative impacts or the broader sub-regional perturbations of local impacts—are giving the public more advanced notice of decisions than has ever been the case before.

Lawsuits, which admittedly highlight discord, are also serving an important function in this pluralistic process. Litigation may not be the most comfortable or efficient way to regulate the competition over resources, but it does provide a reasonably thorough and decisive means of solving problems not otherwise manageable or adequately dealt with in legislative halls and executive offices.

So, until a higher level of agreement and public support for environmental planning is achieved, its proponents must continue to work with segmented situations through a myriad of decision-making channels.

A PROPOSAL FOR INCREMENTAL CHANGE: CRB
INTERGOVERNMENTAL COORDINATION ACT

When I accepted the invitation to explain my views I thought to myself, "What a perfect forum for unveiling a proposal for a basin-wide interstate compact commission, amply empowered to comprehensively plan, monitor and control environmental impacts!"

As an intermediate institution that might be a stepping stone to a full-fledged basin-wide management authority, I had in mind a Regional Environmental Planning and Assessment Commission, composed of Federal-State-Tribal-Local Government representatives and containing two well-staffed agencies. First, a Regional Environmental Planning Agency would be charged with the duty of coordinating and developing a comprehensive environmental plan for the basin. Second, a Regional Environmental Assessment Agency would operate a basin-wide environmental monitoring program and make independent environmental impact assessments of all major actions in the basin.

The possibilities seemed intriguing and endless. Then I made a fatal mistake. I stopped to ask myself, "Can you imagine your native state of California, represented by some three dozen members in the House of Representatives (several of whom sit on the Interior and Insular Affairs Committee), knowingly taking a seat on a regional commission where its voting strength would be the same as Wyoming's?" Would Wyoming accede to allowing California to have more voting power than it would have?

I went on to ask myself, "If the incentive of economic development has not thus far resulted in a sustained basin-wide union of the states and other major interests of the basin, what hope is there that those states and interest will rally around the flag of regional environmental planning and management?"

It is enjoyable to dream up fictitious institutions that could alleviate complex and pressing problems if only given a chance. What is needed, however, is a strategy that starts with the here and the now.

We should refrain at this time from trying to fore-ordain an optimal institutional arrangement for the basin. It may be that a river basin commission, for example, is not the best model for the Colorado River Basin. More than two and a half dozen interstate compacts dealing with various facets of water resource planning and development have been undertaken during this century. Some seven river basin commissions are operating under the Water Revenue Planning Act of 1965. There has been considerable experimentation with these regional institutions in this nation.[17] Yet, river basin commissions have not produced an impressive environmental planning record to date, even in settings with less multiplicity of jurisdictions and interests than the Colorado River Basin. It is simply not clear whether the Delaware River or Sesquehanna River Compact Commission model,[18] for instance, could be transplanted successfully to the arid West.

The best immediate strategy for improving the posture of environmental planning and management in the basin is probably that popularized by Charles Lindblom under the rubric, "disjointed incrementalism." We should probably give most of our initial attention to institutional alternatives that are "only incrementally different from the status quo."[19] But in suggesting that the preferable form for institutional change is incremental, I want to urge that the rate of change ought to be rapid. The pace of change and development in the basin requires prompt attention to the deliberate improvement of environmental planning and regulation.

But incrementalism will not work without some economic incentives. Federal revenue sharing, conditioned upon participation in a regional planning and management organization, has been suggested as one possible economic incentive.[20] Another approach might be simply to provide direct federal subsidy, as repugnant as that might

[17]See National Water Commission, *Water Policies for Future, Final Report to President and to Congress of United States* (Washington, D.C., 1973), Section D, "Organizations for Water Planning and Management for River Basins and Other Regions"; also, Henry C. Hart, "Institutional Arrangements: River Basin Commissions, Inter-Agency Committees, and Ad Hoc Coordinating Committees," Legal Study 13 for National Water Commission.

[18]See Delaware River Basin Compact (1961) and Act of September 27, 1961, 75 Stat. 688.

[19]David Braybrooke and Charles E. Lindblom, *A Strategy of Decision* (New York: Free Press of Glencoe, 1963), p. 86.

[20]Dr. Helen Ingram, Government Department, University of Arizona, communicated this suggestion to the author. In her paper, "The Challenge to Multi-State Regional Organizations in Environmental Decision-Making," in *State Planning Issues* (Chicago Council of State Governments), May 1973, Dr. Ingram has identified certain criteria for effective regional arrangements: program integration, geographical integration, information generation, coordinative leadership, adequate representation, implementing actions and political viability.

be to the market economist. I hope that any subsidized beginnings could lead to a situation in which the costs of environmental planning could be internalized in some way.

With my assumption stated that economic incentives and incrementalism will characterize the basin's institutional future if regional environmental planning is to become a reality, let me give an example of the first incremental step that might be taken.

Congress might be asked to consider the enactment of a Colorado River Basin Intergovernmental Coordination Act. The act could be patterned to a degree after the Intergovernmental Cooperation Act of 1968 (82 Stat. 1098), which was designed to improve the coordination between urban-oriented state and federal programs. The act could contain a public declaration that the land, air, water, wildlife, wilderness, and recreational resources of the Colorado River Basin make it a region of unique national importance and, as such, it is the intention of Congress to foster the improvement of local-state-tribal-federal coordination of planning, development, and environmental protection in the basin. The act could provide for:

1. The creation and funding of an outgoing inter-agency policy review commission, composed of federal, state, tribal and local government representatives, charged with the responsibility of (a) reviewing current environmental management policies; (b) identifying conflicting and compatible local, tribal, state and federal policies; and (c) recommending uniform policies and guidelines for consideration and adoption by the various local, state, tribal and federal agencies.

2. The creation and funding of a program to promote the sharing of technical assistance and information, including the establishment of an integrated, basin-wide, computerized information system.

3. The creation and funding of an office of regional research responsible for (a) developing carrying capacity indices for the basin; (b) determining the feasibility and cost of a comprehensive environmental monitoring system for the basin; and (c) encouraging greater coordination and efficiency in the ongoing research efforts relating to resource allocation and management in the region.

Such an Intergovernmental Coordination Act would not replace the Water Resources Planning Act or the expected National Land Use Policy Act,[21] but rather would augment those approaches by trying to link the disparate sanctions and incentives which already exist for planning parts of the environment into coordinated whole for this particular river basin.

Conclusion

Let me summarize by emphasizing that simply counting the number of governmental jurisdictions within the basin does not disclose the true nature of the problem facing environmental management.

The major obstacle to basin-wide planning lies in the multiplicity of purposes and values represented by governmental jurisdictions and other interest groups within and without the basin. It is the diversity and distribution of political and economic power among these various institutional actors whose decisions affect the environment of the basin that holds the key to the future of basin-wide environmental planning.

It will take some imaginative and forceful incentives and sanctions to bring about an institutional alignment in which meaningful planning and effective management can begin to flourish.

Broad-based research delving into the institutional dynamics of the basin and examining various institutional futures for the basin is obviously needed.

So, my parting request is that you will list the social, political, legal and economic institutions of the basin as subjects needing serious research attention. Unless we speed up the transfusion of new ideas and information into our institutions, the current enthusiasm over enivronmental indices may be for naught.

---

[21]For a summary of the pending bills, see "*National Land Use Policy Legislation*, 93 Cong., An Analysis of Legislative Proposals and State Laws," Committee Print, Senate Committee on Interior and Insular Affairs (April, 1973).

CHAPTER II

Management Objectives in the Colorado River Basin: The Problem of Establishing Priorities and Achieving Coordination

David L. Crandall*

From its source in the Rocky Mountains, the Colorado River flows through some 1,440 miles of mostly arid and semiarid lands of the United States and Mexico to the Gulf of California. The drainage basin includes about 246,000 square miles or about one-seventh of the area of the Continental United States. Elevations in the basin range from over 14,000 feet to 248 feet below sea level at the Salton Sea. Through much of its course then, the river flows through a land quite deficient in water. It is, of course, a scenic land containing many national parks, monuments and recreation areas. Generally, the climate is healthful and stimulating, making it a good place to live if sufficient natural resources are available. Water supply and water quality thus influence the location and nature of human use of the basin. A number of large urban areas lying just outside the basin have, in their quest for water, reached out to the Colorado River for part of their supply.

The extensive use of water from the Colorado River, beginning with developments in the early 1900's, has eventually resulted in a river that is quite thoroughly committed. Although for many years no water from the Colorado River has spilled to the Gulf of Cali-

---

*Regional Director, Upper Colorado Region, Bureau of Reclamation

fornia, some upper basin states still have rights to develop additional water. So further upstream consumption will curtail even more present lower basin uses.

It is interesting to note that the last general history of the Colorado River was written in 1923. In that history the author, Lewis Freeman, included a chapter on the dams and other water developments that were then being planned. If a historian were to attempt now to write a complete up-to-date history of the Colorado River, he, for certain, could not do it in one volume.

I'll cover some of the factors, but you all know objectives and priorities result from a very dynamic interplay of interests within a complex framework of laws, rules, and traditions, but the process seems to begin with planning.

For many years Federal, state and other agencies have been working and improving the principles and standards used in planning water and related land resources. Most recently a revised set of principles and standards will apply to all new project proposals. The system of planning contained in the principles and standards has evolved as a logical response to merging shifts in public values on the role of water resources and its relationship to environmental and economic concerns. The pursuit of primarily economic parameters expressed as benefit-cost ratios is yielding to a concept of planning to meet the dual objectives of national economic development and environmental quality.

I don't have time to go into all the aspects of multi-objective planning here; however, the important distinction between this approach and conventional planning lies in the formulation of alernatives which reflect varying degrees of emphasis on the two objectives and the display of the alternative economic, environmental, regional and social effects and tradeoffs. For the decision maker, there will be more data, monetary and otherwise, than he ever had before. The full impact of each alternative and consequently the impact of his decision should be more easily identifiable.

Any large storage dam or reservoir on any river imposes controls over the flows below that dam. When Hoover Dam was built, the flows were controlled below that point. Now the flows are controlled below Glen Canyon Dam. But control implies responsibility. Water is not delivered solely for human purposes. Every management decision in operating a river must be consciously and thoroughly planned yet the complex of laws, agreement, and contracts do define choices. An example of this occurred in August and September of this year when releases from Glen Canyon Dam had to be severely curtailed because of a complex law that states that after other obligations have been met, storage in Lake Powell and Lake Mead will be equalized. Since Lake Powell volume was less than that of Lake Mead, the flows were cut back. River runners were inconvenienced by this decision. Also, we had to purchase high priced electrical energy from outside the basin to fulfill our power commitment.

It would be simpler, perhaps, if all the Colorado Basin had was scenery, but the basin has some of the nation's biggest sources of natural energy fuel beneath its colorful rocks, plains, and mountains. Although the nation has an increasing need for scenery, wilderness and open spaces, the need for natural energy fuels grows at an ever higher rate; consequently, we now find giant thermal steam generating plants either in operation or being constructed on the deserts. These plants are or will be using coal found in great abundance over much of the basin. The other resource needed is water—water in relatively large quantities. Although none of these dams were constructed for the specific purpose of providing water for thermal plant use, they do serve to help meet the basin's need for energy.

Other fuel sources besides coal may be given additional priority in the picture. Oil shale deposits, for instance, in the Colorado Basin are some of the most extensive in the world. Although intensive development of oil shale may not occur during the next two or three years, it would not seem likely that this vast deposit of fossil fuel would remain forever undeveloped. In the processing and the retorting of oil shale and for associated communities large quantities of water are needed.

One of these developers is now negotiating with the United States to obtain the needed water to further develop coal through gasification. The two plants now contemplated would deliver about 250 million cubic feet per day.

Development of other minerals requires water. One of these is trona which is found in abundance along the upper Green River in Wyoming. Right now four trona plants north of Green River are using Colorado River water.

Increasing use of water throughout the part of the Colorado Basin lying in the United States has of course, decreased the quantity of water left available for Mexico. In a 1944 treaty, Mexico was guaranteed 1,500,000 acre-feet each year but nothing was stated as to quality required. It has since been found that if only this amount of water is delivered to Mexico, the quality is often too low for it to be used for general agriculture. If more water were available, it could be released to dilute the salinity but no such water supply is available; the salinity problem has to be attacked directly.

Salt loading in the Colorado Basin comes from a variety of sources some natural, some man-caused. One of the largest salt sources is the very colorful Blue Spring which continually bubbles out 225 cubic feet per second of 2,500 parts per million of water into the Little Colorado and then into the Grand Canyon. Many other salt springs also contribute to the salinity problem in the Paradox Valley. Along the Colorado-Utah border the Dolores River flows over a huge deposit of natural salt and some of this gets into the water. Man increases the salinity of the river merely by withdrawing some of it so that what is left becomes more concentrated. Irrigation water picks up soil which finds its way into the river.

The Bureau of Reclamation is currently conducting an intensive water quality improvement investigation. This investigation is aimed at controlling point and diffuse sources wherever possible. It is also aimed at making irrigation agriculture more efficient so that less water is used and less salty return flow gets back into the river. Irrigation scheduling has been under way in the Grand Valley of Colorado for two years and a similar program is now beginning in the Uintah Basin of Utah, the lower Gunnison area of Colorado, the Colorado River Indian Reservation in Arizona, and the Palo Verde Irrigation District in California. Successful results of these projects will open the way for other areas where more efficient methods can be applied.

Recent negotiations between the United States and Mexico have resulted in an agreement which provides that the waters delivered to Mexico upstream from Morelos Dam will have an annual average salinity of no more than 115 parts per million dissolved solids greater than the annual average salinity of Colorado River waters arriving at Imperial Dam. To comply with this agreement, the United States is proposing a large desalting plant to treat the highly saline drainage water from the Welton-Mohawk Irrigation and Drainage District.

While all these other demands are increasing, other projects are being developed that will deliver the water directly to irrigators and to cities and industries. The biggest of these projects, still under development is, of course, the Central Utah Project. Further construction of the Bonneville Unit of the Central Utah Project is now awaiting decision by the Secretary of the Interior to proceed with authorized and funded construction contracts in the Uintah Basin.

Also, under construction is the Navajo Indian Irrigation Project which will deliver 500 thousand acre-feet per year from the San Juan River to the Navajo Reservation area south of Farmington, New Mexico.

The first water delivery from the Navajo Indian Irrigation Project is expected around 1976, but the amount delivered should go up as the canals are extended.

One of the largest reclamation projects to get underway recently is the Central Arizona Project, which will supply water from the Colorado River to the Phoenix and Tucson areas.

In addition to the present dams and projects on the Colorado River and its tributaries and to those under construction, there are also a large number of projects authorized but waiting funding. Although most of them are relatively small, their development would decrease available flows down the river and would certainly add to the water quality problems.

Rights of Indians within the Colorado Basin is of paramount importance. Many undeveloped and prospective water rights are for Indian use. Realization of the full range of benefits from a water right depends on construction of facilities necessary to put the water to use, and this construction depends upon Federal Government financing. Successful completion and operation of the Bonneville Unit of the Central Utah Project, for instance, depends upon an agreement which was worked out with the Ute Indians in the Uintah Basin in 1965. The Ute Tribe agreed to postpone development of their water until the year 2005 provided that facilities for their use could be constructed and in place by that time. From the Central Arizona Project the Indians on the Fort McDowell Reservation will receive both irrigation and municipal and industrial water. On the one CAP Reservoir that will cover part of their land, the Indians will be given special recreation privileges and public lands will be exchanged to them for the area covered by the reservoir. Animas-La Plata and Dolores Projects are authorized projects with important Indian relationships and values.

In addition to all these needs and demands for water, we have the need of recreation of fish and wildlife. This sometimes, but not always, means leaving water in a stream. Reservoir recreation has, of course, been increased tremendously by the addition of dams to the Colorado River. River running sometimes suffers somewhat, but the additional regulation provided by the dams has added to the river running season. Although power demands fluctuate throughout the day, reaching a peak in late afternoon and a low point somewhat after midnight, we try always to have at least 3,000 cubic feet per second flowing out of the Glen Canyon Powerplant, the minimum to prevent boaters from being stranded on the rocks in Grand Canyon.

Certainly it is easier to catch fish now and the fishermen come back with greater returns from the reservoir than they ever did from the muddy stream that preceded it. The Gunnison River, though, was a high quality fly-fishing stream partially covered by a reservoir. Losses do occur. Also there is increased quality fishing in rivers directly below the dams. In Utah the Division of Wildlife Resources has classified 62 miles of river as Class No. 1 Trout Fishing Streams. Almost all of this lies directly below dams. The complex question of fishery values involves considerable personal choice.

Water development projects affect wildlife most adversely. Mitigation measures are undertaken through development of refuges and replacement areas.

When possible, releases from Glen Canyon Dam in the spring of the years are kept fairly high so that Lake Mead will slowly increase in depth, at least not drop. This is to assist the spawning bass. We have no absolute commitment to make this release to Lake Mead but every effort is made to do so.

While I have not specifically referred to environmental concerns, I believe that they are implicit in practically every decision that we make. Looking at it another way, environment is not a separate priority but its consideration is a fundamental element throughout.

In summary, the priorities that the residents of the Colorado River Basin States assign to the use of water are in a state of evolution. In years past there has always been ample water for whatever use we wanted to make of it. There was, for example, plenty of water for all the land we could find to irrigate but this is no longer the case. As government agencies trying to obey the law and to fulfill our contracts and obligations, we cannot arbitrarily depart from the priorities that have already been assigned. We can in some instances make small managerial decisions that may provide assistance in a bad situation, but we cannot make any large changes. Basic changes and the setting of priorities must come from the expression of the will of citizens and organizations in local and state governments and finally in Congress.

I believe that we have an interesting future in store for us in dealing with the uses of the Colorado River, but it will not be without controversy. I believe, however, the controversies will be resolved and that the ideas obtained will help all of us to make the best decisions.

CHAPTER III

The Role of Environmental Indices in Regional Management

J. Clarence Davies, III*

I hope I will not startle anyone by beginning with the proposition that the world is a complicated place. Furthermore, it will not come as a great revelation that environmental management and the development of environmental policy is a particularly complicated undertaking. I hope that I can also count on agreement that environmental management and policy should be as rational and democratic as possible. Environmental indices provide one important tool for making a complicated world more tractable and thus for making environmental management and policy more rational and democratic.

WHAT ARE ENVIRONMENTAL INDICES?

Because it is useful to the audience, if not always to the speaker, to define terms at the outset, let me begin by describing what is meant by environmental indices.

An index is a quantitative measure which aggregates and summarizes the available data on a particular problem. There are many types and forms of indices. An index can be just a simple ratio, for example, the ratio of average ambient air pollution to a standard, or it can be a complex formulation involving a number of factors and a variety of mathematical manipulations. The nature and complexity of the index used will depend on the subject matter and the purpose the index is to serve. In short, there are three characteristics to an in-

*Resources for the Future, Inc.

dex: it is quantitative, it is a summary of the data, and it relates to some particular purpose or problem.

The best examples of the use of indices in making public policy come from the field of economics. We are all familiar with such economic indices as GNP, the cost of living index, and the unemployment rate. These quantitative measures summarize important aspects of the economic world. In the process of summarizing, a number of arbitrary and sometimes value-laden assumptions are built into the final economic indices, but their utility for policy making has been well proven and their use as means to communicate to the public is attested to by the daily papers and by the layman's familiarity with the terms.

In the environmental area, which for my purposes here I am limiting to the physical environment, indices have not received adequate attention. For the past three years, the President's Council on Environmental Quality has been promoting the use and development of environmental indices and, as I will describe later, this effort is beginning to show results. A large number of newspapers and radio stations have for several years used daily indices of air pollution, but the crudity of most of these indices only serves to emphasize the need for the development of better concepts and better data. On the whole, environmental policy makers have not devoted the effort necessary to improve the data base for making decisions or to summarize the data in a usable way. This is unfortunate for several reasons, which will become apparent if we examine the utility of environmental indices.

THE UTILITY OF ENVIRONMENTAL INDICES

For policy makers indices serve the vital function of making a large number of factors and bits of data comprehensible and usable. Indices can be an essential tool in developing policy apppproaches to problems, in assigning priorities among alternative programs and policies, and in evaluating the performance of a program or the outcome of a policy.

At least in the environmental area, the development of policies almost always entails considering a large number of factors. For example, Professor Harper's position paper on fossil fuels, written for this conference, describes 18 distinct types of impacts from power generation in the Colorado River Basin. These impacts are general categories, such as air quality, and thus there are numerous sub-factors within each category, such as each of the different types of air pollutants. If a policy is to be developed for dealing with the impacts of power generation it must take all those factors into account. This can be done in two ways. It can be done through large-scale computer modeling or through the use of summary variables, in other words, indices. Computer modeling is expensive and time consuming, and it is often mistrusted or misunderstood by those who have to make decisions. Thus, the use of indices may often be considered the preferable method for choosing a policy, although in many cases modeling and indices are really inseparable because indices are often based on mathematical models and, conversely, large-scale models frequently require indices as part of their input.

Inherent in the problem of dealing with a large number of factors is the problem of making trade-offs. All policy decisions of any consequence involve the sacrifice of some values to achieve others. Whether the method used is cost-benefit analysis, cost-effectiveness analysis, common sense, or intuition, indices can be of tremendous assistance in making trade-off decisions. They can provide this assistance in either of two ways.

First, by summarizing the key factors, they can tell the decision maker what the choices really are. If we had an index of air pollution and an index of water pollution, a policy decision which improved air pollution but lowered water quality could be evaluated in succinct, comprehensible terms which stated *how much* improvement in one factor could be gotten at *what cost* to the other factor. This, incidentally, is not a theoretical problem. Battelle Memorial Institute is now under contract with CEQ and EPA to develop indices which can summarize air pollution vs. water pollution trade-offs.

The second way an index can assist in making trade-offs is through the numerical "weights" often used in formulating environmental indices. An overall index of air pollution must assign certain weights to each component pollutant. It must be decided, for example, that SO_2 is twice as important or causes twice as much damage as carbon monoxide. Thus, if we have an overall air pollution index (or water pollution or recreation index), trade-offs among different pollutants can be made fairly readily. We could determine, for example, whether a policy which increased levels of SO_2 while lowering levels of carbon monoxide resulted in an overall improvement in air quality, as measured by the index. We would have a way of answering questions such as whether X dollars put into automobile emission controls would buy more air quality improvement than the same amount of money put into SO_2 stack gas controls.

Another major function which indices can serve for policy makers is in evaluating program performance. All too often, the success or failure of a policy is judged on the basis of the latest newspaper commentaries or the subjective testimony of a few random witnesses testifying at a hearing. In the environmental area, questions of program performance are often quite susceptible to hard, quantifiable answers. But such answers all too rarely are given because the necessary data is not collected or, when collected, it is not analyzed and put into index form, and thus remains incomprehensible to those who need to use it. We have more than 8,000 monitoring stations in the United States measuring water quality. And yet we cannot give any good quantifiable answer to the question of whether water quality in the United States has improved or become worse. Even questions like whether construction of a particular waste treatment plant or the holding of an enforcement conference have improved water quality are usually answered by a blank stare or by an unanalyzed ream of computerized data, full of symbols and numbers signifying nothing. The use of indices would not only give significance to the raw data, it would also make it more likely that the right data was collected in the first place.

This discussion assumes, of course, that the policy maker really wants to know whether or not a program has succeeded. Very often he does not. But the remedy for this does not lie in any tools or methods of analysis. Indices will only help those who want to help themselves.

The line between what I have been calling "policy makers" or "decision makers" on the one hand and the general public on the other is often exaggerated. At some future time, in some engineer's utopia, all high-level policy makers will be thoroughly trained in the use of computers, in statistical analysis, and in econometrics. This is not the situation now. The meritocracy has not yet fully arrived. The quantitative and technical skills of the typical congressman, state legislator, or upper-level bureaucrat are little different from those of the man in the street.

One of the key functions of environmental indices is to facilitate communication to the general public about environmental conditions. As Tom Thomas has said, "The major goal in development of indicators is a translation by a scientifically defensible method of the many components of environment into an optimum number of terms with maximum information content. To do this, we accept some reduction in precision, but in return we gain the ability to communicate."[1] The distinction between the function of communicating to the general public and the policy making functions is not a sharp one, because the language of the policy makers is often no different from the language of the public.

When the people ask questions like, "is the air quality in my hometown getting better or worse?", they are entitled to get an answer, not only so that they can perform their democratic duties of participating in the decisions but also so that they are not at the mercy of any office-holder or candidate who has his own personal answer. Only through the use of indices can we provide authoritative answers, because there is no other way of effectively communicating the complexities of environmental conditions to the layman.

The use of the set of indices which could summarize changes in environmental quality would raise the whole level of political dialogue about environmental matters. The dialogue now consists mostly of slogans and vague generalizations. Imagine what our political controversies over economic matters would be like without the existence of any economic indices. That is where we are now with respect to environmental discussion and debate.

The use of indices is certainly no panacea. It will not by itself solve any of our environmental problems. But it is a vital tool which can make the solution of these problems considerably easier than it is now.

PROGRESS IN DEVELOPING ENVIRONMENTAL INDICES

Over the past few years interest in the development and use of indices has grown considerably. As I noted before, the President's

---

[1] William A. Thomas, ed., *Indicators of Environmental Quality* (New York: Plenum Press, 1972), p. 2.

Council on Environmental Quality has been one of the major forces in promoting this interest. The council's 1972 annual report stated that, "One of the most effective ways to communicate information on environmental trends to policy makers and the general public is with indices." The first chapter of the report was entitled "The Quest for Environmental Indices." The Council has used its research funds to sponsor studies on the development of indices for air and water pollution, land use, radiation, pesticides, recreation, and wildlife.

Because the National Academy of Sciences has taken a strong interest in the development of indices, it is forming a committee which will undertake a preliminary study of the use of indices in the environmental field. The study is being jointly funded by the Council on Environmental Quality, the Department of Commerce, and the United States Geological Survey.

San Diego County has received a large grant from the Ford Foundation for an integrated regional environmental management program and a central part of this program will be development of a set of environmental indices. The first environmental quality indices for San Diego County already have been published.

In North Carolina, a Council on State Goals and Policy, composed of 14 citizens from across the state and chaired by the Governor, was established in 1971. One of its first tasks was to develop a set of environmental indicators. Some of these indicators will be published in a brochure intended for use by both the general public and decision makers.

Other examples of the use and development of environmental indices could be cited. For example, the Canadian Department of the Environment has completed the ambitious task of calculating a complete Environmental Quality Index for all of Canada. However, it has not yet been issued because of misgivings about its technical accuracy and its political ramifications. In the United States, an increasing number of banks, insurance companies, and other private firms are experimenting with environmental indices as one method for keeping tabs on the fulfillment of their social responsibilities. The fact that this conference is giving considerable attention to the subject of environmental indices is in itself an encouraging sign.

The requirement for environmental impact statements from Federal agencies should have proven a major prod to the use of indices but this so far has not been the case. The impact statements must focus on the question of trade-offs, and they are intended to be read by both the public and the non-technical decision maker. The use of indices thus would result in a significant improvement in the quality of the impact statements, but few agencies have employed them. Battelle Memorial Institute has provided the Bureau of Reclamation with a detailed and imaginative scheme for using indices in the bureau's impact statements, but so far as I am aware the scheme has not actually been put into use.

If we turn to particular aspects of environmental quality and ask what progress has been made in developing indices to describe those aspects, we find that progress has been uneven.

The area in which the most work has been done is air pollution. There exist almost innumerable air pollution indices of one kind or another, and some of them, such as those developed by the Oak Ridge National Laboratory and the Mitre Corporation, are quite sophisticated. Although major problems still exist in the development of a "perfect" air pollution index (if such a thing is possible), much work is being done and the state of knowledge regarding the possibilities and pitfalls of air pollution indices is advancing rapidly.

Water pollution indices present much greater problems. The large number of pollutants, the variety of uses to which water can be put, and problems of data collection all pose serious obstacles to the development of water pollution indices. The National Sanitation Foundation has been testing a proposed water quality index, and the results of the field tests appear promising. EPA has been using a "PDI" (for prevalence-duration-intensity) index of water pollution for several years, but the PDI index allows for considerable subjective input by the field personnel calculating the index values.

Land use indices or indicators are comparatively unexplored. The conceptual problems are very difficult because land use questions underlie so many other environmental problems. The Council on Environmental Quality concluded that, at least for many aspects of land use, it made little sense to try to develop national land use indicators, and that "most measures or indicators will have to be developed and applied by local, state, and regional authorities." This, I think, is a real challenge to groups such as those concerned with the Colorado River Basin. Can you develop ways to measure how land use in the basin is changing, whether it is changing for better or worse, and what the effectiveness of government policy is in changing land use practices?

Some work has been done on indices for other aspects of the environment. I have already mentioned work on wildlife, recreation, radiation, and pesticides. CEQ has identified more than 80 environmental factors which should be being measured, so there is a very long way to go before we have anything resembling a complete set of indicators or indices of environmental quality. Let me now turn to some of the obstacles to accomplishing this task.

Obstacles to the Development of Environmental Indices

Although good progress has been made in the development of environmental indices, there remain many difficulties in both their development and their use. These difficulties relate to conceptual problems, to problems of data, and to the users of indices.

There is a conceptual problem in terms of what aspects of the environment are of major significance. Our definition of what "the environmental problem" is changes constantly as we take steps to cope with the problems we recognize as we learn more about aspects of the environment and their interrelationships. This evolving process of definition must and should determine which aspects of the environment we seek to measure. As recently as five years ago would much time have been spent on indices of mercury pollution or even of land use?

An even more dificult set of conceptual problems arises when we consider the separate facets of the environment. An index, to be of maximum utility, should have a desired direction of change. In other words, when the numerical value of the index increases we should be able to say whether this is good or bad, other things being equal. This obviously brings a strong component of value judgments into an index, but then indices are essentially policy tools, and policy inherently involves the application of values.

The problem comes in the determination of what changes are good and putting quantitative values or weights on the "goodness" of particular changes. For example, in air pollution there is really no conceptual problem—we know that an increase in air pollution is "bad." But is there a threshold value of damage below which an increase really makes no difference? And how much do we weigh a change of a given amount of SO_2 as against the same amount of carbon monoxide? These are basic questions in the formulation of indices, but the scientific knowledge often is simply not good enough to give us answers in which we can have much confidence. In some areas, there are just basic conceptual problems. The best example is probably land use, where it is very difficult to come up with a set of measures capable of indicating desirable or undesirable change.

Data limitations are a severe constraint on the use of many potential environmental indices. I could discourse for some time of the shortcomings of existing monitoring programs in the United States, but I shall refrain. Suffice it to say that there are difficulties with site location, with collection methodology, and with the methods of analysis used. The most frequently discussed problem is the shortage of funds to start new stations and to adequately equip existing ones. This is a real problem, but all too often it ignores the question of what will be done with the data. The tendency to collect data for the sake of collecting data, to amass ten-foot stacks of automated readings and then leave them unanalyzed in some closet or file drawer, is, I fear, more widespread than we would like to think. It is essential that we know what analyses will be performed *before* we collect the data, and that data collection requirements be shaped by the needs of data use. Obviously, environmental indices are one such use. I hope that we will begin to see a trend toward moulding data collection to indices rather than the other way around.

Finally, there are the obstacles posed by the users of indices. There are a multitude of problems here too; I shall only indicate a few. I have already touched upon the possible reluctance of program administrators and policy makers to having an objective measure of program effectiveness. This is a real problem, and there is no solution except to get more sympathetic administrators and to keep the pressures on those who are unsympathetic.

Technical personnel also may have troubles with indices. Indices inevitably involve some sacrifice of detailed precision in exchange for being comprehensible. This sacrifice of detail bothers many technicians who are, after all, often the ones who collected the detail and thus hate to see it lost. Put another way, we can envision a continuum running from the raw data at one extreme to some grand overall quality of life index at the other. Many technicians are quite uncomfortable if they stray too far from the raw data end of the continuum.

Human whim and and ignorance are also obstacles which must be recognized. One of the best examples occurred in New Jersey where the State Department of Environment Protection developed a daily air pollution index for use by the newspapers of the state. The department went to great lengths to make the index easy to use. It was simple, graphic, easy to understand, and the department put it in a format such that all the newspapers had to do was plug in a couple of numbers and it was ready for printing in the next edition. About a dozen papers started using the index, but each of them used it in a form different from the other papers, and only one of the papers used it in the format which the department had gone to such great lengths to design. So much for the best laid plans.

CARRYING CAPACITY

The announcement of this conference asks the question, "What indices are most useful for analyzing trends and assessing the capacity of this arid environment to support additional development?" I would, therefore, like to diverge for a few minutes to discuss the concept of carrying capacity which is, in some respects, a possible framework for developing indices.

Carrying capacity is a very useful concept and its use is essential in many kinds of environmental planning. But it is also a concept of which I am very wary. It was originally developed to describe the environmental conditions or behavior of antelope, lemmings, and other sub-human species. Humans are in many respects just another animal, and we can never afford to forget it. But humans also have many characteristics not common to other living things, and it is the failure to take these other characteristics into account which frequently worries me about the use of the notion of carrying capacity.

Consider, for example, the geographic scale on which we are to measure carrying capacity. There is very little inter-herd trading among antelopes, to say the least. But humans today live in a complex interrelated world with a highly-specialized division of labor and system of exchange. The division of labor is geographic as well as social. For example, Dr. Thomas notes that the Colorado Basin contains more than seven acres of cultivated land per person compared with a need of only one acre per person. As he says in his position paper, "This represents a tremendous base and indicates our potential to supply other parts of the United States and other nations of the world." The national and international trading system allows this potential to be realized. Given the extent of international exchange and division of labor which currently exists, it is questionable whether human carrying capacity can be calculated on anything less than a global scale.

A second question that must be raised is that of life style. Human wants and values are almost infinitely varied. The differences between a Calcutta slum dweller and a member of the Rockefeller family are so great that it is hard to remember that they are members of the same species. When considering either what human demands are placed on some facet of the environment or in judging what the capacity of the environment is these differences in wants and values play a crucial role. Mr. Stankey puts one aspect of this problem well in his position paper on recreation: "Because *any* recreational use results in some change in the physical-biological regime, decisions regarding capacity must ultimately rely upon value judgments by decision makers." In short, determination of carrying capacity must almost always rest, explicitly or implicitly on some human value judgment, and this value judgment is not scientifically determinable.

A third set of difficulties is man's ability to change natural carrying capacity through his actions. Our technological powers are sufficiently great so that there are few instances where the purely natural capacity of an area is a realistic limitation on man's actions. There are, of course, some. We are not likely to develop a technology for "building" wilderness areas. But in most cases the social and political questions entailed in the application of technology are likely to overshadow the scientific questions of natural carrying capacity. In the Colorado Basin the limiting natural factor is water. But the key questions to be addressed by gatherings such as this conference are not whether there is enough natural supply of water. Rather they are questions of applying technology — should water be imported or exported, and so forth. These questions require scientific knowledge of natural limits if they are to be answered rationally. But they cannot be answered scientifically for they are basically political and value judgment questions.

If I were to summarize my concerns about carrying capacity, I guess I would say that it seems to me often to imply the idea of a strict limit, a scientifically ascertainable capacity which, if known, will determine policy decisions. The image is that of an elevator which has a capacity of 15 persons. If a 16th gets on the elevator, the cables will snap and catastrophe will ensue. I submit that almost *none* of the environmental policy problems we face are of this character. They do not involve strict limits but rather varying shades of gray. They do not involve scientifically determinable capacities but rather a host of political and economic tradeoffs. We desperately need the scientist's input, but such input is rarely decisive.

However, let me emphasize that I am not in any way opposed to using the concept of carrying capacity. It is an important and useful way of looking at many environmental problems. But it is a concept subject to much vagueness, abuse, and confusion, and therefore when we use it we should be very careful that we know what we are talking about.

ENVIRONMENTAL INDICES AND REGIONAL
MANAGEMENT

To return to the use of environmental indices, I think it is clear from what I have said that I believe that indices are a vital tool in the formulation of rational environmental policy. I should hasten to add that I do not consider "rational" and "scientific" to be synonymous. Important policy decisions will always be political—political both in the broad sense of involving the values of the society and in the narrow sense of being of a partisan struggle for power among competing interests. But decisions can be both political *and* rational. They can be rational if we use the knowledge and data we possess to narrow down the area of value judgment left to the political process. Indices provide a critical link in making such knowledge and data available to the decision makers and thus in sorting out what is legitimately determinable by the facts and what truly involves a conflict of values and interests.

Indices can be of great utility at the regional level. I have mentioned the advantages of the region as the level for formulating and using land indices, and most other aspects of the environment lend themselves well to measurement on the regional scale. But it is important to point out that indices are a *tool* for management or decision-making. If they are to be really useful there must be a capacity for managing or for making decisions. Regional indices will be of only passing interest if there is not also the ability to make regional policy. This conference represents an important step in making that ability a reality. I have no doubt that if we can overcome the obstacles that lie in the path of regional policy making we will find that the use of environmental indices will greatly assist in the formulation and evaluation of regional policy.

CHAPTER IV

*Environmental Carrying Capacity: An Integrative Management Concept**

*Peter W. House***

CAN WE GET THERE FROM HERE? THE CARRYING CAPACITY OF A REGION

Not too long ago a book entitled, *Limits to Growth,* appeared which has attracted more widespread attention from the educated community than any book in recent memory. Some of the critics of this effort feel that it has very little scientific accuracy. Nonetheless, the book does call attention to the shortcomings of many of our fondest assumptions. For years planning, both public and private, has practiced its art assuming a "fruitful" earth. Problems were usually touched in terms of efficiency. For example, a comprehensive or master plan was prepared for a community to answer questions of its ultimate size and the most efficient way spatially to distribute the people and their activities. A few of the better or more recent plans have included social amenities or other qualitative (or soft) goals. Few of the plans questioned the possibility of achieving their own goals. The purpose of this paper is to analyze the possibility of social and economic growth under conditions of available resources and with minimal environmental damage, and to describe a possible technique state of the system (SOS) — for accomplishing the analysis.

*Director, Environmental Studies Division, Washington Environmental Research Center, Office of Research and Development, U.S. Environmental Protection Agency, Washington, D.C.
    **The author wishes to thank Mr. Ted Williams of Chase, Rosen, & Wallace, Alexandria, Virginia, for his help in writing this paper.

With this preamble in mind, let us reflect on the goals of local and regional areas to provide the better things of life for their citizens. In the past few decades, our cities have greatly increased economically, but have often failed to provide benefits to the majority of the society. This need has been recognized and has resulted in the burgeoning appearance of the planning profession. The nation soon saw the appearance of the "master" plan and more recently, the comprehensive plan. The latter plan was envisioned as the way the community could (and should) take into consideration the total growth of its locale including population, labor, urban form, transportation, tax laws, and easement and land rights.

Today, we are beginning to question the very possibility of unlimited growth. Thus the comprehensive plans of localities need to be tested for validity in a situation in which resources are limited and environmental qualities have been established. That is, they must be related to a region's "carrying capacity."

Since we are concerned with defining and studying environmental carrying capacity, it is useful to begin with a description of ecological carrying capacity in the classical wildlife biologist's terms. "Carrying capacity is the ability of an ecosystem to support a given number of consumers and remain healthy and productive."

Population Characteristics of Species. Population dynamics are, of course, an integral part of carrying capacity. The growth of a species population will generally have the form shown in figure 1.

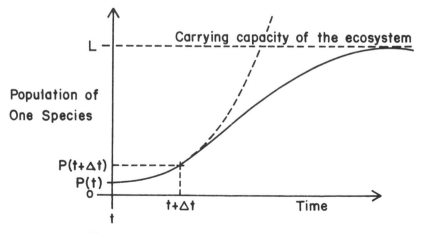

Figure 1. *Graph of a Species Population*

Under most circumstances population grows "exponentially," i.e., according to the formula:

$$P(t+\ t)=P(t)*\exp(r*\ t)$$

where $P(t)$ is the population at time t

    r is the net growth rate (births minus deaths)

    t is any time increment.

This relationship is reflected in the graph by the lower portion of the solid curve, and the dashed extension. Such an increasing trend cannot be expected to continue indefinitely due to limits in food supply and space, and to the actions of disease and natural predators.

The carrying capacity is variable and changing at both the community and species levels. Even when speaking of the carrying capacity of one particular species, one has to look at the entire ecosystem and the relationship of the population of the particular species to other species and communities.

Limiting Factors. The ability to identify limiting factors is important in determining the carrying capacity of an ecosystem. In proportion to the needs of an organism or a collection of ecosystem components the requirement that is present to the minimum extent is the limiting factor. Factors in an ecosystem that can be limiting include food, climate, space (e.g., land) in ecosystem, cover (habitat and protection), the extent of the ecological "niche," and water (amount and distribution).

The reduction in growth rate, as the carrying capacity (line L in the graph) is approached, can be approximated by defining a variable net growth rate using:

$$r=r'*L\text{-}P(t)\ /L$$

where r' is the unconstrained growth rate

    L is the carrying capacity.

When $P(t)$ is small relative to L, this relationship results in net growth rate, r, that is approximately equal to r'. On the other hand, as $P(t)$ approaches L, the net growth becomes smaller ultimately zero if $P(t)=L$.

Each species population in an ecosystem will occupy an "ecological niche"—a combination of species function and habitat.

A somewhat more complex treatment of population growth should, however, include consideration of the competitive drives among the species who inhabit a locale. As the carrying capacity of the locale is approached by any one species, the growth rates of all local species are affected.

RESOURCES OF THE HUMAN ECOSYSTEM

As suggested in the proceding section, the carrying capacity of an ecocystem is greatly influenced by the availability of resources and the manner in which they are utilized, especially by man. Thus a key element in the State of the System (SOS) Model is the treatment of resources. This section presents the concepts upon which the model's consideration of resources is based. Two of the anticipated contributions of the SOS model are the attempt to anticipate adaptive changes through substitution of resources of similar types (or strata) and by taking into consideration the discovery and delayed development of new areas of resources as a function of resource prices.

The idea of ecological accessability as a limitor has meaning in resource constraints also. Because resources are not distributed equally across the earth, the insulation of a society from catastrophe is a function of its access, via ownership or trade, to scarce resources of production. The possibilities for resource acquisition are numerous, and can result in changes in the population's growth rate.

The availability of resources at any particular time is the result of the interactions among the nature and size of man's requirements, the physical occurrence of the resource, and the means of producing it. Estimates of the future availability of resources, therefore, require the assessment of:

1. The particular combination of economic and technological conditions that determines present production,
2. the level of production that would take place under different economic conditions,
3. the level of production that could take place under different technological conditions, and
4. the nature and quantity of the total physical stock of both "renewable" and "nonrenewable" resources.

GROUPING RESOURCES FOR THE SOS MODEL

The State of the System Model essentially follows the traditional definitions of resources used in manufacturing and services. Along with the traditional list of six resource groups, the model includes two resource-like groups to permit consideration of the level of damage caused to the environmental media of air and water. Thus, the model treats the eight resource groups: energy sources, natural resources (durable ores), agricultural resources (food and fibers), land, workers, capital (including R & D funds), air, and water.

The eight groups can be divided into the categories of non-renewable resources (natural resources and energy sources) and renewable resources.

RESOURCE FUNCTIONS

The following general rules can be associated with all resources represented in the SOS model.

1. The available resources at any point in time can be associated with a unit procurement cost. This cost can be used in a number of methods concerned with the detection and the resolution of perceived resource crises.
2. At any period in time, the stockpile of a given resource in absolute terms is unknown. However, the quantities available as resource reserves at any unit procurement cost can be known.
3. For any resource, the indication of a perceived resource crisis is associated with preset stock depletion warning signals. These signals are set when the present resource stocks no longer can product a unit of the resource at the usual unit cost.
4. The resources of ores, foods, fibers, and land have resource strata within the general resource category. Energy can be viewed as a single strata. Within any strata the mix of associated resources used to make up a single unit of that resource strata is maintained without change unless a stock depletion signal occurs for a resource in that strata.
5. If a stock depletion signal for a resource or a strata occurs, a check of allowable substitutions is made to determine if

another acceptable resource mix or replacement (generally called a substitution) can be made that generates a lower unit cost. If this condition is met, the substitution process is initiated.

6. For any substitution process or change in input-output processes, the full change may require several time periods. The level of attainment achieved for each subsequent time period is calculated and the appropriate level of mixed strategy is used in production processes.

7. In addition to the expansion of a critical resource base by substitution (which is not only non-linear but asymtotic to some unknown upper limit), the availability of resource total stocks is checked to determine if the unit cost will cause a greater stockpile of the resource to be transferred to the reserve status. Such increments are carried out using a time delay function for activating the new reserve sources. Expansion of the resources of land and labor are subject to additional constraints in that labor must maintain its partition structure and the total amount of land is constant; hence expansion of one land or labor strata implies decreases in other strata.

8. The natural resources and sub-categories of other resources can include a recycling expansion of available ores. The rate of recycling is based on maintenance of a minimum unit cost from the complementary sources of extraction and recycling.

9. In its present form, the original source of transportable resources (ores, energy, foods and fibers) is not considered. The selection of stockpile levels and increments is a function of the price need to be calibrated to reflect the availability.

MODEL OVERVIEW

PURPOSE AND APPLICATIONS

The State of the System Model is being developed as an attempt to meld the growth desires of a population with the limitations of the locale in which the populace will continue to exist. To handle this growth vs. environmental paradigm, the model has been designed to test various assumptions about the desired growth of an area for a set of side conditions (boundaries, constraints, or thresholds). Feasibility is demonstrated if the desired growth can be achieved without violating the side conditions.

As examples of the side conditions, the model would translate higher level laws (federal and state, for example, if the model is of a local government), health thresholds, natural boundaries and the local desires into quantitative side conditions. Specifically, one could set values such as a minimum level of subsistance per family, a maximum unemployment rate, the various environmental standards, housing and other industrial-commercial codes, density levels and minimum education levels.

Implementation of this model would allow testing of both the present growth trend and potential variations. Such a model could be used to analyze at least three types of questions. First, it would be able to test the ability of the present growth trends to arrive at the time frame goals of the locale as defined by a comprehensive plan or similar goal statement. Secondly, it could allow the user to test the probable life of a system, in terms of years, and discover the most viable and critical linkages and constraints, given the resources of the locale and the constraints as set. Finally, analyses similar to the two above could be run using several different policy alternatives as starting points. Such analyses would determine the relative utility of each alternative.

STRUCTURE

The State of the System Model includes four major elements:

1. *Sectors of Growth.* This consists of three components: the population, measured in terms of physical needs—i.e., as consumers; the private production sector; and the public services sector. The two latter components are each measured in terms of level of expenditures maintenance and production—M & P funds—per year. The private production sector and the public services sector each can be subdivided into component categories (e.g., heavy industry or education services) with each category being an independent growth component. While the population growth is not divided into components, it can be partitioned into special need groupings in response to the relative levels of output by the components of the private and public sectors.*

---

*In the discussion these components are often called production components where production may be in goods or services.

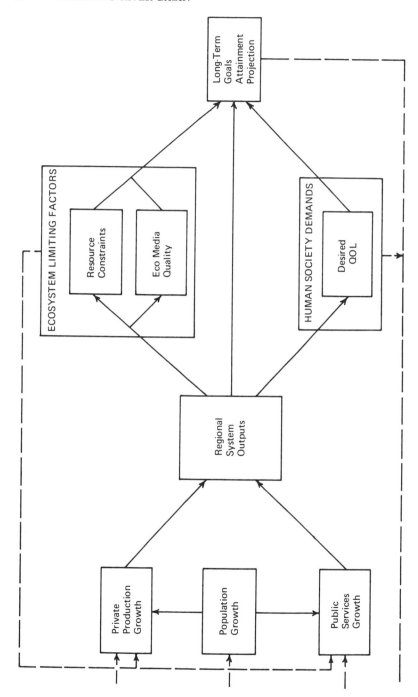

Figure 2. *Conceptual Form of the Model*

because the system reacts to shortages and "brownouts," such occurrences will be handled as system warnings which cause both short and long-run adjustments of resource supply, resource utilization and resource demands.

If the projected output of the system during a particular time period is within the tolerance limits set by the local carrying capacity then the model will continue to the next cycle. If the output demands are beyond the system output capacity, the projected growth rates of funds expenditures will be adjusted. This adjustment cycle will be repeated in future time periods until the projected output is within system limits. Throughout this process, the growth of the system in real output is compared against the stated goals of the inhabitants— the quality of life demand-measures.

The model also responds to the whim of political pressure and public fancy. In addition to the "rational" feedbacks of the model itself, it responds to exogenous perturbations. This algorithm lists the areas of public expenditure, (education, transportation, etc.) and checks to see whether each area has (1) recently had an infusion of public funds, and (2) is an area where more funds would have a noticeable effect on the Quality of Life. The resultant output from the algorithm is a vector of weights for each public services component as an index of popularity.

SYSTEM INPUTS

Total Production Growth. The model takes its impetus for iteration from yearly growth and development rates. The closer the regional system is to closure, the more the rate of change is endogenously determined. The efficacy with which the growth rates are changed by the feedback loops is the key to the success of the allocative portions of the model. However, while the growth rates can change, the total input to the regional system cannot. The total amounts of input funds available for a cycle includes two sources— the endogenous funds generated based on the past period production, ous funds could represent national to regional transfers and in some cases negative.

The exogenous funds are made up of two elements, the net exports balance which may be cumulative representing regional savings, and a cash transfer capability that is not wholly a function of the pre-

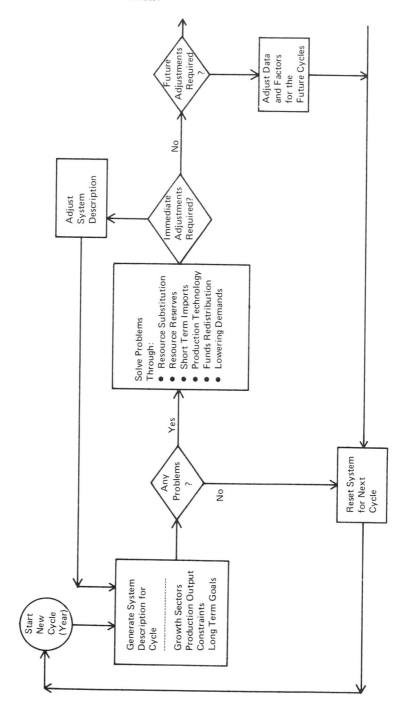

Figure 3. *Model Procedural Flow*

vious period. This second factor is set to vary based on a probabilistic range about an expected transfer value that is region-specific.

This level of regional funds sets an upper constraint on input to the production sectors and components for the current cycle. The process of funds allocation to production components is done subject to the condition: the funds of the components are equal to the total regional funds. The allocation process has two major steps. First, an expected allocation of funds is provided assuming that the relative growth rates set and adjusted for each component in the past cycle are followed. Additional growth or reduction of growth rates is introduced as functions of net exogenous-funds-available and the population preference for goods or services this cycle.

The Production Sectors. The sectors of regional growth, other than regional population, are the production and services components of the private sector and the public sector. The dimension of growth for both sectors, and hence their input to the system, is the level of funds used annually to procure and transform resources into capital and ecosystem maintenance* and sector production outputs (M&P funds).

Due to the need to partition the sectors into more meaningful elements, both the private sector and the public sector are divided into components that represent typical real-world subdivisions. For the private sector, production components are established; e.g., heavy-polluting industry, light-polluting industry, commercial goods and services, agriculture, and household-related industries. In the public sector, typical service components could be education, welfare, safety defense and administrative services, health and transportation/communication. In the model each of these components has related with it at a rate of yearly M&P funds growth.

As implied in the above formulation, the model is visualized as being responsive to changes in many parameters of the public and private sectors. The model takes direct notice of endogenous "rational" changes through the adjustment feedback mechanism discussed later. In addition, the model can also reflect exogenous and endogenous economic and political pressures and public fancy in relation to growth in the various components. Generally the latter will be reflected in the preference function of the growth rates.

The Population Sector. Population growth as such is not seen as significant in the sense of regional limits until it is related to territory—the larger the physical space in which the population is housed, the less pressure is exerted on the group in the sense of food and living space demands—other things being equal.

The limiting factor of population growth may not be land, food, organization or transportation as described in the society's own domain but may be caused when its growth intrudes on the territory of another society.

For the purpose of this paper, we shall assume that the necessary organizational structure required to support a given level of population will exist when it is required. Changes in population birth and death rates are outside our perview except when the level of life in a region reaches catastrophically low bounds. The model causes most variation in population growth to be because of changing area attractiveness. The actual primary rate-change mechanism is through the net migration rate.

Population Characteristics. The demographic structure of the population is of interest for two reasons. First, the population is grouped in two ages. This grouping allows a representation of the resource of labor in terms of level and ability of the regional population to expand rapidly the work unit supply based on production sector labor demands. Secondly, the population age groups are partitioned to determine the expected consumption rates of the population as affected by the size of the various partitions. Included in this process are a number of factors that can be correlated to the regional outputs to represent the present socio-economic level of the society. Typical partition characteristics include:

length of immaturity/educational time
rates of short-term and long-term infirmity
ratio of educational units to work units achieved in each age grouping
death rates by age grouping
size of worker force, further partitioned as:

employed, paid workers
unemployed, paid workers
workers not in paid status (housewives, volunteers)

The population characteristics are assumed to change directly with the production and services levels of the private and public sectors. These changes are shifts of population elements from one partition to another, e.g., from unemployed to employed.

SYSTEM OUTPUTS

The major measures to be used for system output are the expenditures of the various production components to produce the output. The input, i.e., the investments discussed earlier, include not only production funds but also maintenance funds.

Maintenance as considered here has three major elements and, thus, differs from the usual maintenance expressions that consider only offsetting plant and equipment depreciation. In addition to this capital depreciation offset, the model considers the ecosystem equivalent, i.e., the costs of effluent treatment. These eco-media treatment costs are assumed to be related to the component output level. The third maintenance element represents the annual rate of capital investment to increase the production facilities of the component.

It will be noted that the maintenance components are not constant over time. The depreciation offset cost is considered variable with time since these costs can be deferred for future times to allow a short-term increase in production funds. Expansion of facilities can change cost over time because of change in the costs of the resource. The effluent treatment costs vary over time based on the variation of overall media pollution compared to the system's natural regeneration.

STATE OF THE SYSTEM

The major measures of the state of the system are the levels of available resources and the level and quality of life. Only resource levels will be discussed in detail here. Development of appropriate formulations for quality of life measures is a major part of the future effort for the mode. The example model described in the next section illustrates one approach to QOL treatment as non-scaler system measures.

Resource Utilization. In addition to the utilization of capital funds and volumes of eco-media within the maintenance element of the expenditures, the outputs of the various growth components use resources in a production-transfer system that is postulated in the model as being directly related to the units of real goods output.

Effect of Technology on Resource Utilization. A major consideration for this more general form is the determination of when, and at what cost, technology changes are allowed. The model as conceived admits as future facts that institutional and technological change occurs. To provide for "idea(s) whose time(s) have come" requires an appropriate treatment of timing and impetus for change.

The procedure provided in the model for incorporation and scheduling of technological change is the cumulative expenditure of capital toward research and development. The model assumes that R&D expenditures for technological improvements in utilization of natural resources, energy resources, agricultural resources and land density are made at a rate relative to the level a component expends to procure the resource. These R&D investments are as cumulated for each resource category and as the threshold of the cumulated capital is passed to cause a technological improvement, the production processes for all components are then adjusted to reflect the input/output transfer improvement due to technology.

Effect of Consumer Preference on Resource Utilization. A second reason for changes in the input/output transfer function is a more gradual trend over the time limits of the model and represents the shift in production output mix demanded by the population to maintain a production level that is considered constant over time. Unlike the change due to technological improvement, this change and its resultant change in types of resources utilized is considered to be continuous and reasonably linear over a model run of one or two decades. For longer periods of analysis more complex functional forms may be represented.

Available Resources. A key feature of the model's consideration of resources is that the "available" reserve level is the amount that can be extracted (or otherwise obtained) at a relatively fixed unit cost (see the earlier discussion of resources). Thus resource levels can be increased by improved processing techniques or by accepting a higher unit cost. The latter process is discussed under System Adjustment that follows: Determination of resource availability levels for fixed unit costs are discussed below for the various resource categories.

Energy. At any time the total energy stock available to a region is the sum of the amounts of the various energy sources. At the present level of the model no energy utilization strata (for example, stationery vis-a-vis moving energy consumers) are made.

Natural Resources. Natural resources, like energy, are normally viewed as a non-renewable category. However, there are two important hedges in considering the actual stock reserve at any one time. First, for many of the ores a high level of substitution of other resources in the production process is possible.

A second hedge available to natural resources, but not available to any great degree in the most used energy sources, is the ability to recycle debris from processed and consumed goods to regain natural ore in the form of salvage. This procedure, tempered by the mobility of the various component products in passing from ore to goods to debris, sets a resource reserve that is once again variable by cost, i.e., the recycling costs that will determine the level of ore salvage from the system debris.

Land. Within a given region the total amount of land does not significantly change. The relative change in total land form is judged insignificant for consideration at the total stock perspective. However, land generation, when its specific utilization or worth characteristics are viewed, may require consideration due to its high intrinsic value to the local population.

Methods for expanding reserves of a land-use category are developed similar to other resources. The maximum potential for transformation at various cost levels is defined and, if added to the existent stock of land, represents the total stock level for a region at a given land cost. From these data a resource reserve generation procedure, as used in non-renewable resources, is possible. In this procedure land use succession is activated for a given land use type as the unused reserve reaches a stock depletion warning level. At that time additional reserves for that land use are generated by a minimum cost algorithm. The major difference in this category from ores is that generation of new reserves in one land use category requires its removal from others.

Agricultural Resources (Foods and Fibers). Based on research in the field of resource availability, a greater emphasis should be placed on the agricultural portion of the resource base, more specically, on its output, food and fibers.

Capital. Capital is also an important renewable resource used as an intermediate step between raw materials and final consumption.

Labor. Labor as a resource is measured in work units. The partition for paid workers provides at any time the instantaneous maximum labor supply level. The labor cost unit is a function of the rate at which this level is utilized at this time—the full labor force employment rate. Additional labor units can be generated as a function of this rate by transferring, in later time periods, work units from the population in training or in unpaid work activities.

Air. Unlike with other resources, the model is not concerned with the "level" of air. Rather, it is the pollution in the air which is of concern.

Water. Water, like air is measured in terms of pollution generated. This level is expressed similar to the air formulation where the parameters are defined similar to their air pollution analogs.

Level and Quality of Life. The major elements of the State of the System are measured in terms of societal perceptions—a set of judgments dealing with various components of level and quality of life. Our particular system must be area-specific, plus represent the planning system that would accomplish the adjustments of growth and output to achieve an acceptable state. Hence, only a general formulation of measures can be provided here. First, consider each of the two planning systems discussed earlier as they relate to these state of the system indicators.

In the first alternative—achievement of the comprehensive plan goals—the procedure is reasonably straightforward. Each goal by itself is a specific threshold to be realized. The relative importance assigned the goals in the plan provides a set of weighting coefficients to determine priorities in establishing tradeoffs, given that total achievement of goals cannot be accomplished. Thus the only requirement in setting of goals is to restate the goals in terms of parameters developed in the model operations. These parameters will be primarily measures of real growth; e.g., production component outputs as related to total system requirements, indicators in the form of per capita outputs, the rate of population growth, and size of specific population partitions.

The second alternative is the system that requires achievement of certain minimum values to achieve an acceptable state. It involves supplementary measures relating to the resilience of the system in remaining above the minimums. Each of the collection of measures has a dissatisfaction threshold and a resilience capability measured in terms of the relative level above the threshold. Unlike the first system, where the measures are generated directly from the comprehensive goals, a set of measures must be selected in terms of the area-specific needs and desires of the society in the region. The general forms of these measures will be similar to those of the plan above with the exception that a minimum acceptable value rather than a goal of achievement is set. Of greater difficulty is the setting of relative weights to combine the composite set of measures. However, this need not be accomplished. Instead an iterative process can be carried out, which measures the state of the system and then adjusts M & P fund levels among the production components until all thresholds are met. Given that this is accomplished, the determination of minimum resiliency and variance among the measures provides a useful statement of the health of the system.

An extension of the procedure of setting thresholds of minimum acceptable values is to have the threshoid values change based on population expectations. To account for this phenomenon, the thresholds of each measure can be set as a function of the historic (simulated historic) output trends.

System Adjustments

For any method of measuring the state of the system, if the present state is found unacceptable, a set of adjustments should be effected to allow future states to become acceptable. The adjustments are performed in the following order until the projected trends indicate acceptability:

(1) Short-term adjustments:
    (a) short-term deferral of capital maintenance and/or
    (b) expenditure of net export balances to achieve additional production output funds for the purchase of additional resources or the importation of goods
(2) Long-term adjustments:
    (a) changing input/output production functions to achieve the minimum cost mix for components contributing to unacceptable value

(b) reallocating the total projected M & P funds level within a sector to better balance projected growth rates and needed outputs of deficient components (The adjustment of RG9c, t-1) referred to in the formulation of system inputs).

(c) scheduling on a permanent basis the annual transfer of funds from one sector to the other and then repeating procedure (b). (This, of course, is used only if all components of one sector are not delinquent.)

(d) adjusting the rates and direction of net migration to reduce per capita consumption needs if significant unemployment exists in the region.

RESOURCE BASE ADJUSTMENTS

Finally, the resource base is melded into the general carrying capacity model.

If none of the long term adjustments produce a satisfactory correction of the projected state of the system, one final form of adjustment can be made to permit the model operation to continue. In this situation the system goals (for the plan analysis alternative) are modified to lower levels. This will allow a possibility of maintaining the regional growth projections at the cost of a less acceptable level and quality of life. Figure 6 illustrates the adjustment procedure. The

Finally, the resource base is melded into the general carrying capacity model:

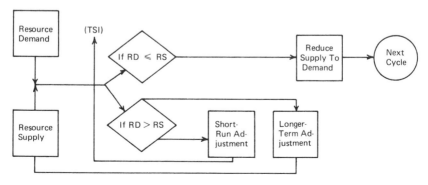

Figure 4. *Resource Base Adjustment Process*

final step is modified if time-variable threshold of QOL measures is used in the model form.

The systems reaching a natural limit to its carrying capacity may merely suggest a short-run imbalance of the demand and supply of a specific resource. This imbalance can be corrected by changing the rate of extraction and distribution of the resource in question. If, on the other hand, the reaching of a depletion symptom at a particular point in time heralds the beginning of a serious shortage of a particular resource, there are numerous possible responses:

The rate of extraction could be increased, despite increasing costs, increasing economically available reserves.

More supplies could be demanded from other regional systems at higher costs.

Make adjustment in the resource use by substituting a more available resource mix.

If these procedures to expand the base are not sufficient, demand must be changed by changing:

The population's demand function which drives the sytem input mix.

The growth rate of specific sectors in the system.

SUMMARY

In general terms the mode, described in its simplest form, will allow the user to iterate through time until one or another of the system resources is exhausted. This means that the system can be conceived of as having several limits or thresholds which will prevent its further growth. As one, or all, of the systems resources begin to be scarce and relatively expensive, there is a tendency first to skimp on maintenance to a given level and then to curtail growth. The indicators of public-private output levels compared to system needs begin to decline. Unless drastic steps are taken, the system may be in terminal decline.

This form of the model, however, is of limited use to local regions and to the policy maker who must make day-to-day decisions based on limited information. Consequently, the State of the System Model is seen to have a number of adjustment loops representing local reactions, permitting it to serve as a local policy device. In particular a large set of resource adjustment capabilities provide a better representation of resource constraints by using costs and economic substitution.

A model of this type can be used to test the operating or comprehensive plan of a specific region. The test is of the type which makes the assumption that either plan has teeth in it and that the region will make whatever adjustments are necessary to implement the plan. With this design in mind, the model iterates through time constrained by the desired end goal of the local inhabitants. Whenever a specific value (or series of values) at a time is out of phase with the desired plan, the model will adjust itself to refocus the iterations toward the end goal.

The questions addressed by the model then are whether the region has the capability of arriving at their desired goals given the existing problems and the area-specific adjustment processes.

CHAPTER V

Colorado River Management and International Law

Cesar Sepulveda*

As compared to other branches of international law, the law of international river currents had remained behind, almost static, with no evolution whatsoever. Its general theory only dealt with the functions of rivers for navigational purposes or as a boundary between two or more states.

Fortunately, this branch of law started to develop, making up for lost ground in the last three decades. During this period, a considerable body of conventional and consuetudinary law started to develop. It guarantees that the main problems between the nations served by these international rivers may be solved with precision and efficiency.

One might point out that Mexico, the United States and Canada have been the nations that have made the greatest contribution towards the development of new international river law and it might also be maintained that the Colorado River matter has specially given rise to quite a few institutions, methods and rules that have become a part of the international legal system.

The task of developing bilateral norms to regulate the use of the waters of three international rivers shared by Mexico and the United States has not been an easy one. However, the understanding,

---

Colorado River Management and International Law, President International Law Association, Mexico City

is important here is the existence of some contractual basis, which allows for flexible accommodations later.

But perhaps one of the positive achievements of the 1944 Water Treaty was the pursuance of the already existing Boundary Commission into a Commission of International Boundary and Waters (Artciles 2, 23, 24 and 25), and the assignment of new tasks to this body. For even though it did not grant it the authority or sufficient power to operate throughout the basin, it is a body that, through its operation, is likely to provide a source of new law from the pact itself. Furthermore, it is a body that, suitably enough, issues resolutions equivalent to third-party decisions, therefore each government feels less committed politically to approve such resolutions. Its recommendations, based on technical grounds, are easily attainable.

The Commission of International Boundary and Waters has operated since 1889, and has served as a conduit for adjusting by technical means differences that arise out of the operation of the 1944 treaty. This commission, whose fine work has still not been analyzed systematically and comparatively in international literature, offers considerable possibilities, since it allows technical solutions to governments, uncontaminated by politics. Such professional solutions permit the leaders of each country to avoid complicated diplomatic negotiations, replete with emotional burdens, public pressure, and partisanship. The problems of international rivers obviously require apolitical, tecnhical solutions, and it is obvious that a specialized, technical institution is better endowed for this purpose than the departments of foreign relations.

Since these inter-governmental bodies are staffed by experts, experiences can be shared and compared daily. Also, because of their propinquity to the problems, they become impartial, neutral bodies that observe difference from the point of view of adjustment, thus carrying out a disinterested public service.

Due to the particular functions that the Boundary and Water Commission have its resolutions when approved, are practically the equivalent of an executive agreement that does not require the complex intervention of the legislative branch in the form of approval or ratification, and whose fulfillment and execution are carried out singly by the executive itself.

In examining the various steps followed in solving the dispute concerning salinity in the Colorado River, one must surely recognize that it has been the work of the joint commission which has laid the groundwork for building a satisfactory technical, pragmatically acceptable, permanent and valid, arrangement.

Let us go back into history. In 1961 an unfortunate episode of saline discharge at Wellton Mohawk occurred, which caused vast damage around Mexicali. Mexico filed a diplomatic complaint in December 1961, accusing the other country of violating the 1944 Treaty. The reply of the United States was evasive and neither kind nor heartening, and the dispute became embittered.

Nevertheless technical judgment prevailed. All the water specialists agreed that the technical handling had not been correct. In 1965 the commission proposed an agreement, contained in Minute 218, which was accepted by both governments as a transistory arrangement for five years. The United States committed itself to building a channel for carrying saline waters coming from Wellton Mohawk pumping stations in order to keep them from flowing into storage dams. To a certain extent, the arrangement contained in Minute 218 represented a temporarily satisfactory measure. Furthermore, it implicitly constituted an admission of responsibility on the part of the United States with respect to the quality of the water to be delivered to Mexico. It likewise enlarged the content of the treaty. However, this meant an inequitable reduction in the water supplied to Mexico.

In 1972, both President Echeverría and President Nixon accepted Minute 241 of the Boundary and Water Commission. The saline waters would flow into the Gulf of California through the canal built by the United States in 1965. Half of that volume of unusable water would be substituted for equal quantites of useful water, usable water would be substituted for equal quantities of useful water, supplied in the course of the Colorado, thus reducing salinity to 100 parts per million. This constituted an advancement. It implies recognizing a fundamental principle of fluvial law, that the riparian downstream should be supplied with a liquid of the same quality as that received by users upstream. The principle of not accepting polluted waters is thus established. To a certain degree, it is an admission of the Mexican plea that the water treaty was not being fulfilled, since waters from the Colorado River were not being supplied according to the terms of the pact. Finally, Minute 241 is important because it consecrates the norm that is important in international rivers, water of a certain quality should be purveyed. The only unsatisfactory point is that Mexico lost 122 million cubic meters of Colorado water a year from its allotment.

Finally, in 1973, both governments approved Minute 242 of the Boundary and Water Commission, which provides new and acceptable technical reccommendations. It stipulates that Mexico will receive the full amount of water allotted in the treaty with a salt content of no more than 1,030 parts per million. In order to arrive at this, the United States has agreed itself to disburse over one hundred million dollars on a desalting plant upstream in Arizona and a canal that will run through Mexican territory to the Santa Clara swamp on the Gulf of California in order to discharge the Wellton Mohawk waters and the resulting brine.

As one can see, the commission has acted as a unique kind of clearing house for giving substance to the ideas of adjustment, encouraging technical measures to be taken along the course of the Colorado River, suggesting means of settlement, work construction, and the best use of the water current. I sincerely believe that the commission has been a significant factor in bringing about the final settlement regarding the matter of saline water in the Colorado, and that its powers for regulating the basin should be furthered.

The final settlement of the question of salinity, through Minute 242 of August 30, 1973, merits a few brief comments. It shows, in the first place, that Mexico and the United States are able to solve complicated problems regarding international rivers, including industrial contamination that might arise therefrom in the future, through friendly negotiations.

The settlement is quite satisfactory. In my country many people would have hoped that Washington grant a complete pecuniary indemnification for the loss and damages received by farmers in the Mexicali Valley due to the saline pollution, thus expressly recognizing that responsibility. However, we realize that under the current state of the international legal order, it is difficult to ensure a claim of this nature. The theory of the international responsibility of the state is still in its infancy. On the other hand, this demand has found certain satisfaction in the fact that the United States has formaly bound itself to provide non-reimbursable economic assistance "on a basis mutually acceptable by both countries" to rehabilitate the Mexicali argricultural zone, as well as supporting Mexico's efforts to obtain unrestricted credit at low interest and on a long-term basis. Washington's powerful influence in international financial institutions is a known fact, which makes this next to a reality. Looking at the settlement from another point of view, a probable indemnification has been substituted for a tangible reality of ensuring for the future the rightful volumes of constant and good quality water. Something aleatory has been converted into a certain and positive thing, through negotiation.

Another interesting aspect of the settlement is that both neighboring states agree to reciprocal consultations before initiating, any new development in the border zone of surface waters or underground waters or carrying out any substantial change that might adversely affect the other country. This practically eliminates any surprise damage, as the saline discharge from Wellton Mohawk in 1961.

Another aspect that has been taken into consideration is the future problem of the underground waters in the border area of Arizona and Sonora. A pumping limit of 160,000 acres-feet yearly has been established for each country, until a complete international agreement is reached concerning these waters. This would be the first time anywhere that an agreement regarding subterranean waters has been reached. When the pact is concluded, it will have strengthened the idea of the unitary international drainage basin, including the subsoil waters, which permits an integral management of the whole basin of the international river.

This is not the time to carry out an in-depth study of the agreement concerning the Colorado, although it does extensive and detailed analysis. But it can be pointed out that with this settlement an irritating cause of friction has been removed that affected the whole panorama of Mexican-North American relations, and a practical solution to the problem of damages inflicted has been found.

The settlement contributes considerably towards the sparse collection of international river law norms. Even though it be only implicitly, the principle of state judicial responsibility for man-caused pollution of international waters in detriment to the riparian downstream has been instituted in the agreement. This new and great principle of coexistence on international drainage basins—which is stated as *sic utere tuo*—is incorporated for the first time in a treaty by means of the resolution 242 of the Boundary and Water Commission on the 30th of August. Surely it will then become incorporated into other bilateral and multilateral international instruments.

No less important is that the principle of minimum quality of the water to be supplied in an international river to the state situated downstream is inserted in a compact, which will also be reflected in the future practice of international fluvial rules.

Another advantage is that the Colorado settlement offers brilliant technical solutions and suitable formulae for similar cases in other parts of the world.

The settlement fills in the lacunae of the 1944 Waters Treaty concerning water quality, which now remains defined and guaranteed for the future. In this fashion, future ambiguities and evasions in applying the treaty are avoided which might be prone to produce controversies.

And the most heartening thing here is that one can see in this settlement both countries' intentions to treat the entire Colorado River Basin, including subsoil waters, as an indivisible whole and integral unit, in order to make this great body of water yield the maximum possible benefit to the communities it serves, even though such communities are broken up or segregated by boundaries.

CHAPTER VI

The Future of Regional Planning in the United States

John A. Busterud*

For the first time in many years very basic questions are being asked about regional planning activities in our country and what reforms are needed to assure that they bring about more realistic results. And it is in the Colorado Basin that perhaps more progress has been made in cooperation and coordination of regional planning through the states than in any other part of the country. The compact among the Colorado River Basin States and the Federal Government for the use of water is a fine example of how sound regional planning related to specific problems can produce good results.

One of the recent publications of the Council talks about the "Quiet Revolution" in land use control which this country is undergoing. An important part of that "quiet revolution" is what is happening in the area of planning, both at the local level and on a regional basis. Many of the assumptions that planning has been operating on for a number of years have now come into question. People are beginning to wonder what real effectiveness planning has had in the past in this country. They are beginning to recognize that many other countries in the world have taken far more extensive steps to assure that the planning that is done is actually reflected in what happens on the land. For too many years in this country we have idealized planning and kept our focus on the future; when present realities did not

*Council on Environmental Quality, Washington, D.C.

live up to those plans, we simply decided that more planning was what was necessary. As a result, there is underway today in this country a sense that the planning that has gone on in the past has not been adequate, and that some very basic reforms are needed to make regional planning and comprehensive planning more than mere terms thrown out at conferences.

There are three important trends in this regard. I would like to give attention to each of these this evening. First, it is becoming increasingly apparent that regional planning can only be as effective as the regulatory mechanisms that are available to carry out the plans in the form of day-to-day decisions on individual development projects. To the extent that the planning process is removed from the political and regulatory realities of a given site, it cannot effectively predict or focus the important trends in community growth and development. At the present time this country is undergoing a major institutional shuffle in response to the public's recognition that planning and land use regulation must go hand in hand. This is not to say that regional planning requires that all decisions on land use and development be regional in nature. Sometimes the decisions are best left to local governments or small units combining several jurisdictions. What is important is that the planning that takes place be related to the development that is going on at the same time. There must be contact between those who are making the day-to-day decisions and those who are involved in predicting and planning for the future.

The second new direction for regional planning is related to the need to focus on the degree of growth that is expected and the best way to accommodate that growth. In other words, regional planning is moving from issues of "whether or not" and "when" to issues of "how much" and "where." This requires a keen knowledge of the factors at work in a given region which are going to produce growth and change and expression. At the same time, it also calls for the best kinds of judgments about where the growth should be located and to what extent it can be accommodated without destroying the very values that development is seeking. As an example, let me cite the tremendous expansion in recreational lot sales and seasonal homes which is occurring not simply in the Colorado Basin, but throughout the country. The issue is not whether or not everyone who can afford a second home should be able to have one. The issue is how to best accommodate the demand without destroying the very environmental values that people are seeking in a second home. In the State of Arizona alone, there are already more lots subdivided in the desert than are necessary to accommodate the entire predicted population for 40 years hence. The result is sprawl, inefficiency, and what can generally be characterized as the 'uglification" of the landscape.

At the present time the Congress is considering and is likely to enact legislation to establish land use policies in each state to assure that growth is accommodated in a way that protects environmental qualilty. The approach is to use the existing planning and regulatory institutions that we have, bolstered by a new and expanded role for the states, to bring about the kind of systematic understanding of growth that is required if we are to continue to grow as a nation and to provide a quality environment for our citizens. The bill calls for each state to designate environmentally critical areas where efforts need to be made to hold back on full scale development, to develop procedures for assuring that major growth-inducing facilities are placed in a manner that fully recognizes their potential for causing environmental degradation and development problems, and a method of properly siteing large-scale developments.

The third and final recent trend in regional planning is the growing realization of the importance of proper timing and construction of public facilites as a tool for pacing development. Let me give you an example of this. We used to think that when we built highways and sewers around the outskirts of our cities that we were providing necessary services for the development that was occurring there. We are now beginning to understand that to a large extent sewers and highways and similar public facilities can induce growth. To an increasing degree regional planners are beginning to learn that it is the pace at which public facilities are laid out that often times affects the ultimate quality of the development that occurs. For example, if sewers are laid too quickly they tend to cause sprawl and a spread of urban development throughout the countryside with little or no coordination of individual subdivisions. If they are placed too slowly, on the other hand, they do not provide sufficient services to growing areas and cause the wealthier to move beyond and to install septic tanks systems in their new subdivisions. This results in another form of sprawl. So we are beginning to learn that oftentimes it is the pace of sewers and highways and other development projects that is most important in determining what the quality of the ultimate environment that we live in will be.

Regional planning requires careful consideration of the resources in a given area, the limits of those resources, and the demands upon them. It is useful to examine some of the resource and demand problems of the Colorado River Basin in order to understand how regional planning can play a role in this problem of allocation. Let us examine, then, the problems that face the Colorado River Basin, keeping in mind the three trends in regional planning that I just enunciated—namely, the importance of regulatory mechanisms, the need to accommodate the growth that we know is coming, and the importance of properly pacing the installation of public facilities.

The availability of water is a focal point for development within the Colorado River Basin—industrial, municipal, and agricultural expansion are directly dependent on water, as are the services they demand such as power production, sewage treatment, and energy resource development.

With water being one of the limiting factors in the Colorado Basin, there is a need to recognize and address its use and conservation. We have become keenly aware in recent years of what overuse can mean—the Colorado has ended up with a severe salinity problem that has international implications with Mexico. While the Department of State and Special Presidential Assistant Herbert Brownell have negotiated a settlement with Mexico, the immediate costs accruing to the Federal Government will exceed $100 million and could well create significant new environmental problems. I will touch upon this in a minute, but first let's look at some of the factors in the basin that have contributed to the salinity problem.

Salinity increases have been attributed directly to irrigation return flows, for salt pick-up resulting from irrigation is increased when inefficient flood-type irrigation techniques are used. Conversely, irrigation efficiency increases when less water is applied per unit area to achieve satisfactory plant growth potential. Thus, in the water-short Colorado Basin techniques other than flood-type irrigation should be given high priority for implementation. Regional planning can serve as a useful and necessary tool in making these decisions.

Another issue, one of much greater importance and magnitude

to regional planning, is the extent to which additional irrigation acreage should be developed. Recognizing that each of the basin states has a specified allotment of Colorado River water under the compact, it becomes a question of water use priorities within each state. Agricultural benefits accrue to many western states through federally-supported irrigation programs. These need to be constantly re-examined to assure that they are in line with national objectives and the Administration's intent to reduce Federal spending. In general, regional planners should consider what is going on in other regions of the country before setting a priority on agricultural use of the scarce water resources of the Colorado. They might find in doing so, for example, that the Midwestern "bread basket" of our Nation has the agricultural potential to serve many of our national food needs—even in light of the current shortages of some food items—and can do so in a more efficient manner than is the case in many of the western states. If regional planners do not take this fact into account, they will be caught up short when Federal budget decisions begin to recognize this reality. More and more people are returning to the age-old concept—let the market place and agricultural competition establish where the production will take place. I am suggesting that a key issue for regional planners, particularly in the western states, is to take into account that over time they need to look to the market place rather than to Federal subsidies to determine agricultural production and to reallocate water priorities accordingly. Such a shift in priorities would aid in solving the salinity problems by freeing water now used inefficiently for irrigation.

Just what are more efficient uses of water? By efficient uses I am referring to those which are not totally water dependent and which do not involve high rates of consumptive use. For example, the Colorado River Basin is richly endowed with present and potential recreation opportunities. Maybe emphasis should be directed more toward capitalizing on this recreation potential. Maintaining lakes and free-flowing streams would be a focal point in developing these natural assets for public recreation use.

In addition, pressures for economic growth will continue to mount. The job of the regional planner will thus become one of weighing and balancing the competing demands, particularly for water. As urbanization occurs, environmental solutions should be built into the growth process. Adequate local and state land use regulation is essential. Air and water pollution should be dealt with before they become serious problems. To this end, the regional planner must provide the necessary perception and forethought to assure a satisfactory and protective growth policy.

Relating my foregoing points regarding the use of Colorado River Basin water to its implications for the regional planner, I might return to the salinity problem and the Mexican dispute. We have now committed ourselves to a solution of the salinity problem but we have made no definitive plans to assure that the salinity levels will not increase. In fact, the Bureau of Reclamation has predicted a major increase in salinity levels as planned irrigation developments in the basin are implemented and as the basin states begin to utilize fully their water allotment. Such projects as central Arizona and central Utah will remove considerable flows from the Colorado River, thereby reducing the downstream flows currently being accumulated in lakes Powell and Mead and released downstream to Mexico. Thus the salinity problem will be aggravated on two fronts—increased return flows from expanded irrigation and reduced dilution potential through a reduction in downstream flows.

The major feature of the current proposal to reduce the Colorado River salinity is a desalinization plant located on the Wellton-Mohawk Canal. A structural solution such as this might appear to set a precedent for other similar situations. But I believe that would be an erroneous assumption. The Colorado salinity problem has been resolved with Federal money because of its international implications. It should not be taken as a precedent for Federal funding to correct regionally-spawned problems in other areas. The solutions for those should be developed regionally and paid for regionally. Now admittedly, previous Federal spending for irrigation programs has led to the salinity problem, and it is not unreasonable that further Federal dollars should be spent to rectify the situation. But there is no assurance that the problem will not continue to worsen and possibly create additional demands for desalinization capacity.

We must break the Federal funding cycle and replace it with sensible priorities set through regional planning and adequate land use controls carried out through localities and states. Salinity problems will not be abated unless the region is willing to make the tough decisions about water allocation and irrigation. The days of Federal money to encourage practices which increase salinity followed by more Federal money to abate salinity are numbered. Strong regional planning, and effective and fair regulartory mechanisms in states and localities to carry out that planning, are what is called for to assure growth and economic prosperity throughout the region.

Now all of this is not going to happen over night. What is important is that we begin to think now about the kinds of institutional arrangements for proper planning and regulation of future developments within the Colorado River Basin. In this regard, the key concept is rationality. A system must be developed regionally which can set priorities, make allocations, and provide leadership and guidance to states and localities so that they may maximize their resources. The Federal Government should be called upon only when necessary, and every effort should be made to avoid using Federal money in ways that just create more problems in the long run. Otherwise we are in danger of developing an addiction that saps the vitality of states and localities to make their own way.

Much cooperation has already resulted in progress toward regional planning in the basin. But so far the effort has been primarily in terms of long-range projections and has focused on the process of planning itself. The new trends in regional planning will have the same impact in the Colorado Basin as they are having throughout the country. To go back to the points I made earlier, in at least three ways you will be facing in coming years a challenge to make planning work. First you will need to resolve the issues of who has the power to regulate the actual decisions that are made on a day-to-day basis by all levels of government. Second, you will need to develop mechanisms to accommodate the growth that is inevitable in ways that maximize the environmental conditions that result. And finally, you will need to use your money wisely, whether it is Federal, state, or local. The decisions you make on public facilities and other public expenditures will be critical in determining the future pattern and pace of development within the Colorado Basin. To make those decisions intelligently and in a timely fashion is a challenge that will be difficult to meet. But to fail to make those decisions will mean insecurity about the future, irrationality in the planning process, and continued dependence upon the Federal Government for ultimate solutions.

There is no debate over the fact that the decisions that face the Colorado Basin region in coming years are critical and essential to its continued vitality. It is also clear that many important decisions will need to be made on a regional basis. I feel confident, on the basis of my experience with the growing interest of the public in issues of comprehensive planning and land use regulation, that you have a real opportunity to take advantage of public support and enlightenment in a way that will permanently improve the quality of life for all of the residents of the Colorado Basin.

CHAPTER VII

Future Directions in Environmental Legislation

Carl Braithwait*

The conference managers asked me for a bit of "predicting" about environmental legislation. As anyone who follows the headlines can easily tell, 1973 has not been a good year for those who make their living by gazing into the crystal ball and telling us what lies ahead. Who would have guessed Watergate? Who would have guessed that the nation would now have a new Vice President? Nevertheless, in spite of better judgment, I will attempt to address some of the implications that follow from environmental legislation recently enacted or likely to gain approval in the near future. The list of potential topics is staggering: land use, strip mining, changes in NEPA and its requirements for impact statements, legislation that establishes broad rights of environmental class action, new protection for endangered species, legislation to rapidly develop new sources of energy, power plant siting—the list is almost endless.

Environmental legislation is a fast-moving area. Attempting to pin down its implications is a bit like trying to nail jello to a wall. An examination of the broad range of issues mentioned earlier suggests a conclusion not readily grasped by all, but one that merits a hearing: Environmental legislation that is now charged with being restrictive will actually benefit the long-term growth of the Colorado

*Representing Frank E. Moss, U.S. Senator from Utah

River Basin. Limiting pollution, limiting environmental degradation, and protecting and enhancing natural resources will actually preserve the potential of development and growth in the region.

ENVIRONMENTAL LEGISLATION—PLUS OR MINUS?

Legislation to protect the environment is often depicted as restricting opportunities, foreclosing actions, or eliminating options. These laws are often viewed as "taking away" something rather than "giving" something. Some who live in the basin itself are among the first to make such protests any time new proposals that bear the "environmentalist" tag come along. And they see such legislation as stopping action they would like to take. This viewpoint is very understandable, for many of the environmental groups proclaim such legislation as a tool for stopping, for halting, for eliminating, for outlawing.

I believe both sides in this argument are going to be surprised. Why? Because it is pollution that limits growh in most cases. Laws to restrict that pollution will therefore enhance growth potential. The crunch often comes in the short run, while we are adjusting to new requirements, phasing out old activities, and planning new ways of using resources while avoiding the bad side effects of previous practices.

Those previous practices have often made our society appear to be a little like the cartoon character "Mr. Magoo," who teeters along from point to point, oblivious of the virtual disasters continually crossing his path. The legislation now on the books and legislation currently working its way through Congress, will provide us with better tools to avoid those disasters. Let me give a concrete example.

Legislation to impose requirements on surface mining activities recently passed the Senate of the United States. Senator Moss proposed an amendment to that legislation which was successfully adopted on the floor of the Senate. Its intent was to require mining operators who were applying for a mining permit to outline in detail the effects their activities would have on the available water in the surrounding area. It also required extensive monitoring of water tables and surface waters, and required that any aquifiers disturbed by mining would be restored in a way that would enhance and preserve the recharge capacity of that aquifer.

To many this may have appeared as a "limiting" amendment. In the short run, it may do that. But in the long run, it definitely will not. True, a mining operator may be foreclosed from carelessly and quickly extracting coal resources by surface mining techniques, but to a responsible operator, this provision will merely cause some short-term delays while information is gathered to be submitted with the permit. If it turns out that he cannot mine the area without doing irreversible damage to the water resources, then it is essential for the long-run growth of the area to know that such resources would in fact be permanently damaged. To allow the damage to occur would curtail the long-run potential of the area and actually have a much more limiting effect on our options than would the restrictions placed on the miner when he applies for the permit.

Frequently our choice is to preserve long-run growth instead of promoting short-term booms. This is not really a limitation—it is simply wise planning.

There appear to be a number of unintended consequences accompanying environmental legislation. Many of these are going to be beneficial, in my view. In the process of moving to protect a new set of values, we have frequently started processes in motion that may heal some of the infected areas of our present social structure. As an example, I would predict that the requirements of many of our pollution control laws will in some cases help restore competition to the free enterprise system. Requirements for technology to develop pollution control methods will have the potential of breaking up what has come close to being a monopoly activity in some segments of American industry. It will be very difficult for some of the large sectors of the American industry to say that a certain clean-up job cannot be done when they find that a small research and development firm has not believed the propaganda spouted by industry for many years and has in fact done the job that was impossible.

The Environmental Protection Agency will this week begin public hearings on the status of sulfur oxide removal technology in the electrical utility industry. These hearings are very likely to reveal that the pressures of pollution control legislation has created new options that open up ways of controlling pollution, therefore, avoiding the necessity of halting the Kaiparowits Power Plant.

In a similar area, there is little doubt that the pollution control requirements relating to automobile emission standards have brought a new element of competition and diversity into the automobile market in America. If seen from the proper perspective, the concerns of the environmental movement have actually given a shot in the arm to the competitive factor in America's economic system.

Competition is healthy, and it is a positive fallout from environmental legislation which was enacted to reach other goals. Needless to say, the carrying capacity of the Colorado River Basin will be greatly enhanced if we keep our precious water from being inadvertently disturbed and lost and are successful in forcing the development of technology that would allow the use of coal without the accompanying destruction of air quality. These benefits are positive, not negative.

There are surprises for all in the fallout accompanying the wave of environmental legislation that has been brought forth in the last few years. Some of the voices contributing the loudest to the debate in recent years have trumpeted what is basically an antitechnology feeling. A surprise may be in store for these people, because the legislation they have pressed forward will actually help create new technology that will increase the carrying capacity in many parts of the country.

Let me give another specific example. Senator Moss has been pressing for years for a reversal of our wasteful patterns regarding precious natural resources. He has completed six days of hearings on broad legislation introduced by him and by Senator Hart to give much stronger impetus to recycling and resource conservation efforts. In the process of investigating this subject he uncovered a very interesting project being developed by the National Academy of Engineering, the National Aeronautics and Space Administration, and the Department of Housing and Urban Development. This is a joint effort to create a total "spaceship" community based upon the concept of integrated recycling systems.

This work is designed to produce an actual working small community patterned on the "closed system" used in space flight. Waste heat from electric generating plants that now goes into the atmosphere would be diverted into a heat production process for the homes and the community. Sludge removed from waste water treatment would be used as fuel rather than dumped as a pollutant. The concept applies to the recycling of all sorts of processes and products. The goal of this group is to produce a practical, reasonable project, not simply a pie-in-the-sky science fiction story. In many areas of the Colorado

River Basin, such a concept would be ideal. Where resources are scarce, the application of such technology may well increase the development potential of the area without producing significant adverse effects. This would allow people to live in beautiful areas that were previously incapable of sustaining much life.

We are approaching a possible threshold in the test of our will to implement the environmental preservation goals we have established as a nation. The nature and the extent of the costs involved are beginning to loom large. The very real benefits which will flow from a cleaner environment have not yet made a similar impression upon our consciousness. The average citizen in Los Angeles has not yet seen the point at which the skies will actually improve and the rivers will become cleaner. We must summon our will and press on through this threshold. It would be a terrible mistake to fail to realize that the benefits of a clean air environment and a higher quality of living will far outweigh the costs. Lower medical costs, improved health, crystal clear view across mountain ranges, and an unspoiled place to take the family for recreation are all tangible, direct, concrete benefits.

The contention that environmental programs will reduce our standard of living must be rejected. This is utter nonsense. A few cents more on our electric light bill for the accompanying reduction in health-damaging sulfur in the air we breath will not reduce our standard of living. It will, in fact, improve the quality of life. Excessive emphasis on the cash side of our standard of living ignores the fact that even in a very product-conscious society such as ours, most of our values lie outside the simple "cash" accounting system. Soundly managed environmental programs will make a substantial contribution to the quality of all our lives.

We always grumble a little when we have to change our ways, but change our ways we must, if we are to accomplish the goals we have set as a nation in environmental enhancement and preservation. The effect of all this, however, will definitely be positive. Our past practices were rapidly closing some of our alternatives. The new legislation will expand them.

A Note of Caution

These comments must not be interpreted to imply that the positive benefits of environmental legislation will simply fall out easily as some kind of unintended consequence. This is simply not the case.

If our anxiety over the conflicts surrounding environmental legislation immobilize our will, we will end up in a nightmare. A very careful stewardship of the resources in the basin will be necessary to accomplish our goals.

One of the most important pieces of environmental legislation may well stand in the way of our attempts to accomplish these goals. This legislation does not appear on the list mentioned at the beginning of this address. It is the legislation that results from the budget proposals of the President and issues forth in the form of appropriations bills that wind their separate ways through the channels of executive and congressional processes. Yet this may be the biggest fight of all.

The deep cut in environmental programs proposed in President Nixon's FY 74 budget are a cause of grievous concern for all those who see the necessity of increased budgetary resources for the enhancement and protection of other resources. This protection is a vital component of any plan to develop the growth potential of the Colorado River Basin.

Let me list a few of the cuts proposed by the President in his budget: Funds for protecting and utilizing national forest lands were slated for a cut of $56 million. Planning and construction of park facilities were scheduled for a reduction of $60 million from the level established in the budget two years earlier. The Bureau of Sport Fisheries and Wildlife was given virtually no new funds, in spite of greatly expanded programs to protect and enhance the wildlife resources of the nation. More than half of the funds used to clean up America's waterways were impounded. Solid waste disposal problems were labeled a "local headache," and the funds for grants for these programs were reduced from $30 million down to $5 million. A token increase was slated for energy research and development, but the level was a mere $25 million. In virtually all of these areas, Congress has forced the President's budget up to a somewhat more respectable level. But in virtually all cases, the funding level is still inadequate. Such decisions may well limit the growth potential of the Colorado River Basin. Let me give an example.

Progress in energy research and development has a good chance of allowing the growth potential of the Colorado River Basin to be utilized without significant environmental degradation. For example, if coal gasification technology moves forward rapidly, it could well replace some, though certainly not all, of the coal-fired mine-mouth electric generating plants planned in the area. The environmental degradation will be greatly reduced by the pollution control technology I mentioned earlier, but coal gasification will reduce the environmental impact of such energy conversion plants even further.But if the Federal government continues to provide paltry funds for such purposes, the basin, along with the rest of the nation, will suffer. The same holds true for needed developments in oil shale, geothermal power sources, and other forms of fuel production and energy conversion.

The same stewardship principle just mentioned in regard to national resources also applies to the use of Utah's precious resources, particularly its water and coal. We have an obligation to help meet national energy needs. But while we continue this first phase of the development of power plants such as Kaiparowits, we need to begin thinking of the long-run use patterns of our scarce Utah resources.

The jobs, tax revenue, income, and spin-off accompanying Kaiparowits and similar energy producing developments will perhaps fill our immediate needs long enough to allow us to begin an examination of the long-range uses we want for the remainder of our Utah resources. We will need to be particularly careful about our water, for new development plans, particularly industrial development may well surpass the optimum use pattern if not examined carefully. The question of mortgaging our water to out-of-state interests may well become a focal point of contention, particularly if the development plans do nothing to avoid the boom and then bust cycle that would follow from fifty years of intense use and ultimate depletion of the resource.

Legislation on the books, and other legislation presently working its way through Congress, should provide protection and allow adequate development while we produce strategies and philosophies that will answer these questions.

In summary, the environmental legislation that has resulted from the wave of public opinion calling for increased emphasis emphasis on environmental values will actually benefit the growth potential of the Colorado River Basin, rather than simply restricting that potential as many have charged. Protecting the environment can well be a game in which no one loses.

CHAPTER VIII

Criteria for the Determination of Recreational Carrying Capacity in the Colorado River Basin

George H. Stankey*

The Colorado River Basin contains a variety of recreational opportunities. This diversity provides a backdrop for activities ranging from primitive camping in the Colorado Rockies to four-wheel driving in the Utah desert to water skiing on Lake Havasu. A wide variety of tastes, preferences, and motivations can be fulfilled within this spectrum of opportunity. Policies and programs have been implemented at different institutional levels and in both the public and private sector to insure maintenance of these opportunities. However, these efforts are often isolated from one another, focused on a relatively short timeframe, and oriented heavily to the goals and objectives of the particular organization making the decision. Cohesiveness and coordination seldom characterize the planning process of the various land management agencies. This is particularly unfortunate, for the kinds of recreational opportunities provided and the subsequent kinds of satisfaction fulfilled will be direct products of the multi-organizational decisions

*Research Social Scientist, Intermountain Forest and Range Experiment Station, Missoula, Montana

made regarding allocation and management. Thus, a major challenge confronting resource administrators and managers consists of the development of strategic designed to insure the maintenance of a diverse spectrum of opportunities.

PURPOSE OF THE PAPER

In this paper, we will discuss the concept of carrying capacity as it applies to recreation and how this concept can serve as a major criterion in the allocation and management of recreation resources. Then, given an understanding of the various implications of alternative carrying capacity strategies, we will focus on several concepts that can serve as criteria for policymakers to evaluate in allocating resources to meet a mix of recreation demands and in establishing management programs to achieve specific objectives. Finally, we will suggest some of the implications that seem likely if an integrated and regional perspective is not brought to traditional resource management programs.

The principal orientation of the discussion is conceptual rather than empirical. Although a reasonable body of empirical literature has developed regarding carrying capacity (Stankey and Lime, 1973), the lack of systematic, conceptual framework to guide research and decision-making has been a significant shortcoming and has resulted in most of the empirical work being non-accumulative (Frissel and Stankey, 1972). The concepts and criteria outlined herein are aimed at improving the situation.

THE CONCEPT OF RECREATIONAL CARRYING CAPACITY

Carrying capacity has received abundant attention in the recreation literature, both as a concept for management and as a topic for research (Dana, 1957; LaPage 1963; Wagar, 1964; Chubb, 1964; Lucas, 1964; Frisell and Stankey, 1972). It is a fundamental concept in fields such as forest ecology and range management and it is within this context that most persons apply it to the management of recreation resources. This biological concept of carrying capacity has unfortunately fostered the notion that recreation lands have a natural level of productivity within which use must be controlled (Wagar, 1968). While a relationship does exist between the productivity of the recreation resource and use, productivity is not measured by the nutritional value of the forage or the rate of biomass production, but rather, by the rate and mix of satisfactions provided recreationists.

In discussing recreational carrying capacity we must recognize that two distinct but interrelated dimensions must be considered. First, any recreational use of a site results in changes in the physical-biological characteristics of that site. Ground cover is lost, soil compaction occurs, coliform counts rise, and so forth. Second, the various dimensions of the recreational experience are subject to change as use increases and as management alters the character of the site. Wagar hypothesized the relationship of principal dimensions of the recreational experience; for some, such as solitude, even very low intensities of use resulted in adverse impacts while for others, such as companionship, increasing use yielded increasing benefits (to some unspecified level) (Wagar, 1964).

In the discussion above, we talk of "change" rather than "damage." The term "damage" signifies a judgment that the change which has occurred is undesirable. Undesirability, in turn, is judged by the relationship of the change to the management objectives that govern an area. Because any recreational use of an area results in some change in the bio-physical sphere, decisions regarding capacity must ultimately rely upon value judgments as to the acceptability of anticipated impacts. Recreational carrying capacity is largely a matter of social judgment rather than bio-physical determinism; as Davis (1963) notes, "the question of carrying capacities too often sounds like a physical problem when its heart is really a matter of interpersonal quality effects." Deciding upon the "limits of acceptable change" (Frissell and Stankey, 1972), then, becomes a matter of determining the point at which change in the bio-physical regime, the recreational experience, or both, constitutes an excessive deviation from some pre-determined standard (a standard described by an area's management objectives) (Frissell and Stankey, 1972). If such a condition develops, use may be limited, the impacts may be offset through various management programs, or the objectives themselves may be changed. Thus, recreational carrying capacity is a dynamic concept that permits us to describe the relationship between the type of recreational experience, the recreational resource, management objectives, and a particular pattern of use.

CATEGORIES OF RECREATION PREFERENCE

Describing this relationship for all activities, however, would be very difficult. Instead, we can consider the range of recreational activities in light of how different activities cluster together, based upon certain similar characteristics. Expressed preferences for participation is a particularly useful way to consider these aggregations because they allow us to consider what people would like to do rather than just what is available for them to do.

In a study of recreationists in car campgrounds and national park and national forest wilderness in the Pacific Northwest, Hendee et al., (1971) asked respondents to select from a list of 26 leisure activities, the six activities they most preferred, in descending order of preference. Those activities chosen as "most preferred" were grouped together into five conceptually-linked categories called "activity preference types." The categories were labeled according to the general type of motivation they fulfilled. The categories were:

1) *Appreciative-symbolic.* Included such activities as mountain climbing and seeing natural scenery. The focus here is on appreciation of environmental qualities and preservation.
2) *Extractive-symbolic.* Hunting and fishing are examples. These activities are characterized by the extraction of "trophies" from the environment.
3) *Passive free-play.* This category includes painting, relaxing, and sightseeing. The activities typically require little effort and are generally not limited to a forest environment.
4) *Sociable learning.* This includes such things as nature study, visiting with other campers, and viewing exhibits. Interaction with others is the primary source of satisfaction.
5) *Active-expressive.* Includes water-skiing, playing games, and driving motorcycles or snowmobiles. As with passive free-play, these activities do not require a forest setting and are largely focused on the instruments of the activity rather than the setting in which it takes place.

By considering the vast number of recreation activities within this preference typology, we are able to identify aggregations that possess similar generic appeals. Likewise, each of these groupings share certain general similarities with regard to their impact on the physical environment as well as the type of experience they provide. We can consider how each of these categories relates to various aspects of recreational carrying capacity.

Several capacity factors can be identified. First, the use intensity— the level of use an area receives—has obvious implications for both the bio-physical and social dimensions of the capacity equation. Related to this is the degree to which change in the physical environment can be accepted. The level at which managerial investment can be applied without altering the type of opportunity provided is a third factor. Finally, the principal type of interaction that characterizes a category needs to be defined. For example, does the activity under concern involve man interacting with man or man interacting with nature? Are intra- or intergroup relationships more important?

The Relationship of Preference Categories to Carrying Capacity

The five activity preference categories previously identified relate in different ways to these four capacity factors. In table 1, we have attempted to identify these relationships.

Consider an activity such as wilderness backpacking. In the typology, this activity would fall in the "appreciative-symbolic" category. Use intensity would be relatively low and qualities such as solitude would be important (Stankey, 1972). Naturalness of the environment is also generally important and relatively small amounts of change could significantly detract from the user's satisfaction. Within classified wilderness, the extent to which management could undertake activities to "harden" sites is limited. The enjoyment of naturalness would generally preclude any extensive investment of managerial modifications to enhance capacity. Finally, the principal interaction that characterizes an appreciative-symbolic activity such as wilderness backpacking would focus on close, interpersonal relationships and on the interaction between the visitor and the environment. Socialization with others outside one's group is generally rejected (Catton, 1969; Stankey, 1972).

We can contrast these conditions with those that would prevail if we consider an activity such as trail bike riding, an activity we would classify within the typology as "active-expressive." Use intensity

TABLE 1: *Relationship of Activity Preference Categories to Carrying Capacity Factors*

Typology	Use Intensity	Degree of Environment Change Permissible	Level of Managerial Investment in Facilities	Principal Interaction
Appreciative-Symbolic	Low, solitude important	Low, naturalness important source of satisfaction	Generally low	Oriented to environment and intra-group relations
Extractive-Symbolic	Can range from low to moderate, depending on specific activity	Variable, change related to effect on activity	Can range from low to high	Variable, ranging from principal focus on environment to social interaction
Passive Free-Play	Moderate to high, depending on specific activity	Generally high	High	Social Interaction
Social Learning	High. Social interaction important source of satisfaction	High	High	Social Interaction
Active-Expressive	Typically high. Social interaction & display significant source of satisfaction	High	High	Social Interaction

for such an activity would be relatively high, particularly when considered in relation to the previous example. Safety might be an important factor in determining the appropriate level of use. Extensive modification of the environment could be carried out as naturalness would be a relatively unimportant quality. The level of managerial investment could be quite high. Paved roads, artificial hills for climbing, obstacle courses, and so forth could be provided. Materials resistant to excessive wear-and-tear could be used. Finally, social interaction with others and the opportunity to display one's skill and equipment would be important sources of satisfaction to participants.

Although the capacity standards for the two activities just described vary considerably, it is entirely possible that both activities might be equally viable uses for the same tract of land. A decision to allocate resources for wilderness preservation, thus providing an opportunity for the first activity, would lead to one set of implications for such questions as: how many people can be served?; what types of satisfactions would be fulfilled?; what would be the costs of providing the opportunity?; a decision to develop the same tract for mechanized recreation would lead to a different set of implications for the same questions. Used in this manner, carrying capacity becomes a criterion for allocation by helping define the trade-offs between the relative number of persons served for one alternative as opposed to another. However, carrying capacity can also serve as a criterion for management.

Consider hunting, for example, an activity included within the "extractive-symbolic" category. When considering use intensity as a factor, several alternatives can be considered. Big game hunting would typically involve relatively low intensities of use; put-and-take pheasant hunting could support considerably higher levels. For some styles of hunting, socialization and display would be important sources of satisfaction; for others (e.g., the solitary bowhunter), the principal interaction would be between the individual and the environment. Given different management objectives, the criterion of carrying capacity could serve to identify the relation between the various capacity factors and the specific type of hunting opportunity to be provided as well as the controls and limitations that might be necessary to insure that opportunity.

A Criteria Framework for Determining Carrying Capacity
Strategies

Although the activity typology outlined above and its relation to
the capacity factors helps describe the implications of alternative decisions regarding recreational allocation and management, there is a
need for criteria that will maximize the social value of these decisions.
For example, what guidelines can be utilized in making a decision
regarding whether or not to maintain an area in its natural state or
to develop it for mechanized recreation and for other uses? What
criteria can be utilized, in conjunction with the constraints imposed
by alternative carrying capacity, in allocating and managing recreational resources? In the following pages, we propose a framework of
five criteria to assist policymakers in dealing with such questions.
These criteria include (1) irreplaceability and relative abundance;
(2) substitutability; (3) demand-preference relationship; (4) complementarity-competitiveness relationship; and (5) costs. Combined with
the criterion of carrying capacity, they provide guidelines for a strategy
to maximize human satisfactions and benefits from recreational resources.

Moreover, by carefully reviewing the potential consequences associated with the alternative carrying capacity strategies, policymakers
will be better able to define the nature of the social impacts stemming
from alternative decisions. For instance, one could specify the types of
satisfactions to be provided (as well as those which are not), who
the principal clientele would be, what recreational options have been
precluded, etc. Such an assessment of social impact is required by the
National Environmental Policy Act of 1970, but little has been
accomplished in the way of articulating such impacts.

Irreplaceability and Relative Abundance. Through a variety of
institutional structures, our society has identified certain environments
as meriting especial guarantees of protection. Wilderness areas, national parks, wild and scenic rivers, the "Red Book" of rare and
endangered species, and similar efforts reflect this social concern.
Motivations to promote such protective devices vary, but are bound
together by the similar belief that preservation is of value to society
(Kriger, 1973). Such environmental qualities are typically scarce
and, relative to the value to be derived from them in a developed

state, would be excessively costly to reproduce (Krutilla, 1967). The role of a technological "fix" in supplying such environments is very limited.

On the other hand, there are many environments that exist in relative abundance and which moreover, are highly susceptible to the tools of technology; i.e., the input of technical know-how, processing, etc., can result in essentially identical reproductions. Thus, there is an asymmetry between these respective environments, with only limited implications for the role of technology in the replication of the former and a rather significant role with regard to the latter.

For example, reservoirs for which recreation is a purpose, are a relatively easy thing to provide. To be certain, an adequate supply of water is needed, the percolation rate of the soil can affect its holding capability, and certain sites are better than others. There are both time and money costs in creating a new reservoir. However, these constraints are readily susceptible to our technology; we can pipe water over considerable distance, we can cover the bottom of reservoirs to prevent leakage, we can build dikes to hold the reservoir. But consider that in deciding to build a reservoir, a free-flowing stream must be dammed. Our technological capacity to reproduce that stream is very restricted. We will have gained a reservoir, a commodity exhibiting considerable potential for reproduction, at the cost of a resource of limited quality and very high demands on our technological skills.

The contrasting susceptibility to technological reproduction can, by itself, serve as a criterion for decision makers to consider. However, because our focus is on the human values that flow from recreation resources, we can further consider what kinds of experiences such areas provide. Certain kinds of recreational satisfactions are area-based or site-specific; they are dependent upon a particular environmental complex, which, if absent, precludes fulfillment of certain motives. For example, studies of wilderness users have consistently reported that for a significant proportion of the users, the presence of a natural environment, unencumbered by conveniences, is the major source of satisfaction (Hendee, et al. 1968; Stankey, 1971). Such satisfactions are highly site-specific; if the limited number of areas capable of providing such experiences were eliminated, this particular clientele's desires would not be met.

Additionally, the knowledge of authenticity might be quite significant (Krieger, 1973). Certainly, it would play a major role for those
persons deriving satisfactions from rare displays of natural phenomena.
Although one could conceivably envision the reproduction of a Grand
Canyon carved out by atomic blasts, the knowledge of how the reproduction was effected, the knowledge that the exposed Vishnu
Schist was a result of man's command of the atom rather than eons
of river carving might very well markedly affect the satisfactions
derived by the clientele described above.

Generic satisfactions tend to not be area based. Socializing with
one's companions, for example, is an important generic satisfaction
that can be derived in a variety of settings. For instance, should a
local picnic area be closed, users can *relatively* easily find alternative
locations to picnic. If need be, such areas can be developed through
the input of technological skills. Or, the picnickers may adopt some
new leisure activity (e.g., bowling) which still provides an opportunity
to socialize. This point is, loss of the recreational resource does not
necessarily mean irretrievable loss of the satisfaction.

The demand curve for activities associated with a resource of
limited quantity, such as we might find on our free-flowing stream
example above, may very well be quite steep and the value of that
opportunity subsequently higher than that associated with relatively
abundant opportunities (Knetsch, 1971). This could be the case despite rather large differences in the number of participants at the
respective alternatives.

Substitutability. Substitutability refers to the extent to which recreation activities can be interchanged in terms of satisfying participant
motives, wishes, and desires (Hendee and Burdge, forthcoming). The
focus of this concept is on the similarity of social, psychological, and
personal variables that lead to interchanges in activities, rather than
on the physical characteristics of the activity setting. Thus, cross-
country skiing would not necessarily represent an appropriate substitution for downhill skiing, as the motives and preferences of participants in these two activities might be different. Downhill skiing and
surfboarding, however, might be fairly substitutable.

The substitutability criterion requires us to determine what the
various alternatives are for the different activity types. One might
hypothesize that activities grouped together in any one activity cate-

gory shown in table 1 would tend to exhibit a greater degree of substitutability than between activity categories. Knowing what relationship does, in fact exist, would be particularly important in allocation decisions, for the loss in satisfaction (if any) that results from providing one type of activity rather than another might be offset by the greater capacity of that activity, its relative availability, demand, etc.

There is increasing evidence that for perhaps a majority of auto-access campers, the experience sought is a social one rather than environmental (Hendee and Campbell, 1969; Campell, Hendee, and Clark, 1968; Clark, Hendee, and Campbell, 1971). However, because the principal motive is social, it might very well be possible to provide users with a satisfactory camping experience in settings other than forest environments. For instance, plans were recently announced for the construction of a 20-story high rise campground near downtown New Orleans, complete with covered parking, utility hookups, and artificial turf (*Conservation News,* 1973). Judgments that such a development isn't "real camping" fail to realize the changing nature of the camping experience and reflect a traditional bias with only limited applicability to the value system espoused by many modern campers. Failure to be sensitive to these values will lead to the continued expenditure of public resources and funds for programs that fail to satisfy public desires as well as create situations that invite violations of norms and regulations judged inappropriate by visitors (Campbell, Hendee, and Clark, 1968).

The substitutability concept also has important implications in terms of defining what is not substitutable. Those activities that exhibit little or not substitutability need to be defined so as to minimize the possibility of decisions occurring that might disenfranchise participants in such activities. Typically, these activities will be area based, such as wilderness use, forms of big game hunting, or the enjoyment of areas of significant scientific value (Hendee and Burdge, forthcoming).

Demand-Preference Relationships. Numerous studies on recreation demand have been completed, both for the nation as well as various sub-regions. In order to qualify for Federal funds under the Land and Water Conservation Act of 1964, the states have had to prepare recreation plans based on use projections derived from demand studies. Although the recreation-demand study has become one of the principal planning tools used by resource managers and policymakers, almost all suffer from a major methodological shortcoming related to their definition of demand.

Technically, "demand" refers to the quantity that would be consumed at various prices (Knetsch, 1969). However, what most recreation demand studies and the subsequent use projections utilize is a measure of participation given existing opportunities, generally at little or no cost to the individual. This, in turn, leads to judgments that "*n*" numbers of users will "need" or "demand" some particular type of facility in the year 2000.[2] This completely ignores the fact that existing patterns and rates of participation are a function of what is available. Time and money are other constraints that prevent people from doing what they prefer to do (Brewer and Gillespie, 1967). Participation is not a surrogate for satisfaction. Continued reliance upon traditional demand studies will lead to a concentration of funds and resources in facilities perhaps already abundant at the expense of opportunities that might be more preferable in the judgment of recreationists. The marginal utility of such latter developments would be quite great as compared to the former, particularly in terms of the social welfare they would contribute.

The traditional treatment of recreation as a "free good" also confuses the relationship between participation and preference. If pricing systems were applied uniformly to recreation resources, the resulting patterns of use might lead us to some rather different conclusions regarding their relative value to the public. Pricing might result in an effort by the public to expand their resources more efficiently; i.e., spend their money to gain the most satisfaction.

The criterion of demand-preference relationships alerts us to the potential discrepancy between reported demand estimates and potential recreationist preferences. Rigorous survey research will help describe the range of preferences that exist, thereby providing cues to policy-makers as they allocate resources to various purposes and develop mangement strategies to achieve various objectives.

Complementarity-Competitiveness. In a region like the Colorado River Basin, a wide range of economic and social activities compete

---

[2]"Need" is another term used very loosely in recreation demand studies. For an excellent review of this concept, see David Mercer "The Concept of Recreational 'Need' ". 1973. *Journal of Leisure Research* 5(1): 37-50.

for limited resources. Capital investment, design, and multiple use are examples of strategies devised to provide more intensive utilization of resources among competing uses. Among the various activity sectors (e.g., agriculture, mining, forestry, tertiary economic enterprises, etc.), competitive and complimentary relationships exist that directly affect the productivity of the different sectors. For example, the pollutants of a factory can adversely affect the productivity of nearby forests or agricultural fields—a negative externality.

We often tend to see the relationship between other activities and recreation from a negative perspective. The conflict (competitive relationship) between wilderness and timber harvest is well known. Agricultural practices that eliminate game habitat are another common problem. While a major purpose of this criterion is to promote programs and policies that minimize such negative impacts, it can also serve to encourage attention to the development of positive programs, designed to produce complementary relationships between activity sectors.

Consider hunting, for example. Participation in hunting has been adversely affected by a variety of factors, but declining opportunity as a result of shifts in land use patterns and agricultural practices is a major cause (ORRRC, 1962). Controls over residential subdivisions, incentives to diversify agricultural practices (e.g., hunter financed subsidies), or changes in forest harvest systems could result in substantial yields at the margin for hunting with only limited (perhaps negligible) impacts on these other activities.

Competitive and complementary relationships exist among the various recreation activity categories. Activities that provide satisfactions primarily from social interaction among participants could conflict with those which depend largely on the interaction between the users and natural, undisturbed environments for motive fulfillment. By specifying the variable human impact associated with different activity categories and the complimentary and competitive relationships that exist among them, it may be possible to spatially allocate recreation resources to minimize conflict and maximize concordant relationships. For instance, a recreational area in which a pattern of concentric zoning places user-oriented activities on the periphery and gradually shifts to the more resource-oriented uses at the center could eliminate many conflicts between different recreationists' value systems as well as provide a coherent transition from one activity category to another.

Costs of Providing Opportunities. The costs of providing alternative recreation opportunities or of providing recreation as opposed to some other form of land use represents a final criterion. Recreation is generally recognized as a merit good. The costs of its provision are seldom met by the user; rather, it is subsidized by the public at large on the grounds that important benefits accrue to all of society (Manthy and Tucker, 1972). As discussed earlier, the lack of a price system means that the normal channel of feedback to administrators is missing. However, the relationship between the costs associated with the provision of recreation from a limited stock of public resources and the benefits derived from that use needs to be defined.

When investing scarce financial resources in recreation there is the tendency to try and maximize anticipated monetary return. Efforts to determine average per day per person expenditures so as to calculate the potential economic impact of, say, a reservoir for the purposes of cost-benefit analysis reflect this emphasis. As has been pointedly demonstrated, however, this approach tends to favor those uses that attract large numbers of people and discounts those uses that might appeal to a minority (Knetsch, 1971). Moreover, it can lead to the allocation of resources already relatively abundant because, as outlined in the earlier discussion on demand-preference relationships, we tend to translate participation rates at existing opportunities into straight line projections of need and demand. Areas already supporting high use levels become, through this self-fulfilling prophecy, the areas most in demand.

Costs associated with providing different types of recreation vary considerably. Intensive forms of recreation may require substantial investment in facilities, maintenance, law enforcement, but the per person costs of providing such an opportunity might be quite low, given high use levels. Dispersed forms of recreation, on the other hand, might require only limited expenditure of funds, but because of the low intensity of use, per capita costs might be high. Such relationships are extremely variable, however. For example, should opportunity costs be calculated in the equation? What costs may be legitimately included in such a calculation?

There is also the problem of relating the costs associated with one activity with the marginal gain in benefits, which in the case of recreation is measured primarily by human satisfactions. One might describe a case where the costs of providing alternative A involve per-visitor per-day costs of only $1.00 as opposed to alternative B where this cost equals $5.00. Such a difference could certainly represent an economic constraint over which there is little control. But consider that both are economically viable alternatives. The important question then becomes "What is the relative gain in benefits per unit expenditure of costs?" Alternative A appears cheaper, but assume it is also an alternative relatively abundant in the area; the marginal benefits accruing from its provisions would be small. Alternative B, on the other hand, is perhaps a relatively scarce opportunity in the area and studies of preference suggests a high demand for such an opportunity. The marginal benefits accruing from its provision then would be quite large. The per-person per-day cost criterion must be weighed with other factors.

THE NEED FOR AN INTEGRATED REGIONAL PERSPECTIVE

We have outlined five criteria that may serve to provide policy-makers and resource managers with guidlines for the allocation and management of recreation resources. Ideally, we seek to promote a situation where a diversity of recreation opportunities, fulfilling a spectrum of leisure tastes and preferences, exists. But the highly fractionalized and compartmentalized nature of resource administration can effectively hinder this objective.

To date, little has been done by resource management agencies in the way of defining what recreational opportunities they are best suited to provide in terms of staff abilities, types of lands administered, the location of land holdings, etc. The recreation opportunity spectrum concept has not been operationalized in any meaningful way. It is unlikely that any one public body can or should provide opportunities along the whole spectrum. However, "each public agency could aim clearly at a part of the demand, and refer people who want something more, less, or different to a more appropriate area" (Lucas, 1963). By clearly defining the management objectives for the various opportunities as well as the responsibility for providing them, it will be much more likely that we will be able to maximize human satisfactions from recreational resources.

The failure to follow this or some similar strategy could lead to some severe consequences. We will describe a likely scenario. The manager of a small, rustic campground, with 10 units, a dirt road leading to it, a hand pump for water, and an outdoor toilet, finds that while only five years ago the use of this campground typically consisted of a couple of families each night camped in a tent, today there also are three motor homes, four pick-up campers, and six tent trailers crowded into the camp. Multiple occupancies at the same site are common. Some of the mobile units have flushed their holding tanks to the nearby stream. Dust from the road makes sitting outside unbearable. The list of problems could continue.

To cope with these conditions, the road is paved, flush toilets are installed, the design capacity of the camp is doubled, sites are equipped with electric plug-ins, drains, and water, and so forth. The problems have been solved through technological input.

Or have they? We must ask, what about the clientele that used to visit this small rustic campground? Perhaps they have changed their camping style and still visit it. Or, perhaps they were able to find another similar location. Or, perhaps they "dropped out" of the recreation market, casualties of a planning system that failed to recognize the importance of maintaining a diversity of opportunities and that was unable to coordinate the provisions of this diversity. Studies of recreation participation in the Northeastern U.S. have reported a decline in annual participation by campers over a five year period and speculate that increased congestion and shifts in management to contend with such problems might be responsible (LaPage and Ragain, 1971).

There is another alternative our hypothetical campers might adopt. They may choose to begin using the next most desirable location on the recreation spectrum. Thus, these rustic campers may become users of a nearby wilderness. These persons bring certain expectations and demands with them, notions that might be contrary to the norms of wilderness. Pressures for developments and facilities within wilderness could build. Such changes, coupled with the increased levels of use, would gradually cause the original wilderness clientele to begin its own process of adapting or moving. Unchecked, this process of "invasion and succession," (Hendee and Campbell, 1969; Clarke, Hendee, and Campbell, 1971) could gradually bring more and more homogeneity to our recreation resources. Subsequently, the ability of these resources to provide satisfactions for diverse tastes would be greatly restricted. This would be particularly disastrous for those persons whose principal satisfaction is derived from participating in non-substitutable activities or irreproducible resources. Once this clientele is displaced, the supply of suitable options is virtually non-existent.

Conflicts between the various uses we have described are common. Much of the debate has placed the resolution of this conflict in an "either-or" framework—do we provide dispersed or concentrated recreation? Or, the argument has advanced as a question of "how much?" A more appropriate focus for public policy is the development of a continuum of recreational opportunities (Lloyd and Fischer, 1972). Moreover, the continuum concept must be recognized as dynamic, with new demand, arising (e.g., the recent growth in off-road recreation vehicles) and other demands gradually diminishing (e.g., spas). Again, diversity in opportuntity is the key.

The scope of the needed regional perspective must be broad. Certain unique resources, such as Grand Canyon and Zion National Parks and the associated flora and fauna of these areas are treasures of the nation, not just the Colorado River Basin. The maintenance of vignettes of the primitive American landscape has been suggested as a major social objective (Leopold et al., 1963). Recent efforts by the National Park Service have defined the relative degree of representation within the National Park System of historical and natural history themes (National Park Service, 1972a and 1972b). Such an effort provides criteria for the assignment of priority for action to insure the fullest extent of diversity. We have argued at length for such diversity on the grounds of the "recreational" values flowing from such resources, but reasons of species maintenance, reservoirs of gene pools, and an understanding of natural processes and the extent to which they have been altered by man may also be included (Dasmann, 1973).

Preservation of a diverse resource base capable of providing a variety of satisfactions and values to people must become the coordinated objective of public agencies at all jurisdictional levels and the private sector.[3] The alternative of independent and unrestricted planning will surely "... result in grand opportunities foregone or in irreversible damage to the environment" (Wildavsky, 1967).

BIBLIOGRAPHY

"Ah, Wonderful Nature. 1973. *Conservation News* 38 (15:7).

Brewer, Durward and Glenn A. Gillespie. 1967. "Estimating Satisfaction Levels of Outdoor Recreationists." *Journal of Soil and Water Conservation* 22(6):248-49.

Catton, William R., Jr. 1969. "Motivations of Wilderness Users." *Pulp and Paper Magazine of Canada, Woodlands Section.* WS Index 2528 (F3) ODC 907.2. pp. 121-26.

Campbell, Frederick L., John C. Hendee, and Roger Clark. 1968. "Law and Order in Public Parks." *Parks and Recreation* 3(12):51-55.

Chubb, Michael 1964. "Outdoor Recreation Land Capacity: Concepts, Usage, and Definitions." Unpub. M.S. Thesis, Department of Resource Development, Michigan State University, East Lansing.

Clark, Roger N., John C. Hendee, and Frederick L. Campbell, 1971. *Depreciative Behavior in Forest Campgrounds: An Exploratory Study.* USDA Forest Service Research Note PNW-161. Pacific Northwest Forest and Range Experiment Station, Portland, Oregon, 12 pp.

Dana, Samuel T. 1957. *Problem Analysis Research in Forest Recreation.* USDA Forest Service, 36 pp.

Dasmann, Raymond F. 1973. "A Rationale for Preserving Natural Areas." *Journal of Soil and Water Conservation* 28(3):114-17.

Davis, Robert K. 1963. "Recreation Planning as an Economic Problem," *Natural Resources Journal* 3(2):239-49.

Frissell, Sidney S. and George H. Stankey. 1972. "Wilderness Environmental Quality: Search for Social and Ecological Harmony." Paper presented to the annual meeting of the Society of American Foresters, Hot Springs, Arkansas, October 1-5, 1972.

---

[3]For an interesting discussion on the significance of diversity, see Kenneth E. F. Watt, 1972. "Man's Efficient Rush Toward Deadly Dullness," *Natural History* 81 (2): 74-77, 80, 82.

Hendee, John C. and Rabel J. Burdge. 1974. "The Substitutability Concept: Implications for Recreation Research and Management." (Scheduled for publication, *Journal of Leisure Research,* Winter, 1974.)

Hendee, John C. and Frederick L. Campbell. 1969. "Social Aspects of Outdoor Recreation—the Developed Campground." *Trends in Parks and Recreation.* pp. 13-16.

Hendee, John E., Richard P. Gale, and William R. Catton, Jr. 1971. Typology of Outdoor Recreation Activity Preferences." *Journal of Environmental Education* 3(1):28-34.

Hendee, John C., William R. Catton, Jr., Larry D. Marlow, and C. Frank Brockman. 1968. *Wilderness Users in the Pacific Northwest —Their Characteristics, Values and Management Preferences.* US- DA Forest Service Research Paper PNW-61. Pacific Northwest Forest and Range Experiment Station, Portland, Oregon. 92 pp. illus.

Knetsch, Jack L. 1969. "Assessing the Demand for Outdoor Recreation," *Journal of Leisure Research* 1(1):85-87.

Knetsch, Jack L. 1971. "Value Comparisons in Free-Flowing Stream Development." *Natural Resources Journal* 11(4): 624-635.

Krieger, Martin H. 1973. "What's Wrong with Plastic Trees?" *Science* 179: 446-55.

Krutilla, John V. 1967. "Conservation Reconsidered," *American Economic Review* 57(4):777-86.

LaPage, Wilbur. 1963. "Some Sociological Aspects of Forest Recreation." *Journal of Forestry* 61(1):32-36.

LaPage, Wilbur and Dale P. Ragain. 1971. *Trends in Camping Participation* USDA Forest Service Research Paper NE-183. Northeast Forest Experiment Station, Upper Darby, Pa. 22 pp. illus.

Lloyd, R. Duane and Virlis L. Fischer. 1972. *Dispersed Versus Concentrated Recreation as Forest Policy.* Seventh World Forestry Congress, Buenos Aires, Argentina, October 4-18, 1972.

Lucas, Robert C. 1963. "The Status of Recreation Research Related to Users," Society of American Foresters Proceedings, 1963. Boston, Mass. pp. 127-28.

Lucas, Robert C. 1964. *The Recreational Capacity of the Quetico-Superior Area.* USDA Forest Service Research Paper LS-15. Lake States Forest Experiment Station, St. Paul, Minn. 34 pp., illus.

Manthy, Robert S. and Thomas L. Tucker. 1972. *Supply Costs for Public Forest Land and Recreation.* Research Report 158. Agricultural Experiment Station, Michigan State University, East Lansing.

Mercer, David. 1973. "The Concept of Recreational Need." *Journal of Leisure Research* 5(1):37-50.

National Park Service, 1972. *Part One of the National Park System Plan—History.* U.S. Department of the Interior. Washington, D.C., 164 pp.

National Park Service. 1972. *Part Two of the National Park System Plan—Natural History* U.S. Department of the Interior. Washington, D.C., 140 pp.

Outdoor Recreation Resources Review Commission. 1962. *Hunting in the United States—Its Present and Future Role.* Study Report 6. Washington, D.C., 180 pp.

"Reports of the Special Advisory Board on Wildlife Management for the Secretary of the Interior 1963-1968." 1969. *Transactions of the North American Wildlife and Natural Resources Conference,* Vols. 28, 29, and 33.

Stankey, George H. 1971. "Wilderness: Carrying Capacity and Quality." *The Naturalist* 22(3):7-13.

Stankey, George H. 1972. "A Strategy for the Definition and Management of Wilderness Quality." In *Natural Environments: Studies in Theoretical and Applied Analysis,* ed. John V. Krutilla. Baltimore: The John Hopkins University Press, 88-114.

Stankey, George H. and David W. Lime. *Recreational Carrying Capacity: An Annotated Bibliography.* U.S.D.A. Forest Service General Technical Report INT-3., Intermountain Forest and Range Experiment Station, Ogden, Utah, 45 pp.

Wagar, J. Alan. 1964. *The Carrying Capacity of Wild Lands for Recreation.* Society of American Foresters, Forest Science Monograph 7, 23 pp.

Wagar, J. Alan. 1968. *The Place of Carrying Capacity in the Management of Recreation Lands.* Paper presented to Third Rocky Mountain-High Plains Park and Recreation Conference, Fort Collins, Colorado, February 21, 1968.

Watt, Kenneth E. F. 1972. "Man's Efficient Rush Toward Deadly Dullness." *Natural History.* 81(2):74-77,80,82.

Wildavsky, Aaron. 1967. "Aesthetic Power or the Triumph of the Sensitive Minority Over the Vulgar Mass: A Political Analysis of the New Econmics," *Daedalus* 96 (4): 1115-1128.

CHAPTER IX

Strategies for Environmental Planning in the Upper Colorado River Region

Robert H. Twiss*

THE NEED FOR ENVIRONMENTAL
PLANNING

The Upper Colorado River Region is at a turning point in its history of development and conservation. A number of major decisions are now being made which will vitally effect the social, economic and environmental well being of the entire region. Is this area to be sacrificed to the national energy crisis? Can the energy development of the region be handled in a manner superior to that of water management? Must the fate of the region be decided by external pressures? Or, can we consider the Upper Colorado as a planning unit in its own right and seek to design a workable, habitable environment. As a society, we cannot take pride in our planning accomplishments to date. While there are scattered examples of successes in pollution control and recreation planning we must say that on the whole, the process of land development has been a destructive one.

A human community is a finely spun web of interactions. The capacity of a region to sustain a certain way of life must be judged in terms of compatibility of land uses, population density, social infrastructure (transportation, education, recreation, community services, housing) and the capacity of the natural environment to withstand or recover from development pressures.

*Professor of Environmental Planning, Department of Landscape Architecture, University of California, Berkeley.

The environmental quality of the region will not be preserved and managed merely through the identification and acquisition of parks and recreation areas. Neither will it be well managed if we meet air and water pollution standards. Architectural design of buildings, and landscaping of housing developments and roads will do little if these developments are inappropriate in the first instance. Planning, if it is single purpose, is bound to fail. That is, no measure of recreation planning, highway planning, energy planning, health planning alone is likely to succeed. These facets of planning are all interlinked through the land uses which they enable, the intensity of development which the engender, and the composito pressures which they place upon people and the natural environment.

It is sometimes helpful to think of regional development as a staircase of decisions and at each step there are many planks which go to make up the level. Figure 1 shows the major development de-

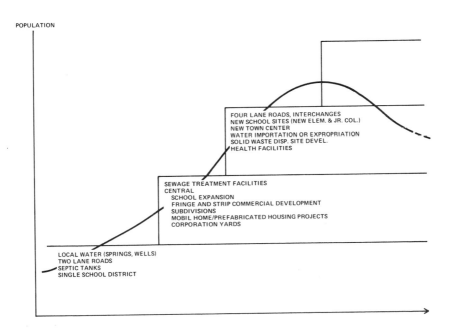

POPULATION

FOUR LANE ROADS, INTERCHANGES
NEW SCHOOL SITES (NEW ELEM. & JR. COL.)
NEW TOWN CENTER
WATER IMPORTATION OR EXPROPRIATION
SOLID WASTE DISP. SITE DEVEL.
HEALTH FACILITIES

SEWAGE TREATMENT FACILITIES
CENTRAL
  SCHOOL EXPANSION
  FRINGE AND STRIP COMMERCIAL DEVELOPMENT
SUBDIVISIONS
MOBIL HOME/PREFABRICATED HOUSING PROJECTS
CORPORATION YARDS

LOCAL WATER (SPRINGS, WELLS)
TWO LANE ROADS
SEPTIC TANKS
SINGLE SCHOOL DISTRICT

Figure 1. *Major Investments and Decisions vs. Population Growth for an Urbanizing Small Town*

cisions that might face a hypothetical small community and planning unit. These major steps are very often funded by outside agencies as part of single purpose planning programs. Figure 2 shows the many smaller steps which might be made by a local government. Given this kind of simple model one can think in terms of clusters of decisions related to the size of community structure. Also, we may consider the capacity to absorb additional increments of growth in terms of levels of social infrastructure. To the extent that infrastructure capacity gets ahead of population growth it builds in pressures for growth that would reduce per capita costs of social services. To the extent that infrastructure lags, one sees failing water systems, crowded recreation areas, schools and alike. Other models of carrying capacity have, of course, been devised relating capacity to natural resources, crowding and lifestyle conflicts, and land-use incompatibility. The key point, however, is that we must begin to treat regional growth, as a manage-

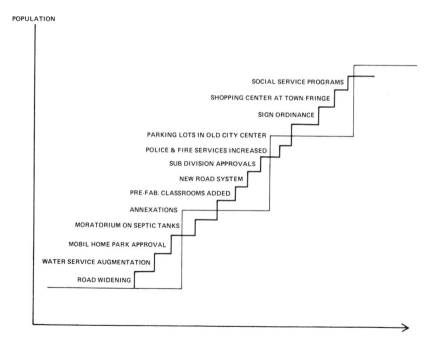

Figure 2. *Incremented Local Governmental Decisions vs. Population Growth*

able phenomenon, recognize the interdependence of projects and programs, recognize the relationship between recreation and work activities and the land-use intensity in which they can take place; and proceed with a comprehensive and multi-faceted program of environmental planning.

Inevitably, does this mean that we must have "master planning" of the region before we can proceed? No, but it does mean that we must have improved decision-making at many places and levels, and involving short and long-run decisions, so that we move incrementally toward an improved state of affairs.

THE CONTEXT OF DECISIONS OVER THE SHORT AND MIDDLE RUN

In discussing regional and environmental quality, we must be realistic. Thus far, the Federal government has essentially closed its eyes to the land use problems its actions create. Only a handful of states have even begun to exercise their responsibilities in the area of land use planning. We have only one real regional government in the entire United States. Local governments zoning powers have not been effective as a regional growth management tool. So, given that we cannot expect too much out of the governmental structure of the Upper Colorado River Region; what can we reasonably expect?

To sharpen discussion, I would like to give one man's forecast of what is likely to happen (realizing at the same time that we all must hope and work for greater progress).

In the Upper Colorado Region we are already seeing some activity on the part of cities, counties and councils of government. But as in the rest of the United States, we can expect only very marginal success with traditional zoning as the major land-use control. In a few instances, we may see local governments enacting ordinances requiring environmental impact statements to sharpen their permit powers.

There is perhaps a 20% chance that one or perhaps two states will pass well designed state land use laws. These are likely to be normative and advisory in essence and may result merely in years of study rather than immediate assistance. In general, local governments will have to maintain their local, competitive perspective. There is perhaps a 50% chance that one state will invoke meaningful state and regional powers through the initiative process.

A National land-use policy act will very likely pass in two years, but this will result mainly in subsidies to state governments for studies, and to develop general statements of goals and objectives. To the extent that these efforts fail to come to grips with the physical and spacial implications of policies, policy conflicts, and the tradeoffs necessary to make land use planning decisions, these efforts will be essentially a waste of time.

The Federal agencies may improve their coordination efforts but will very likely continue to avoid playing a strong role in land use and growth decisions.

The vacuum in regional decision making will very likely be filled by public interest law firms and citizens' groups forcing compliance with existing legislation. A limited number of key decision points will very likely be taken over by "no growth" advocates. These groups are not likely to be extremists in a normal sense of the word, but rather will be ranchers, long-time land owners, conservationists, or young people with a well developed sense of purpose. These groups may not be opposed to growth *per se* but will realize that since the overall growth process is irrational their only leverage is to seek to acquire veto power. These groups will likely become effective in blocking and confounding those development decisions which have glaring inadequacies, inconsistencies or exploitive effects. In the resulting chaos it is unlikely that economic, social or environmental aims will be furthered.

What can be done to improve society's ability to make rational decisions in the land use and environmental planning field? The following section outlines a number of approaches to planning which may perhaps prove useful. First, levels and types of land-oriented planning are discussed, and then in the following brief section a number of ways of incorporating environmental features in the planning process are discussed.

LEVELS AND TYPES OF PLANNING

Speaking in very general terms we can think of two main types of planning activity: mission oriented planning, which includes policy program, and project planning activities; and place-oriented planning, such as site plans, area plans and regional land use plans. Figure 3 depicts this simple classification.

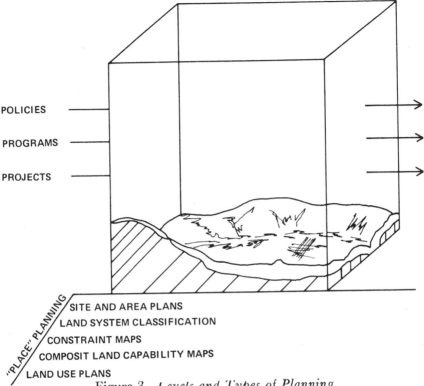

POLICIES

PROGRAMS

PROJECTS

"PLACE" PLANNING

SITE AND AREA PLANS
LAND SYSTEM CLASSIFICATION
CONSTRAINT MAPS
COMPOSIT LAND CAPABILITY MAPS
LAND USE PLANS

Figure 3. *Levels and Types of Planning*

MISSION-ORIENTED PLANS.

Policy-only plans. The "highest" level of planning I term "policy-only" planning. It connotes decisions which have important environmental and land use *effects* but which are couched in terms which preclude the determination of site specific and environmental effects. For example, at the policy-only level decisions are being formulated today in the energy policy which will have sweeping ramifications for the Upper Colorado Region. These general policies are aimed at magnitude of energy output and have only secondary implications for particular places or environmental concerns. Decisions on oil import quotas, Alaska resource development, off-shore oil, exploitation and the safety of nuclear reactors all have extremely important implications vis a vis strip mining for coal and oil shale in the Upper Colorado Region. At stake is the strip mining of large areas in Wyoming, Utah, and Colorado, the proposed detonation of possibly hundreds of nuclear devices for natural gas stimulation, and the inevitable lowering of air quality from fossil fuel burning power plants. Energy policy would divert water from agricultural and recreational uses for consumptive use in power plants. In short, the environmental health of the region is directly linked to these higher level policies. However, at the moment, there is no sure linkage between the special and physical effects in the Upper Colorado and the data being utilized to make national energy policy decisions.

Program Planning. The most common type of planning today is that at the next level, that of program or functional planning, e.g., planning for highways, lumbering, housing, sewage treatment, recreation and the like. These programs, of course, have special and environmental implications, but as at the higher level of planning, it is not commonly clear within the planning process exactly which areas of land or which environments will be effected. For example, a timber plan might outline the level of cut and the National Forest from which the cut is to be derived, but the exact location of the logging shows, the watersheds to be roaded, and so on will be left to later more detailed decisions. Similarly in energy planning a certain resource such as coal or oil shale might be assigned a target output figure but the acreages to be mined would be left for subsequent study. This type of mission oriented planning has been perfected to something of a fine art over the past two decades. Yet, because these plans suboptimize, and since they are single purpose, they have come under increasing fire from the public and the courts. A further problem is that it is always presumed that the single purpose plans are somehow coordinated with other similar plans, that is, that the highway, timber, recreation, housing, energy, and related plans are somehow, somewhere made compatible and synthesized into a final planning operation. My review of Federal agency planning operations as well as those of state and local government lead me to believe that nowhere does one find an integrated set of single-purposed plans such that a comprehensive decision can be made.

Project Planning. It is at this next level of planning that policies and programs impinge upon the ground and where the ramifications of general policies and programs become clear. Since the passage of the National Environmental Policy Act project planning has become the key focal point for environmental and land use planning. This is no doubt the best level for determining site specific environmental effects.

At Berkeley, Professor Luna Leopold and I are reviewing the more than 50 Federal impact statements for the Upper Colorado Basin. We do note an improvement in the quality of these statements and in the ability of all agencies to foresee the environmental implication of specific projects. However, a continuing shortcoming that most impact statements face (since they are conducted at the project level) is that the regional development implications, project interlinkages (e.g. water required for power), land-use effects and the like are very difficult to handle in a project-by-project format. For example, the six volume impact statement on the Interior's oil shale leasing program is now out, with a conclusion that in spite of all the data on the specific lease sites, the most important impact will be that of regional development, which is really beyond the scope of the impact statement itself.

PLACE-ORIENTED PLANS

The second generic type of planning is that which is oriented toward jurisdiction of place. These are county and city master plans, Bureau of Land Management unit area plans, Forest Service unit plans, Park Service composit plans, site plans as prepared by developers, or other sets of documents, maps and policies tied to a specific, boundaried area. Although this type of planning is traditional, it is now just coming into its own. True, general plans and master plans had relatively little effect on streams of decisions we've just been discussing. But with growing public awareness and new legislation, we are beginning to see some projects which flow into them.

Perhaps, at this point, it would be useful to define what is meant by environmental or land use planning, and that is: the conduct of policy, program and project planning as it effects—and is effected by—a given jurisdiction or planning area. It is the meshing of decision streams with an areal or spacial perspective and responsibility.

APPROACHES TO INCORPORATING ENVIRONMENTAL CONSIDERATIONS IN THE PLANNING PROCESS

Since there is a gap between place oriented environmental concern and the streams of decisions which are not place-related but do

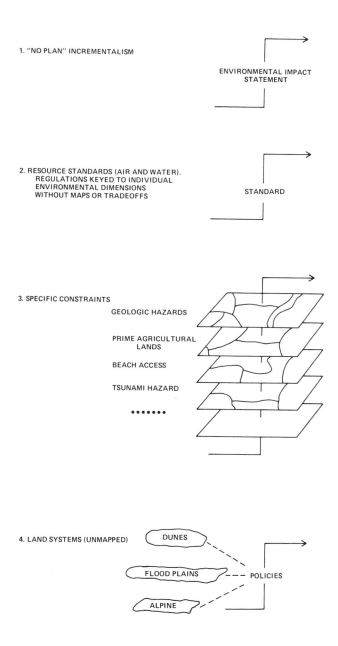

Figure 4. *Nine Approaches to Environmental Planning*

5. LAND SYSTEMS (MAPPED)

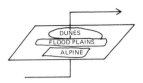

6. COMPOSIT LAND CAPABILITY

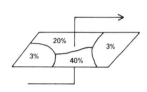

7. TWO MAP PLAN

LAND USE AND DENSITY   – – – – –

COMPOSITE LAND CAPABILITY
(% COVERAGE)   – – – – –

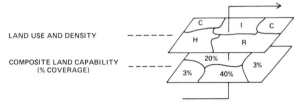

8. MASTER PLAN (LAND USE AND DENSITY)

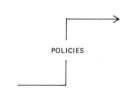

POLICIES

9. MASTER PLAN (LAND USE, DENSITY AND COVERAGE)

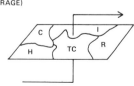

have environmental significance, we must utilize some professional planning tools to insure the incorporation of linkage of environmental information. Figure 4 depicts nine different approaches or archetypes that have been used in an attempt to insure linkage between spacial or mission-oriented and environmental considerations.

1. "No-Plan" Incrementalism. The first approach for the incorporation of environmental variables in planning is that exemplified by the National Environmental Policy Act, in that it focuses on individual projects or programs. No program coordination or overall synthesis is attempted by this type of planning but rather it is hoped that through ad hoc project-by-project review the wost environmental problems can be minimized. It is true that the various projects are "planned" in terms of policy planning or program planning but it is admitted at this level of environmental planning that no specially oriented planning apparatus exists and that impact must be judged in each case *de novo*.

2. Resource Standards. Here the expected outcomes of decisions are compared to standards or regulations keyed to individual dimensions of the environment. The planning process is essentially one of comparing designs against published regulations, as in the fields of air and water pollution control. If all regulations are satisfied, it is presumed that an environmentally sound plan has been created. There is no provision at this level for tradeoffs between air, water and other environmental concerns. The standards exist in isolation as a fiat which cannot be modified except by extraordinary means. Hence, it is possible that, for example, air quality regulations will force industrial development into a region of high seismic risk or high scenic quality, because the planning response is to existing regulations. Those environmental dimensions without a set of standards cannot be taken into account in the decision-making process.

3. Multiple Constaint Maps. In this approach each important environmental concern is expressed in a map depicting the location and intensity of the environmental variable. For example, the land use plan for the island of Kauai in Hawaii essentially consists of a set of constraint maps. One map represents geological hazards, another prime agricultural lands and another beach access, another tsunami hazard and so on. An ordinance is written against each map individually which in effect says, development may occur anywhere on

the island as long as the maps and ordinances are used as a screen in the planning process. The effect is to make development in hazardous or sensitive areas more receptive to environmental problems. The degree to which development can take place depends on the sophistication in design and the expense the developer and consumer are willing to pay. The advantages of this system are that it provides considerable flexibility, leaving the ultimate planning decisions to the developer's and land owner's abilities to work their way through the system. A disadvantage is that there is no way to foresee the likely outcome of these development decisions such that one can forecast and coordinate changes in land use.

4. Land Systems (unmapped). The best example of this approach is that being applied to the state of Washington's coastline wherein regulations are keyed to types of environments, such as sand dunes, estuaries, or cliffed coasts. Policies and regulations can be made specific to the environmental situation expected to cause problems in the planning area and hence, the policies can be more easily administered efficiently and fairly. Some flexibility remains in the definition and mapping of specific environmental units. Therefore, regional planning is difficult in that the designation of zones is left until the specific site plans are prepared. However, regional planners can get some estimate of the situations likely to occur and attempt to take measures toward coordination and amelioration.

5. Land Systems (Mapped). This approach is very similar to that in number 4 except in addition to the specification of environmental types of zones, these areas are mapped in an atlas or set of maps classifying land as to land systems. This makes the procedure more complete in that developers, land owners and planners alike can see how the regulations will play out on the ground, and estimate the effects on social and natural structure. However, it implies that a rather massive effort of environmental inventory and analysis precede the development process. The best example here is the Florida coast for which regulations are keyed in some measure to a coastal environmental atlas.

6. Composite Land Capability Map. Here the professional planning task is taken a step further in that the professionals attempt to synthesize constraint maps and land systems into a single map expressing key environmental features. In other words, the "carrying

2.   The states should enact environmental quality acts to invoke the environmental impact assessment process in state and local actions and permits. This could be done by the states individually, or better, through the interstate compact process recommended above.

3.   A region-wide inventory and evaluation should focus on the preparation of a land systems approach to aid in the planning process (types 4 or 5 of the previous section). This would provide a foil for plans, policies and programs covering the region.

4.   Sets of constraint maps should be prepared by the regional planning agency for local and regional government use. It is much more efficient for these to be prepared at the regional level to take the burden off individual developers and overworked local governments. The application of these maps would still be conducted at the lowest levels of government.

5.   A regional planning information center should be established through a consortium of universities from the concerned states. We face serious social, political and economic questions in the immediate future and a serious need exists for a semi-autonomous and independent source of planning assistance. Since planning data can result in benefits to one county or state over another, the credibility of the information source is important. No industry consultant, or local government report can provide the kind of plan review and evaluation that is going to be neeeded. Granted that no data can be "value free" or unbiased, we must still seek to design a structure of planning support that will minimize bias and provide objective sources of information.

6.   At the Federal level, the Council on Environmental Quality should establish the Colorado River Basin as an environmental planning unit for the purpose of coordinated impact assessment. A set of guidelines specific to the region should be constructed to serve as an aid to impact assessment. This would help insure compatibility between statements and allow those concerned with the social, economic, and environmental status of the region to begin to piece together cumulative and growth inducing or inhibiting effects of the many federal programs. Also, such questions as water quality, minimum stream flow, the use of utility corridors, and other issues could be spelled out in more detail suitable to the Colorado Region's problems.

7.   A single Federal administrator should be appointed by the President to provide a focal point for Federal activity in the region.

His function might be essentially coordinative and this would be of some limited value. But more significantly, the Federal administrator should be assigned responsibility for actions of extreme importance, which reach across agency lines, or are of region-wide concern. A key example here would be that the Interior oil shale leases should be administered not by the Mining Supervisor at the Division Level of the Geologic Survey. This task can be responsibly covered only by a Federal Administrator, responsible to all facets of land, water, and resource development, and with authority to coordinate the activities of the U.S.G.S., the Bureau of Land Management, E.P.A., the Department of Transportation, the Bureau of Reclamation, F.H.A. and other agencies which must be actively involved if the growth inducing and cumulative effects of these leases are to be considered.

Some of these recommendations could be rather quickly achieved by executive order or independent state action. Others will require a concerted effort on the part of many formerly opposing groups. I am sure there are other recommendations which can be developed that will be more viable. But some positive steps must be taken, and soon, to further the process of environmental planning and management.

Recreation Workshop Summary

QUESTION: How can the public best participate in planning decisions?

CONSENSUS: No consensus was reached on this problem except to say that more public participation in the planning process is needed. There are many ways to achieve this, and it was recommended that research be conducted to identify them and make them operational especially with regard to non-resident inputs.

Social values should act as a catalyst or driving force for regional planners. The goal here is for those people who have an interest in the plan to have some input to the planning process, either directly to the plan formulation or to plan evaluation. In this regard, the role of the professional planner is to describe the plan clearly enough so as to make it understandable to the general public.

QUESTION: How can effective coordination among decision-makers and jurisdictions be achieved?

CONSENSUS: There was disagreement as to how much centralization of authority is needed or desirable, but coordination among institutions is required.

QUESTION: How can the planner possibly effectively integrate public preference data, price data, into a comprehensive format when the best economitricians have difficulty doing the same thing to achieve much more narrowly defined goals in private industry (witness the Edsel)?

CONSENSUS: Uncertainty as to future events requires any plan to be flexible; the planner must recognize the range of human response within the realm of the search for experiences, recreational activity, economic security, or anything else. A serious trade-off is presented here in that changing plans implies that private and public developers face uncertain planning constraints.

RECOMMENDATION: Research should be conducted into the different effects of different institutional decision making processes. Processes differ in the reward they give to various kinds of talents in terms of positions, wealth, and activities. Therefore, predictions as to income distribution and other factors which are the results of each institutional framework would be valuable.

CHAPTER X

An Examination of the Environmental Carrying Capacity Concept for the Agricultural Sector of the Colorado River Basin

Gerald W. Thomas*

The "carrying capacity" concept is an excellent vehicle for examing the agricultural industry in the world, the hemisphere, or a particular nation. It is much harder to use the concept when studying a region such as the Colorado River Basin because of, (1) the immigration and outmigration of people and their interrelationships with surrounding territories, (2) the inflow of resources, goods and services and, (3) the movement of resources, goods and services out of the area. However, in spite of these variables it is still a valid and useful tool, particularly when the approach includes:

(1) the capacity of the environment to supply resources for food and fiber activities (*supportive capacity*) and,

(2) the capacity of the environment to act as a sink for wastes produced from these activities (*assimilative capacity*).

Further complications arise concerning "carrying capacity" when one considers the variation in standards of living, impact of technology, and levels of nutrition. It is an established fact that

*President, New Mexico State University, Los Cruces, New Mexico.
Management Conference, Salt Lake City, Utah, October 15-16, 1973.

wealthy people place more pressure on the resource base than poor people. Furthermore, wealthy people create more problems of waste and pollution—although they could, but usually do not—use their advanced technology to overcome these problems. I will give examples of these effects later in this paper.

In order to properly examine the environmental impact of people on the Colorado River Basin, it will be necessary to look first at the world situation—and at the U.S. as a whole. While "agriculture" to me means the total food and fiber sector, I am going to concentrate on food production. This is timely because food is in the news—and *even* American consumers are concerned about food supplies and food prices.

During the past few years we have witnessed *several* remarkable changes in the outlook toward food production. Ten years ago our economists were emphasizing our surplus production capacity and all of our grain storage facilities were full and overflowing. Then, in 1967, the Paddock Brothers issued a very depressing book entitled, *Famine 1975*, raising the issue of mass starvation.[1] Shortly after, new optimism developed with the advent of the "Green Revolution" as a result of the new genetic breakthroughs in the cereal grains. In November, 1971, a headline in a national magazine stated, *"The famine threat is fading in many parts of the world: The reason; scientific breakthroughs—and good weather."* A reference to the impact of the "Green Revolution."

Recently, another dimension has been added to the philosophical debate over the world food problem—another shift back toward pessimism. This comes about as a result of input from the science of ecology The new question is not "Can the world feed itself?", but rather, "Can the world *afford* to feed itself?" In other words, will the environment withstand the pressure of the technological changes necessary as we attempt to feed more and more people?

This latter question is a much more serious question—*because a contaminated environment affects the welfare of rich and poor alike*—whether or not we are all well nourished *or* hungry. It is also a more difficult question to answer due to lack of research information.

Coupled with the ominous predictions of certain environmentalists, pessimism is encourged by the recent food shortages (particularly

---

[1] William and Paul Paddock, *Famine—1975!* (Boston, Mass.: Little, Brown and Co., 1967).

beef) here at home, and the increased demand for our agricultural products by foreign buyers. The average citizen must think "If the pessimists aren't happy now, chances are they will never be!" Even one of the program planners for this event was heard to say, "Ho boy—It's a good thing things are not always as bad as they are most of the time." For myself, there are only *two* things that bother me, one, that *things may never get "back to normal," and the other, that they already have!*

It is apparent from any analysis of this type that, on a world-wide basis, we are nearing the upper limits of world population growth. Of course, some countries and some regions still have much flexibility—partly at the expense of other areas. But, *for the world as a whole, a massive effort must be made to curtail the population explosion and bring people and resources into balance.* Uncontrolled population growth is rapidly eroding away scientific progress, creating unprecedented problems of malnutrition, and reducing the effectiveness of millions of dollars of aid to undeveloped countries. In addition, most of man's activities, whether we realize it or not, have some detrimental effects on our environment. These effects are already very serious, but will reach much more critical stages before the world approaches the 6.5 billion people predicted by the year 2000.[2]

WORLD-WIDE FOOD NEEDS

Throughout man's history, food scarcity has been the accepted way of life. According to recent estimates, this still is a crucial fact for more than half of the world's 3.7 billion people. As recently as 1943, famine took the lives of 3 million people in India and another 3 million in China. Today's headlines still carry depressing stories of widespread hunger in impoverished sections of Asia, Africa, and Latin America. In March of this year an article in *U.S. News and World Report* was headlined, *"Asia's Trouble Returns: Too Many Babies, Too Little Food."* In July a headline read, *"World Experiencing Greatest Peacetime Food Shortage."* And, again on August 11, a headline in the *Albuquerque Journal* read, *"Famine Danger Figure Doubles,"* emphasizing that 12 million people in six North African countries, due to a serious drought, are threatened with famine and another one million in Ethiopia are near starvation. Eighty percent of the live-

[2]Population Reference Bureau, Inc., *1972 World Population Data,* Washington, D.C.

stock in this area have died. Obviously, the "Green Revolution" has not solved all the world's problems. But, as Nobel Prize Winner, Norman Borlaug, has emphasized in one of his frequent addresses,

> We have never maintained that we were solving all problems (with the Green Revolution), but, on the contrary, simply assisting various governments to harness their resources so as to provide more food for its hungry people. What do we hear about this from some of the critics and doomsayers in the affluent countries—such as the U.S.A. and Sweden? 'You are creating more problems than you are solving. You are making the rich richer and the poor poorer. You must know that Malthus was right. You are destroying the environment . . .?[3]

In an answer to the question, "Where would we be without this new genetic material—without the Green Revolution?" Dr. Borlaug states,

> During the past five years a number of the most populous countries in Asia, with whom we have been privileged to work, have made excellent progress in expanding their cereal grain productions, especially wheat. For example, India during 1972 harvested $26\frac{1}{2}$ million metric tons of wheat, making it the third largest producer in the world (exceeded only by the USSR and the USA) contrasted to a harvest of $12\frac{1}{2}$ million tons in 1965. I dread to think of what the plight of India would have been during the past year if it had been forced to import 12 millon tons of wheat in competion with the USSR on the grain-short, price-inflated international market. Despite this excellent progress, India and a number of other developing nations who have been undergoing a Green Revolution, are being criticized by some for their action and progress.

> It is my belief that food is the moral right for all who are born into this world. The question of how many should be born into this world is another issue. Without food, all other components of social justice are meaningless. I am also convinced that world order and peace can not be built nor maintained on empty bellies and abject poverty. This should be readily apparent to even political ideologists and to advocates of utopian environments. (Borlaug, *Challenges*.)

---

[3]Norman E. Borlaug. *Challenges Remain*. Vital Speeches of the Day, Vol. XXXIX, No. 18, July 1, 1973, pp. 554-58.

OUR CHANGING FOOD HABITS

Changing food habits and processing techniques—particularly in the United States—has placed increased pressure on the environment and created more serious problems of pollution.

The first concern of man is for quantity—adequate bulk to dull the pangs of hunger. Where food is available, the total daily intake per person is about 4½ pounds. This total does not change significantly through the years. An American, for example, eats only 100 pounds per year less now than 50 years ago.[4]

Per capita consumption of meat in the U.S. has increased rather consistently (with the exception of lamb). Beef consumption alone has increased from 48 pounds per person, per year in 1930 to over 115 pounds per person per year, today. Each person consumes more fruit— a shift from apples to more citrus and processed fruits. We eat fewer eggs and less dairy products. Sugar consumption per capita is up.

Two rather significant changes deserve special comment. First, direct consumption of cereal grains is down. However, this figure is misleading, because *the grains are going into meat production and into highly refined packaged products.* The U.S. and Canada still utilize over 1600 pounds of grain per person per year, compared with 400 pounds in Iran, Morocco, Japan, U.A.R., Pakistan, Thailand and India.[5] This difference in grain use is four-fold, but, if the world's 3.7 billion people consumed grains at the U.S.-Canadian levels, the total world production would have to be increased 8 times.

Secondly, I want to mention potatoes. I once wrote a paper entitled "Power, Politics and 'Peal of the Potato." This important food product has shaped the lives and destiny of nations. While Idaho has become nationally known as the potato state, the potato is not native to Idaho. Neither did the "Irish potato" originate in Ireland. Rather, the wild forms of potato originated, and were first collected and cultivated, by the native Indians in the Andes Mountains of South America near Lake Titicaca.[6] Early Spanish explorers brought the first small potatoes or "earth nuts" to Europe about 1570.

The potato became, in time, such a popular article of the diet of the Irish that it eventually was grown almost to the exclusion of other

---

[4]Marguerite C. Burk. *Pounds and Percentages in Food,* Yearbook of Agriculture, 1959, pp. 561-600.

[5]Lester R. Brown. *Population and Affluence: Growing Pressures on World Food Resources.* Population Reference Bureau, Inc. Vol. 29, No. 2. 1973.

[6]Donavan S. Correll. *The Potato and Its Wild Relatives.* Texas Research Foundation, Renner, Texas. 1968, 606 pp.

crops. The super-abundance of an easily produced food also caused a population explosion on the Island. These two factors, working together, led to the disastrous famines of 1845-1846, when a blight killed the potato crop. One million people in Ireland died of starvation during this "potato famine" and many more migrated out of the country.

At the time the potato reached Europe the Spanish Conquistadores were intensely preoccupied wih the "rape of South America." In spite of their over-riding concern for precious metals, *in all likelihood they introduced the "real" treasure to the rest of the world in the "potato"*—because, the value of the world's annual yield of potatoes— some 6.5 billion hundred weight—far exceeds the value of all the gold and silver that was ravaged from the South American Continent during the centuries of conquest. Today, the average American consumes about 112 pounds of potatoes per year—only about half the level of consumption reached in the early 1900's. And, ecologically, the substitutes for potatoes as well as for cereals, have placed increased pressure on the environment.

Coupled with our changing diets has been our obsession with intensive processing, refinement and packaging of many food products— even to the point where food values are affected. And, certainly, these built-in maid services are expensive—economically as well as ecologically.

THE LAND RESOURCE BASE

To understand the pressure of man's food needs on the land resource it will be necessary to examine a few basic statistics. Only about 29 per cent of the earth's surface is land area—water covers 71 per cent of the earth. And, *much of the land area is cold, too hot, too dry or too high for traditional agricultural use.* If we study more closely that important portion of the land which is "arable" (land suited for cultivation) we find a critical world picture. I want to do this in the simplest way possible—by looking at the world's cultivated land base in relation to our individual needs for food.

It is estimated that, with the present technology of the developed countries, about one acre of cultivated land per person is desirable to produce enough food for an adequate standard of living. This means that your food needs—and mine—regardless of whether we live in the city or in the country, are related back to this one acre requirement.

At the present time, the Far East has only 0.8 acres per person. Communist Asia has 0.4 acres per person. Is it any wonder that there are still conflicts over land? The amount of arable land per person in Latin America is about 1.3 acres; Africa and West Asia, about 2.3 acres. These latter areas now have a surplus in relation to land needs for food.

For the world, the cultivated acreage now stands at about 3.5 billion acres, or 11 per cent of the earth's land surface. The area actually harvested for crops in a given year is considerably less, due to fallow practices and crop failures—usually about 2.4 billion acres. *This means that we now have only 0.65 acres of usable cultivated land per person in the world compared with our need for one acre per person.*

The last President's Science Panel on the World Food Problem estimated that there are about 7.86 billion acres of land in the world that are suitable for cultivation under optimum conditions and another

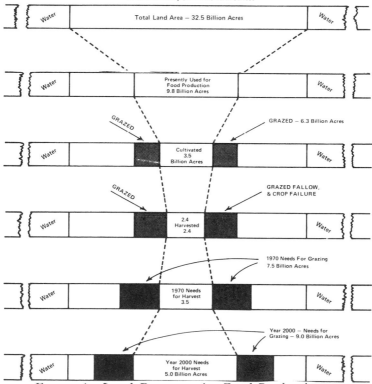

FIGURE 1. *Land Resources for Food Production*

9 billion acres which have a potential for grazing.[7] This optimistic projection is based upon the physical resources only and would be very difficult to attain under realistic social, political, and economic restraints. Figure 1 shows my estimates of present and potential land needs.[8]

Historically man has increased the food supply by expanding the area under cultivation. There are still good opportunities for additional land development in Africa and South America according to the World Food Panel Study. However, it should be emphasized that many densely populated less developed countries have nearly exhausted the supply of new land that can readily be brought under cultivation. These countries are now essentially fixed land economies. If many new areas of potentially arable land are to develop mass migration of people may be necessary and huge expenditures of funds and energy will be needed.

Perhaps here we can bring in some comparisons. When I was working for the Soil Conservation Service right after World War II, we made an estimate of cultivated land needs for a "desirable standard of living." At that time it appeared that each person required about 2½ acres of cultivated land. At that time also, the U.S. had surplus land but the world average fell way short of minimum needs. Since World War II, due to increased yields and improved production technology, we have reduced the 2½ acre requirement to about 1 acre.

These statistics indicate fantastic progress at the farm and ranch level. But, our population continues to grow! Also, we are now exporting the production from one acre out of every four in the United States.[8] These exports have come under critical review during recent months. Never-the-less, we have an international obligation to the rest of the world and perhaps Agricultural sales abroad can help offset some of our balance-of-payments problems since we must import many kinds of goods, services and basic materials for our affluent society.

The United States has about 1.2 acres of cultivated land per capita and a maximum potential of about 2 acres per capita using

[7]President's Science Advisory Panel on World Food Supply. *The World Food Problem.* The White House, May 1967, 712 pp.

[8]Gerald W. Thomas. *The Ecology of Food Production,* KASALS Contribution No. 79. Texas Tech University, Lubbock, Texas, 30 pp.

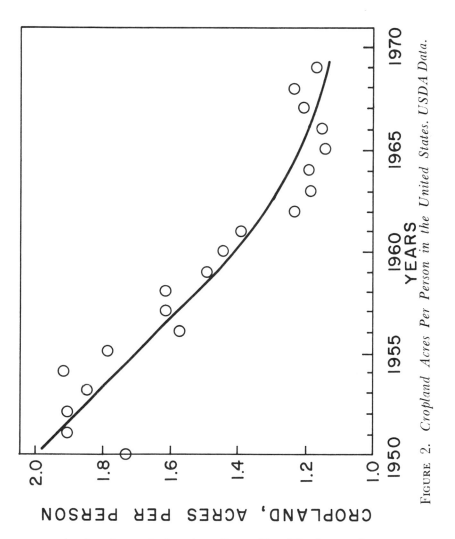

CROPLAND, ACRES PER PERSON

FIGURE 2. *Cropland Acres Per Person in the United States. USDA Data.*

present levels of population (see figure 2). We do not know as yet what the new farm policies will do to the acres per person statistics— nor do we know the effects of expanded acreage on per acre yields. The experience of many countries has shown that most efforts to expand cultivated acreage have resulted in reduced per acre yields. In this country farmers were already using the very best lands for cultivation. However, Carr and Culver[9], in a recent paper on *Agriculture, Population and the Environment* concluded:

> American Agriculture appears capable, in terms of resource adequacy, technology, and structural flexibility, of meeting the challenges to the year 2000.

In the Upper Colorado River Basin we find about 8 acres of cultivated land per person[10] and in the Lower Colorado Region we find about 7 acres of cultivated land per person.[11] This represents a tremendous base and indicates our potential to supply other parts of the U.S. and other nations of the world.

Any analysis of man's impact on the cultivated land base—particularly in the Colorado River Basin—must include an examination of the effects of irrigation. Irrigation, or other methods of water control, makes possible the full use of technology in food production. It brings out the genetic potential of plants. It increases the effectiveness of fertilizers. It allows for crop rotations designed to maintain organic matter or reduce erosion. Water management increases the production of land two- to four-fold and reduces our base land requirements accordingly.

There are approximately 380 million acres of irrigated land in the world—about 11 per cent of the total arable land. The United States now has approximately 42 million acres of agricultural land under irrigation[12] Most of this irrigation—both from surface and underground water sources—is in the semi-arid and arid west. This irrigated cropland, although only 10 percent of the total U.S. cropland, contributes nearly 20 percent of the total farm income from crops.

A high percentage of the cropland in the Colorado River Basin is irrigated and the potential for irrigation is still greater. However,

---

[9]A. Barry Carr and David W. Culver. *Agriculture, Population and the Environment.* Report of the Commission on Population Growth and the American Future, Supt. of Documents, Washington, D.C. 1972, 377 pp.

[10]Upper Colorado River Basin Group. *Upper Colorado Region Comprehensive Framework Study.* Water Resources Council, June 1971, 164 pp.

[11]Lower Colorado Region Group. *Lower Colorado Region Comprehensive Framework Study.* Pacific Southwest Interagency Committee Main Report, June, 1971, 149 pp.

[12]U.S. Water Resources Council. *The Nation's Water Resources.* Washington, D.C., 1968, 175 pp.

in view of the Water Commission Report, the prevailing attitudes of people, and the shortage of water, it is unlikely that the irrigated crop-land acreage will expand. Rather, continued transfers of water will be made from the agricultural sector to municipal and industrial uses. I am alarmed at this trend and I am concerned about statements made—even in the scientific community—that agriculture should move to the humid areas of the United States. If this transfer occurs, we can anticipate further increases in the price of food. Many of our high rainfall areas have poor soils, low fertility conditions, smaller and less efficient farms and more problems with insects and disease. I will enlarge on this concern in the discussion of the water resource.

Uncultivated Land

By far the largest acreage of land in the world is classified as "uncultivated" and part of this is completely devoid of vegetation. For those areas supporting vegetation, grazing by livestock and wildlife is the major use. Forests occupy about 11 billion acres of uncultivated land, with one-third of this forest classified as commercial and two-thirds non-commercial.

Range and forest lands present a complicated ecosystem for study and management. Not only is there a need for research on the energy flow and nutrient cycling at any one time, but a careful evaluation must be made, *through time,* of the vegetation and soil succession-regression patterns.

The ruminant animal, both domesticated and wild, through its ability to convert roughage to edible meat, is the primary means of making productive use of grazing lands. It has been estimated that two-thirds of all feed required by livestock in the United States is derived from grasslands.[13] On a world-wide basis, most of the world's 1.15 billion cattle and buffalo, 1.0 billion sheep, and over 500 million goats spend part or all of their lives on range or pasture lands.

To relate man's needs back to the uncultivated land base is difficult and somewhat dangerous. Also, there are some complicated inter-relationships between range land and cropland. For example, much of the cropland production is devoted to winter feed for range live-stock. I prefer to approach this problem by making some generalized

[13]H. R. Sprague. *The Importance of Grasslands to Our National Life.* American Grassland Council, Jan. 29, 1967, 12 pp.

statements. There is presently, and there will always be, a shortage of uncultivated lands to satisfy man's utopian needs.

For many years we have approached the management of native vegetation resources on the basis of the "multiple-use concept." That is, these lands have value to the individual and to society for more than one purpose. Though the primary income may be from livestock or forest products, the lands also are important from the standpoint of wildlife, recreation, and water yield.

We must now add another dimension to our "multiple-use" approach to uncultivated lands—that is, we must now carefully consider their value in environmental enhancement—particularly air and water quality. It may well be that when all of the data are analyzed, the contribution of our vast uncultivated lands to pollution control and to the total environmental balance will outweigh all other value from these lands.

Many range ecologists believe that it is possible to double our livestock productivity on the vast western range. Such an increase will depend on our ability to manage the vegetation properly as well as on the competitive pressures from recreation and other possible uses. Trends on Federal lands, which occupy about two-thirds of the Colorado River Basin, have been downward during the past several decades. These trends likely will continue (see figure 3).

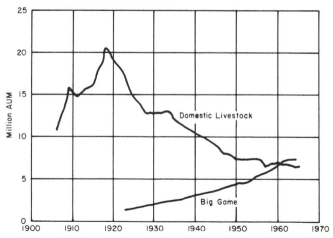

FIGURE 3. *Comparative amounts of Big Game and Domestic Livestock on Federal Lands.*

LAND POLLUTION

Improper land use is one of the most insidious forms of land pollution. Poor land use does not necessarily imply a reduction in absorptive carrying capacity of the environment, but it may cause a reduction in the "supportive" carrying capacity due to the impact on the resource base, i.e., reduction in farm land due to encroachment by urban development. Improper land-use planning and follow-up practices will, however, seriously affect the "quality of life" of the people. It is my firm belief that a desirable living environment is one in which open space is provided for elbow room and an opportunity think and recreate. It is one which preserves the natural features of the environment—the aesthetics of the area. It is one which promotes enjoyable living and enhances the attitudes of people. These and other "quality of life" factors are difficult to measure but important to each of us—and they become more difficult to maintain as population and economic pressures increase.

Disposal of solid wastes can be a form of land pollution or an improper land-use. It will not be necessary here to go into detail and the statistics of the solid waste problem in the U.S. "Of all the agriculture's problems with pollution, one of the most costly to overcome appears to be the disposal of solid wastes. These account for over one-half of the total solid wastes produced in the United States. Every day 3.5 million tons of raw manure are produced, accompanied by a million tons of liquid waste."[9]

The problem of finding land (and in some cases, condemning land) for the so-called "sanitary land fill" is a serious concern of both metropolitan and rural people. Many cities have exhausted their available space for dumps. With present techniques, one acre of new land filled to a depth of 10 feet is required for solid waste disposal for each 10,000 people per year.[14] Elimination of burning in dumps, while it does alleviate the air pollution problem, increases the land requirement per capita for waste disposal.

Changes in the chemical or physical properties of the soil can be a serious form of land pollution. But, keep in mind that soil can also be "improved" by proper management. I was pleased to receive copies of correspondence between Dr. Roy Kottman, Dean of Agriculture at

---

[14]Philip H. Abelson. Waste Management and Control, *Science*. Vol. 152, April 15, 1966. p. 297.

Ohio State University and Dr. Michael Perelman, Professor of Economics at California State at Chico, California. Dr. Perelman made some rather sweeping statements in the October issue of *Environment* which stirred some controversy among agricultural circles.[15] While part of the Perelman paper dealt with energy, there were also serious charges about pollution from heavy fertilization and from the use of pesticides.

Perelman states that "heavy fertilizer applications *upset* the balance of nutrients in the soil and induce deficiencies in our foods." Kottman counters that "the *purpose* of fertilization is to eliminate mineral deficiencies and to improve the balance of nutrients for the *purpose* of improving plant growth and the mineral content of plant products. . . . There is no evidence that the mineral content of plants is rendered deficient by fertilization." Kottman also countered charges of pollution from herbicides with the following statements:

> Further, there is research evidence to show that, contrary to speculation by some, herbicides do not leach into the subsoil in appreciable quantities, that they do not render the soil permanently sterile when they are used in accordance with the label, and that they do *not* occur in meat or milk. Most commercial herbicides now in use are low in toxicity to man and animals.

You will note in this statement that Dr. Kottman confined his remarks to "herbicides" and to "fertilizers." Certain "Insecticides" may be another problem. Never-the-less, the literature indicates a difference of opinion. The problem of nitrates in certain watersheds is unresolved. The movement of certain pesticides in the food chain has not been adequately studied. We have more questions than answers about soil pollution as it relates to the production of agricultural products. But, we do know that the soil is a great acceptor of man's waste products. Soils cleanse carbon monoxide from the air and convert a gaseous pollutant into a gaseous resource.[16] Soils sustain life and are a part of the natural systems. Our challenge is to

---

[15]Michael Perleman. Farming with Petroleum, *Environment*, Vol. 14, No. 8, October, 1972. pp. 8-13.

[16]Gary H. Heichel. Soil Recycles Carbon Monoxide. *Frontier of Plant Science*, May, 1973. pp. 4-5.

understand—to manage—and to prevent soil deterioration or pollution.

Changes in vegetative cover are a serious form of land pollution. These changes can be brought about by over-grazing, by timber harvest, by cultivation, by recreational pressure, or by metropolitan development. We have evidence of desert encroachment in the arid and semi-arid west. Through poor management we have reduced the infiltration of rainfall and changed the hydrologic cycle. Perhaps we have influenced weather patterns. No one really knows. The need for research is obvious.

THE WATER RESOURCE

Water is truly the key to a quality environment in the Colorado River Basin as well as in many other parts of the west. Furthermore, it is probably the most important—and most limiting factor—in growth and development of the area.

The demand for water is increasing at an alarming rate. We need water not only to supply a growing population base, but to take care of increased pressures associated with affluence and technological development. The U.S. Water Resources Council estimated that, before the year 2020, industrial, municipal, domestic and power requirements for fresh water in this Country are expected to reach 1000 billion gallons per day.[17] This is about three times the total withdrawn for *all* purposes today. Such a demand would leave *no* water for agriculture, which presently accounts for 41 percent of the present total withdrawals.

These kinds of projected needs not only alarm the average U.S. citizen, but they really shock those of us already faced with water shortages in the arid southwest. It is time that we ask ourselves some very serious questions about this most valuable resource—and about our future as it may be related to water use and development.

The first and most basic question is, "How much water is required per person?" Is water quantity a limiting factor in "carrying capacity?" This is a single and straight-forward question, but to arrive at an answer is very, very difficult. We know that we need only about two quarts daily for drinking, but even in the early 1900's, our home use of water was about 10 gallons per person per day. Now, each

---

[17]Associated Press News Release, *Albuquerque Journal,* dated Feb. 6, 1969.

of us is using about 200 gallons per day for home use. In addition, we need water to produce food, to refine oil, to manufacture automobiles and to operate our growing metropolis. Our total withdrawals in the U.S. now amount to about 1300 gallons per person per day. So, we might again ask the question, "how much water is required per person—2 quarts? 180 gallons? or over 1300 gallons per day?"

Let's approach the question in a different way. What standard of living are we willing to accept? A recent study in California will serve to illustrate the general relationship between standard of living and water use. In 1968, residents of Beverly Hills, where per capita income was $4929, used an average of 313 gallons of water per day for home use. This compares with 89 gallons per person per day in Compton where the per capita income was only $1727.[17] Should we be satisfied with 89 or go to 313 gallons per person per day for home use, or should we get by with the 20 or 30 gallons common to most people of the world in metropolitan areas?

It should be fairly simple to calculate the per capita water requirements for business, industry and municipalities, but what about water for food production? To grow a pound of wheat in the field will require about 1,500 pounds of water. If we follow this wheat on through the milling processes, with average losses, and to the completed bread, we find that over 2,500 pounds of water are used to produce one pound of bread. To produce one pound of rice may require as much as two tons of water.

As we introduce animal protein or other essentials for balanced diet, the water requirements are increased correspondingly. For example, on some brush infested semi-arid rangelands in the west, from 100 to over 500 tons of water are involved in the process of producing one pound of beef—measured at the supermarket level.

This does not mean that 100 tons of water are "required" to produce a pound of beef—but it does mean that this much water is "involved in" or "associated with" the production of a pound of beef. Much of the water involved in range beef production is dissipated by undesirable weeds and brush or evaporates from the unprotected soil surface. Also, most of the water necessary to the process of photosynthesis in range plants is transpired through the plant and returned to the atmosphere.

Purely from a water efficiency standpoint, we can increase the effectiveness of water use for beef production at least 10 times by producing animal feeds on irrigated lands and confining the animals to a dry-lot during the production period. But this is only part of the story. A "quality" environment involves considerations other than efficiency or economy of water use.

I would like to go back and enlarge on a statement made earlier—namely, that more units of water are required per person as our standard of living rises. Canada and the United States utilize over 1600 pounds of grain per person per year compared with 400 pounds for Iran, Morocco, Japan, UAR, Pakistan, Thailand, and India. This difference in grain use is four-fold, but if the U.S.-Canadian levels were projected across the world's population, the grain use would be nearly 8 times the present world population.[18] In terms of water use, Canada and the U.S. would require 1600 tons of water per person per year to produce their grain needs, but India and Pakistan must get by with 400 tons of water per year—assuming the same level of efficiency.[19]

The U.S. has increased its beef consumption from 48 pounds per person per year in 1930 to over 115 pounds per person in 1973. Japan gets by on about 16 pounds. Even with good efficiency, our water requirements for beef consumption per capita would be over 1100 tons compared with 160 tons per year for the average Japanese.

Research on both cropland and native range areas indicates that, as a general principle, we can increase the effective use of water in the agricultural sector by concentrating our limited resources on a smaller area of land. On range areas this means more attention to mechanical land treatment, land shaping for modified water harvest, contour furrowing, water spreading, and micro-climate modification. On cropland this means level benching, other forms of water concentration and new techniques for irrigation.

With the growth of industry and the development of metropolitan areas, the competition for water has increased. At the present time, water for food production is in a lower priority than the use of water

---

[18]Brown, *Population and Affluence*: Growing Pressures on Food Resources. Population Reference Bureau, Inc. Vol. 29, No. 2, 1973. 45 p.

[19]Thadis W. Box and G. W. Thomas. *Ecology and the Use of Water Resources,* Proceedings of the West Texas Water Conference. Texas Tech University, February, 1970. 19 p.

by metropolitan areas or many industries. Water is also being transferred out of the agricultural sector for recreational land development.

For the Colorado River Basin, it is particularly important to
analyze the National Water Commission Report.[20] The following general conclusions of this Report would have a very serious impact on
the agricultural sector:

(1) *Land will not be scarce by 2000.* Output from U.S. farm and
range lands, including lands now set aside in government programs, will be adequate to meet projected food demands even at
the high level that would be expected if population increases to
325 million persons and some food exports grow to about twice
their 1967-1969 levels.

(2) *Expansion of irrigation is not needed to meet future food needs.*
Quite to the contrary. The most efficient pattern of production
at most projected demand levels would be achieved with a *reduction* in the acreage of irrigated land used for annual crops.

(3) *There will be no general shortage of water by the year 2000.*
Increased municipal and industrial demands can be met easily
(except for isolated localities) since (a) municipal and industrial
uses are very small relative to irrigation uses, (b) irrigation need
not, in fact should not, be expanded, and (c) if a tight situation
does arise, irrigation can be contracted to release the water needed
for municipal and industrial uses at *no increase in difficulty or
cost of food production.*

These conclusions of the National Water Commission Report have
been the subject of much controversy. The best review and critique
of this report, in my opinion, was prepared by the Western Agricultural Economics Research Council.[21] The council challenged some
assumptions of the so-called "Heady Report" on which the commission conclusions were based. The council also pointed to the need for
research:

[20]E. O. Heady, H. C. Madsen, K. J. Nicol and S. H. Hargrove. *Agricultural and Water Policies and the Environment.* CARD Report 40T. Iowa State
Unversity, June, 1972. 25 p.

[21]Western Agricultural Economics Research Council. Review and Critique:
Agricultural and Water Policies and the Environment. Undated.
19 p.

Some implications for agricultural research in Western states can be drawn from the report. There is a clear indication of need for more knowledge about relative costs of production on irrigated lands in comparison to drylands. Better cost and yield data would help to either confirm or refute the study's conclusion that costs are higher on irrigated lands. An improved study of water use and allocation in the region would also help to clear up some questions left by the study. The finding of relatively high costs for irrigated production suggests that research on means of reducing costs would be most helpful to the long-run health of irrigated agriculture. In fact, the study results suggest that cost-saving technology would be more important than water saving technology for most irrigated areas. Finally, improved knowledge and information programs about the process of adjustment for farmers, farm workers, and farm communities, would be very helpful if the study's projected decline for irrigated agriculture does in fact occur.

We are all concerned about water pollution. This problem ranges from direct contamination by improperly treated effluent discharge from towns and cities, to the problems of chemicals such as nitrate or phosphate accumulation and siltation from erosion. Farmers in the United States have made great strides in the conservation of soil and water since the dust bowl period. Yet much remains to be done. Water pollution also seriously inhibits water-based recreational activities. About one-fourth of all outdoor recreation is now dependent upon clean water.

The approach to water pollution control is, of necessity, quite different in the agricultural sector than for other business, industry, or for muncipalities. While water is truly a renewable natural resource, it can be cleaned up, pollutants removed *and recycled in the short run by municipalities and industry* rather rapidly with a technological and economic input. On the other hand, *water used for food and fiber production can be reused only in the long run* as it moves through the complicated hydrologic cycle. The use of this water as it passes through the cycle is the basis for life itself.

ENERGY AND AGRICULTURE

Recent publicity about the U.S. energy crisis has, for the most part, ignored the role of agriculture and the interdependence of agriculture and energy recources. The gigantic food and industry uses more petroleum products than any other industry in this country. Large amounts of energy are consumed in the "supply sector" to provide the farmer and rancher with fertilizers, pesticides, machinery, and other inputs. Large amounts of energy are used in the "production sector" for planting, cultivation, irrigation, care and harvesting of crops and livestock. Large amounts of energy are also consumed by the "storage, processing, packaging and distribution sector" of the food and fiber industry.[22]

Two aspects of energy flow patterns must be considered of vital importance to agriculture:

(1) The capture, conservation and utilization of photosynthetic energy produced by vegetation and,
(2) Energy subsidies (largely fossil fuels) to run the food and fiber systems.

All life on earth is supported by the solar energy in food, captured primarily by vegetation in the process of photosynthesis. *This chemical reaction involving carbon dioxide, water, and sunlight energy to produce food and release oxygen plus water through transpiration is the most important chemical reaction in the world.*

Primitive man harvested wildlife, insects, and wild plants for food energy as they became seasonally available. Under these conditions, the carrying capacity for the earth has been estimated as 10 million, a population smaller than that of London or Tokyo today.[23] As man learned to harvest surplus food, domesticate and cultivate crops, the carrying capacity of the land (for man) increased. The first major increase in carrying capacity resulted from the diversion of "surplus photosynthetic energy directly to man from other biological organisms. The next major breakthrough in carrying capacity came about when man found that he could "subsidize" the system with fossil fuels and thus increase the effective harvest of food and fiber.

Thus, through the diversion of surplus photosynthetic energy, through fossil fuel subsidies, and by other technological innovations, total food and fiber production on the earth has been increased many-

22Gerald W. Thomas. *Agriculture Faces the Energy Crisis.* New Mexico State University, June 15, 1973, 20 p.
23Lester R. Brown. Human Food Production as a Process in the Biosphere, in *The Biosphere,* Scientific American, Vol. 223, 1970, p. 160-70.

fold. The average daily per capita consumption of K calories in food now ranges from about 2000 in the Far East to over 3200 in North America. A daily diet of less than 1500 K calories is not uncommon for some of the world's 3.6 billion people. Yet a desirable standard should be about 3000 K calories per person per day with some variation for age and size of the individual.

A complete analysis of energy flow patterns must take into consideration the capture of energy by photosynthesis, the dissipation pattern of energy flow, and the inputs of outside energy to harvest and utilize the vegetation. Figure 4 presents a concept of energy flow on uncultivated lands. All the energy captured by the producer organisms is eventually consumed by animals (including man) and the organisms of decay.

On range lands, the ruminant animal, both domesticated and wild, through its ability to convert roughage to edible meat, is the primary means of making productive use of these areas. However, the conversion process is rather inefficient. On the average, less than one percent of the sunlight energy falling on a given area of range land is captured by the vegetation in the process of photosynthesis. Less than one-half of this vegetation can be safely consumed by grazing animals. Further reductions are shown in figure 5, which presents a concept of energy partitioning and disposition by ruminants.[24] Cook in Utah reported that ranchers could sell, in a good cow-calf operation, about 10 per cent of the energy consumed by the animal.[25] A study in California showed that 1/1000 of the radiant energy falling on an area was available to cattle and only 1/40,000 of the original energy reaches the food product, meat.[26]

The fossil fuel input for livestock production on range lands is relatively small because there is little energy required for supplies and production. Mechanized equipment on the ranch consists primarily of motor vehicles, tractors, or aircraft used for brush control, mechanical equipment for stock pond construction, etc. There are, how-

[24]Donald N. Hyder. *The Impact of Domestic Animals on the Function and Structure of Grassland Ecosystems.* Range Science Series No. 2, Colorado State University, 1969. pp. 243-260.

[25]C. Wayne Cook. *Energy Budget of the Range and Range Livestock.* Colorado State University Experiment Station Bull. TB 109. 1970. 28 p.

[26]Merton Love. The Rangelands of the Western U.S. *Scientific American,* 222 (2) : 1970, 88-96.

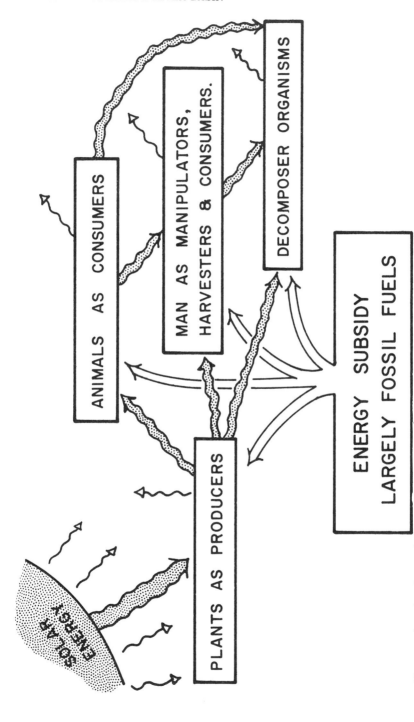

FIGURE 4. A schematic diagram of solar energy capture and utilization on uncultivated lands. Fossil fuel energy subsidies are relatively small compared with intensive crop production.

DAILY ENERGY INTAKE					
	DIGESTIBLE ENERGY				FECES
	METABOLIZABLE ENERGY			METHANE	FECES
			HEAT INCREMENT	URINE	FECES
	NET ENERGY	MAIN-TEN-ANCE	HEAT INCREMENT	URINE	FECES
GAIN		WORK OF GRAZING	TO ATMOSPHERE	URINE	TO SOIL
TO PRODUCT					

not drawn to scale

FIGFRE 5. *Energy partitioning and disposition by ruminants.* (From Hyder, 1969).

ever, higher energy costs in the feed lots, for meat processing and for distribution to the consumer. Few reliable estimates of these energy values are available, although Odum has estimated that a yield of 40 calories of meat requires at least 50 calories of fossil fuel subsidy.[27] Thus, even excessive grazing systems require outside energy to place the animal products on the table at the consumer level. As the intensity of grazing increases, and as more livestock move through the feed lot and packing plants, higher levels of fossil fuel subsidy are required.

A significant breakthrough in the efficiency of sunlight energy diversion to man was made when crop cultivation was developed. Man could select and develop crop plants for his specific needs and concentrate cultural practices on maximum production. Under some modern intensive cultivation systems, the efficiency of sunlight energy capture has exceeded three percent, while the theoretical efficiencies of conversion have been calculated at 5.3 percent of total energy and 12 percent for visible light radiant energy.[28]

An examination of energy flow patterns on cultivated lands reveals some interesting historical trends. In some of the developing countries of the world, about 30-40 percent of the energy input to run the system comes from manpower or oxen power, and the net yields are small. Even in the United States, in the early 1900's there were about 27 million horses and mules on the farms and ranches. Through the years farmers have steadily mechanized and have substituted over five million tractors and many other forms of power equipment for about 22 million of these horses and mules (see figure 6). As a measure of progress, we have released about 72 million acres of land that would have been required to feed the horses and mules and may now be used for direct food production for humans. In addition, we have increased efficiency and output per acre. However, as a result of this increase in efficiency on croplands in the the U.S., energy cycling patterns have been significantly changed. Horsepower, mulepower, oxenpower, and manpower operate on solar energy—an infinite resource for all practical purposes. Tractors and machinery utilize fossil fuel—a depletable resource.

---

[27]Howard T. Odum, *Environment Power and Society*. Wiley-Interscience. New York, 1971, 331 p.
[28]R. S. Loomis and W. A. Williams. Maximum Crop Productivity: An Estimate. *Crop Science*. Vol. 3, 1963, p. 67-72.

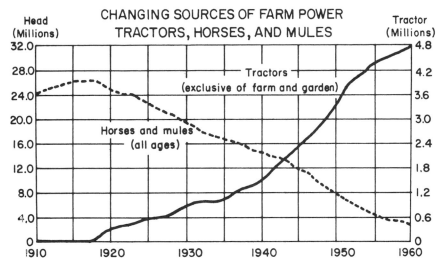

FIGURE 6. *Since 1918, American farms have moved rapidly from dependence upon horses and mules for power to tractors and other forms of mechanized equipment. The present number of horses and mules is back up to about eight million, nearly all dedicated to recreation purposes. After USDA data.*

Figure 7 presents a schematic diagram of energy flow for cultivated ecosystems. Although solar energy capture takes place only at the farm and ranch level, fossil fuel energy subsidies are required throughout the system. Energy is consumed in the preparation of agricultural chemicals, fertilizers, farm machinery, seed and other supplies. Energy is also consumed in the process of planting, cultivation, and harvesting, and large amounts of energy are consumed in processing, storage, packaging, and transportation before the finished product reaches the consumer level. In the United States, one estimate indicates that over 10,000 calories of fuel are required to help capture 3,000 calories of food and place it before the consumer.[29] Other estimates of fossil fuel subsidy range up to 10 or more calories of fossil fuel for each food calorie produced.[30] From an ecological

[29]Gerald W. Thomas, *The Ecology of Food Production,* KASALS Contribution No. 79, Texas Tech University, Lubbock, Texas.

[30]Merton Love. The Rangelands of the Western U.S. *Scientific American,* 222 (2): 1970, pp. 88-96.

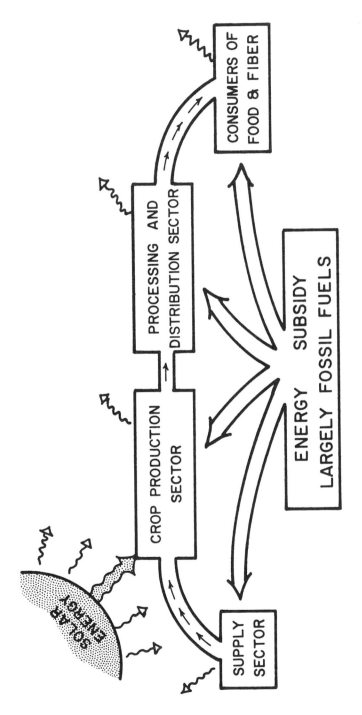

FIGURE 7. An illustration of energy flow and utilization for cultivated land ecosystems. Fossil fuel subsidies are relatively high in order to capture and deliver solar energy to the consumer.

viewpoint, these ecosystems cannot be sustained unless adequate substitutes for fossil fuel can be found.

Limited studies have also been made of energy flow patterns for cotton and other fibers. Table 2 presents a comparison of energy (large fossil fuel) required for cotton and cellulosic and non-cellulosic fiber production.[31] To produce and process a pound of cotton as a finished broadwoven fabric requires about 14,620 calories. Energy consumption for the synthetic fibers are more than double this amount. Wool places the lowest demand on fossil fuel. The raw materials for the non-cellulosic fibers are petrochemicals from petroleum and natural gas. Again, from an ecological viewpoint, the natural fibers (cotton, wool and mohair) have an advantage in that they place less pressure on the energy resource base than synthetic and highly-processed fibers. In spite of these ecological considerations, synthetic fibers are capturing an increasing share of the fiber market. Each person in the United States is now consuming over 20 pounds of synthetic fiber per year. In my opinion, the projections made by Resources for the future will not materialize due to the pressure on petroleum products. Thus, the energy crunch may force us to take another look at the natural fibers, including wool.

TABLE 2. ENERGY CONSUMPTION FOR SELECTED FIBERS.* RAW MATERIALS TO FINISHED BROADWOVEN FABRIC (KILOWATT HOURS PER POUND OF FIBER)

	Cotton	Cellulosic	Non-cellulosic
Consumed as Raw Materials	0.20	1.61	6.28
Consumed in Fiber Production	3.55	22.09	11.36
Consumed in Weaving & Spinning	6.30	7.03	7.03
Consumed in Finishing Mills	6.98	8.52	8.52
Cumulative Total	17.03	39.25	33.19

*Adapted from Gatewood, National Cotton Council of America

Despite the concern over the energy crisis, too little attention has been given to the possibilities for energy conservation and increased efficiency of use in the agricultural sector. More specific research is

[31]L. B. Gatewood, Jr. *The Energy Crisis: Can Cotton Help Meet It?* National Cotton Council of America, Jan., 1973, 35 pp.

needed to determine ways and means to increase photosynthetic energy capture, to increase the efficiency of use of fossil fuels, and to examine and improve energy flow patterns.

Research directed toward increased crop production has had the indirect effect of increasing solar energy capture. However, our effective energy capture could be moved above the three percent level by plant breeding and selection to increase leaf area and arrangement, more research on the process of photosynthesis, studies of artificial increases in carbon dioxide supply, and modification of other environmental factors with special attention to energy. The tremendous losses of energy by insects, diseases, rodents, and wasteful practices could produce substantial savings in food and fiber energy at the consumer level. The United States produces about two billion tons of solid organic wastes which could be utilized. Estimates of the readily collectable organic wastes amount to the equivalent of 170 million barrels of oil.[32] While this represents only three percent of the 1971 oil consumption, the potential is much greater. And, as the price of petroleum increases, agriculture may produce an end-product that is competitive as a fuel or as a source of methane and alcohol to run mechanized equipment.

Unfortunately, until the energy crisis was well upon us, very little concern was expressed over the problem of fossil fuel subsidies to maintain the huge agricultural complex. We continue to mechanize on farms and ranches partly because of the unreliability and high costs of labor. Concern seems to be for increased power rather than increased efficiency in most systems of mechanization. Our national policies still tend to encourage migration of people from farms to cities, with serious ecological implications. Tremendous energy expenditures still go to the transportation sector, and the trend toward specialized processing and built-in maid services extracts large energy subsidies.

As the world's population increases and more pressure is placed on the agricultural industry to provide quality food and fiber, mankind will be forced into *better photosynthetic energy conservation* practices. In the meantime, the search must be intensified to find adequate *substitutes for depletable resource* fuels. We must find ways and means to run the total food and fiber system on renewable resources.

[32]Allen L. Hammond, Fuel from Wastes: A Minor Energy Source. *Science* Vol. 178, 10 Nov., 1972, pp. 599-602.

SUMMARY

The history and ecology of "man and agriculture" permits some broad generalizations:

(1)   The resource base (productive capacity of the environment) will most likely limit man's ability to supply food and fiber to an increasing population rather than the "absorptive" capacity of the environment. In other words, while I see pollution as a serious problem, I see good possibilities for scientific and technological solutions to these problems. On the other hand, we have finite resources and limited possibilities for changing the basic relationships between people and resources.

(2)   Population control and management are essential in either case—both for the wealthy countries and for the developing countries.

(3)   With the projected world population expected to be over 6.5 billion by the year 2,000, the gross acreage of land for both cropland and grazing, even under the most optimistic conditions, will be reduced to 2.7 acres per person. To meet the needs of this many people, using a reasonable standard of living, it would appear necessary to expand the cultivated acreage by at least 50 percent and double crop yields once more. Uncultivated lands must fill the gap by increased production of livestock, wildlife, and possibly more exotic foods such as insects or micro-organisms. Compromises must be made by recreation and certain other uses—an undesirable but necessary reversal of the present trends.

(4)   Improved genetic material in crops, proper use of agricultural chemicals, and improved farm technology tends to *reduce* the land and water requirements per capita. But, to maximize the use of land and water by these techniques will require heavy energy subsidies.

(5)   Organic farming and the production of "natural" foods, if practiced on a broad scale, will *increase* the land and water requirement per capita. This implies the elimination of agricultural chemicals (synthetic fertilizers, pesticides, etc.) and certain other changes in production practices which likely will reduce per acre yields.

(6)   A "vegetarian" diet requires a *smaller* land base than a diet heavily dependent upon meat products. Ecologically this moves man closer to the "producer" organisms where photosynthesis takes place. But, this also places more emphasis on the "sustained yield" concept. Water use and water cycling patterns may also be changed accordingly.

(7)   The substitution of many foods in our diet for the basic cereals and potatoes has *increased* our land, water, and fossil fuel requirements.

(8)   Unnecessary "waste" and unnecessary "processing" and packaging *increase* the pressure on land and other resources. We waste food at all levels in the United States—and particularly when we leave the table.

(9)   The Colorado River Basin has a wealth of agricultural resources compared with the world average or even the U.S. potential. Water will probably be the first limiting factor in "carrying capacity" although substitutes for "fossil fuel energy" must be found very soon. Many forms of pollution present serious problems. However, it my belief that new technologies can and will be developed to reduce pollution to an acceptable level for life support ecosystems. My major concern is with world-wide and nation-wide population pressures as they must inevitably impact on the Colorado River Basin.

(10)   Many of the so-called answers to the problem create pressures at other points in the ecosystem. It is essential that we increase our research on ecosystems and their management.

CHAPTER XI

Agriculture's Management of the Environment in the Colorado River Basin

Leonard H. Johnson*

No sector of society has attempted to manage the environment in the Colorado River Basin more than agriculture. The successful production of food and fiber demanded the control of the hostile elements that endangered agricultural processes. Activities to manage the big six enemies: flood, erosion, drought, fire, disease, and insects dramatically altered the harsh environment which pioneers of the Colorado River Basin encountered. The development and the use of improved seeds, breeds, and production technology adapted to the basin's basic environmental needs have also had their impact.

The indictment that some farmers' and ranchers' efforts to manage the environment might have long-term adverse impacts on the environment demands a critical re-evaluation of agriculture's environmental improvement activities.

The conservation of water resources to protect top soil, control floods, and eliminate the disasters of drought is perhaps agriculture's most distinguished single accomplishment in the Colorado Basin. Nevertheless, projects to conserve water resources are encountering militant opposition in the basin. It appears that both sides of the controversy require broad public exposure and understanding.

California's experience indicates that water conservation and use is much more valuable to the state than the mining of gold. The

*Assistant Director, Natural Resources Department, American Farm Bureau Federation, Salt Lake City, Utah

agricultural crops produced annually in California, primarily by impoundment and the diversion of excess water from natural channels to irrigation, are more valuable than all the gold mined in that state in the past 150 years.

Irrigated agriculture in California contributes some $16 billion a year to the state's economy. Most of this is new wealth which flows into the metropolitan areas to provide thousands of jobs in commerce and industry.

There are by-product benefits to the environment whose value may exceed the economic production. The man-enhanced waterways back of the conservation projects provide recreation for millions of Americans: boating, fishing, hunting, swimming, picnicking, water skiing, camping, and sightseeing.

In 1540 when Coronado first explored the Colorado River, he reported that he found a muddy, turbulent stream occupied by squaw-fish, humpback suckers and bony-tail chub. Today, that same Colo-rado River runs relatively clear compared to 1540. It shelters 18 species of game fish to provide some of the finest rainbow trout and bass fishing in the world. Most rivers might properly be named "Wild Rivers," because, untamed, they are wild. Periodically, they kill and destroy. But water, like fire, when controlled and harnessed, can enrich the quality of the environment.

Doubters of the value of water conservation projects have for-gotten the battles which men have continually fought with flood waters.

The annual loss of life and property due to flood continues to make flood control a priority issue.

The 1972 Rapid City flood took 237 lives, left thousands home-less, and caused millions of dollars damage. Also this past year, the destruction of homes occurred which required relocation of many families on the Snake River in southern Idaho.

The most disastrous flood in the nation's history was "Agnes," which deluged five eastern states with rainfall. It is impossible to place a value on the human suffering, the loss of life, topsoil and prop-erty. The agricultural damage in two states of Pennsylvania and New York has been estimated to exceed $500 million dollars. The homes lost totaled in excess of 117,000. It is significant that the 75 upstream conservation dams constructed under the SCS-PL 566 Small Watershed Program in these five states stood the test: not one failed or came close to failing, and they are credited with preventing millions of dollars of property damage and undoubtedly saved many lives.

Floods not only affect man and his environment, but all other forms of life in their pathway, including hundreds of miles of aquatic and fish habitat.

The framework studies[1] estimates that without additional flood control in the Colorado River Basin that by the year 2000 the damages due to flood will be $310 million dollars annually. With flood control, the annual losses due to flood in the Basin could be reduced to $68 million dollars.

It is in the wise development and use of resources that their highest contribution to the environment is attained. Untamed water in flood stages has been a significant source of devastation in the Colorado River Basin. Conserved and wisely developed to useful purposes, water has become one of the most valuable resources of the Basin.

Undoubtedly, the Basin's environmental goals for the future will be determined in a major way by comprehensive land use plans, plus national water and air qaulity standards. This paper will not examine land use planning or air and water quality standards per se but will attempt to analyze selected basin-wide water policy decisions:

> The current total acreage irrigated? How many acre-feet of water this requires? The economic impacts created by irrigation?
>
> How much additional land in the Basin could be irrigated? Water requirements for irrigation? Impact upon the environment?

A complete inventory of irrigation development in the Colorado River Basin was attempted. However, time was too short to properly research the data made available from the seven states. Limited data is reported to stimulate interest in greater comprehension of the extent of water conservation in the Basin and the benefits which have resulted. A second objective was to create greater appreciation for the opportunities to produce at some future date additional food and

---

[1]*Lower Colorado Region Comprehensive Framework Study of Water and Land Resources.*

fiber products in the Colorado River Basin, in which resides an important national land resource reserve.

Arizona in 1972 had 1,205,080 acres in irrigation, with annual cash-receipts value estimated at $318.5 million dollars. Of these acres 10,900 are located in the Upper Colorado River Basin. The Framework study identifies 34.4 million acres of land in Arizona as having soils suitable for irrigation. Using a ball park figure of five acre-feet of water per acre, the land reserves of Arizona alone might use more water than all the states in the Basin if all the land were in irrigation.

Colorado lands irrigated with Colorado River waters total 1,797,000 acres. Of this total 720,000 acres are located in the South Platte Basin and receive supplemental waters by a trans-mountain diversion. The actual Colorado River Basin acres total 914,000. The economic value to Colorado from this irrigation is about $239 million dollars annually. The Framework studies indicate an increase of 246,300 acres in Colorado in the Basin by 2020. It is projected that to supply this increase in irrigation, would require an additional 461,000 acre-feet of water.

In 1969, Nevada had 825,000 acres in irrigation, of which 27,000 were in the Colorado River Basin. The annual value was $76.4 million dollars, of which $5.8 million dollars was produced in the Colorado River Basin. This state has 14,119,800 acres of land which is suitable for irrigation. If this total, 653,360 acres are located in the Colorado River Basin. To irrigate this land would require 27 million acre-feet of water and the economic value is placed at $1.3 billion dollars. To irrigate just the Nevada lands in the Basin would require 2.4 million acre-feet of water and the value is estimated to be $140 million dollars.

New Mexico is currently irrigating 1,016,000 acres of land: 640,000 acres from groundwater and 376,000 acres from surface waters. Of this total, 69,970 acres are located in the Colorado River Basin, plus 21,000 acres in the Middle Rio Grande Conservancy District receive supplemental Colorado River water. By 1985, New Mexico anticipates the authorized Upper Colorado River Basin projects will develop irrigation of 110,00 acres in the Navajo Indian Project and provide 30,000 acre-feet of supplemental and new-land water for the San Juan Chama Tributory units, and supplemental and full irrigation for 16,700 acres in the Animas LaPlata Project.

It is estimated the total irrigation in New Mexico could peak at 1,300,000 acres by the year 2000. However, this is one state which has no problem in finding abundant acreage suitable for irrigation. The New Mexico State Water Plan identified 9,451,000 acres as *highly suitable* and 22,303,000 as *moderately suitable* for a total of 31,754,000 acres of land.

Utah has 1,436,000 acres irrigated. Of this total, 332,600 acres are located in the Upper Colorado River Basin. The state projects that 75,000 acres of new-irrigation land will be developed in the Upper Colorado River Basin, which included 29,000 acres of Indian lands. The state also projects developing 87,000 acre-feet of supplemental water.

Utah has some 4 million acres which are suitable for irrigation if water were available. Of this 4 million acres, it has 1,167,200 acres most suitable for irrigation. If the total acres were developed, it could require a potential diversion of 12 million acre-feet of water. Obviously, to develop these potentials would require a large scale augmentation of water supplies.

In Wyoming, there are 332,260 acres irrigated in the Colorado River Basin. The gross value of crops from this land is $7,794,460.00. If water were available, this state could irrigate 186,000 additional acres in the Colorado River Basin. A conservative and realistic estimate of the additional acres to be brought into intensive agricultural production is 81,000.

Projections of irrigation development in the Colorado River Basin with water resources that are available:

Year	Acres
1960	2,638,164
1980	2,806,513
2010	2,911,753

Total lands suitable for irrigation in the Basin:

Lower Basin	38,760,000 Acres
Upper Basin	7,058,600 Acres
Total	46,818,600 Acres

Much more data on current irrigated acres in the Basin states is available. That which has been reviewed briefly identifies what has been accomplished with irrigation, as well as what is projected for future development. The total lands suitable for irrigation if water were available indicates one of the great land reserves of the nation is located in the Colorado River Basin.

IMPACT ON WILDLIFE HABITAT

The impact on game habitat, due to water conservation and irrigation on land, might be reviewed at this point. It seems studies are needed to assemble researched answers to many impact questions in this area:

Is it true that the availability of improved forage on irrigated and private agricultural lands is beneficial and reponsible in a major way for the significant increase in total numbers of game animals now residing in the Colorado River Basin?

Have the dams and reservoirs in the Basin really improved the quality and increased the number of game fish available for fishermen?

Is it true that flood damage of stream channels and aquatic and fish habitat justifies greater flood controls? Channelization for flood and drainage control?

What are the impacts resulting from drainage of wet lands?

Do benefits to the habitat of some game species balance out the damages to others?

Is the inundation of key game habitats for water conservation projects justifiable?

WATER QUALITY

Maintaining water quality and cleaning up existing water pollution caused by nature and agriculture while developing the resources of the Colorado River Basin surfaces a number of serious deterrents to continued agricultural production in the Basin. The pollutants include fertilizer and pesticides run-off residues, animal waste, siltation and salinity. The most serious to manage are siltation and salinity. Siltation has been a concern for years and will continue to be a major water pollutant challenge. For various reasons, including international commitments, the salinity build-up in Colorado River waters and land irrigated by Colorado River water is the prime concern to agriculture at this time.

Some of the salinity management questions to be answered would include:

What will be the long-range impact if salinity water management fails to reduce the level of salinity created by irrigation and natural sources in the Basin?

Should the responsibility for salinity management on the Colorado River be divided among user groups and various water institutions?

Have the sources of salinity been adequately identified?

If major sources of natural salinity sources were managed, could the current uses of Colorado River water be continued? Expanded?

Are there additional or alternative uses that would be environmentally more desirable? What are they? What would be the impacts?

Would the desalinization project proposed to improve water quality for international commitments be of greater benefit to the Basin if it were positioned higher up the river?

How extensive will desalinization facilities be required to correct salinity of the river?

How significant to water quality in the Colorado River is augmentation of the river flow with high quality waters?

What volume of water augmentation could be developed and environmentally justified by inter-basin transfers? Weather modification? Watershed management? Water use?

WATERSHED MANAGEMENT

Great local and national attention is currently focused on the protection of federal land resources from "unwise" use and development. The generated public concern for federal land protection and resource conservation is identified by some as a program to stop further development in order to return these great land resources to a "natural" state. It appears that until the general public is assured that the current uses and development of federal lands will protect vital ecosystems and will benefit all groups, there will be opposition to all proposed developments.

This broad public alarm has caused all western public land user groups to recognize that selected developments of past generations did place in jeopardy some valuable resources. Now is the time to analyze carefully what twentieth century users are doing to manage and protect the federal land resources. New federal land laws are needed by which orderly development programs can be designed that will provide for normal growth. This is particularly important in the Colorado River Basin. This group of states is experiencing growth which requires dynamic adjustments to provide new lands for new cities in a growth area.

The basin's population increases indicate one of the great opportunities is to provide the water and other important resource of the Basin by more intensive and more effective watershed management. The principal watersheds in the basin are located on federal lands.

Any Colorado River Basin watershed management program should review studies and findings such as the following:

The National Food & Fiber Commission reported that 25 million acre-feet of water could be saved in the reclamation states by the elimination of phraetophytes from the public and private watershed. While this is a much larger area than the Colorado River Basin, it is indicative of the potential water development on some western watersheds.

The National Water Commission's report issued in 1973 states that phraetophytes constitute a *serious source of inefficient water use.*

Steve Reynolds, State Engineer of New Mexico, reports the management of phraetophytes is one of New Mexico's most serious water problems.

The phraetophyte control work in New Mexico and other states is highly controversial. Resolution of such controversies will take time and developing carefully public understanding of the benefits and the losses. Vegetative management on watershed is being studied in many areas. The United States Bureau of Reclamation's "Rio Grande Water Salvaged Project" in New Mexico is currently reviewing a recommendation to clear 17,800 acres of land and thinning 2,800 acres of phraetophyte vegetation in the Middle Rio Grande.

The federal and nonfederal lands in the Colorado River Basin states constitutes an important watershed. No one has fully inventoried the water and vegetative production that could result by greater management of phraetophytes and other inefficient water-consuming vegetative types from the watersheds of this Basin. There is, however, extensive research as to the potential increases from this type of water-shed activity. The United States Forest Service and the State of Arizona have conducted some of the most intense and extended investigations in watershed management. This cooperative research indicates water yields can be increases, as well as increases in forage and timber production. The Arizona experience and that of other public land state researchers is sufficiently verified to justify the careful review by the Colorado Basin states. There is also a benefit to game habitat and reduced fire hazard by proper watershed management of vegetation.

The Seventeenth Annual Arizona Water Symposium, held September 19, 1973 at Phoenix, was directed to *"improvement of game habitats resulting from vegetative management on watersheds."* The Arizona research has aided in greater understanding of opportunities on western watersheds to improve game habitat and reduce range and forest fire hazards by vegetative management. The use of controlled burning on watersheds is one of the management tools for improving game habitat examined at this year's watershed symposium.

National and world conditions make food and fiber production of increased importance. Such conditions make the federal land watershed in the Colorado River Basin to be a vitally important national land resource. The management of these watersheds to control the less valuable water consuming vegetation and increase the grasses, timber, and forage plants for the benefit of big game animals and domestic livestock will become increasingly important.

RANGE IMPROVEMENT

An unexpected finding of the Public Land Law Review Commission came from the Commission's research of western federal land range forage production. This study by the Commission was made by the University of Idaho. The study revealed that to increase big game numbers and general recreation uses of federal lands would not require reducing domestic livestock grazing. Instead, it shows that increasing the number of both game and livestock could be achieved by intensive management and range improvement. A balanced forage program commensurate with the available feed would allow increases of both.

An American Farm Bureau's study of forage production on public land ranges revealed that the desirable vegetation on most federal lands' watersheds could be doubled by intensive management. The PLLRC range study by the University of Idaho found that the AUM's could be increased 76% by intensive management.

There are numerous studies by western land grant universities verifying the opportunities for increased forage on western federal lands by more intensive management and wise use.

An example of this type research is *The Economic Feasibility and Impact of Present and Potential Range Management Program in the Four Corners Area,* issued May, 1971, by researchers, Dr. J. Wayne McArthur and Dr. Darwin B. Nielsen of Utah State University. The study reported that benefits to agriculture by range improvement in the Four Corners area would be $69,330.00. The benefits to big game and hunting would be $122,787.00, and general recreation, $5,500.00, for a total annual benefit to the area of $197,617.00. The cost of this range big game and recreation improvement, according to the researchers, would be $90,797.00.

In 1966, a report to Governor Rampton, *Report to the Governor on Resources Development of Utah Grazing Lands* the researchers found there were 3.6 million acres of land in Utah which were suitable for seeding and watershed improvement. The study continued and reported that at the current rate of funding, it would take 52 years to complete the range and watershed work identified. The Utah range situation could be duplicated in each Colorado River Basin state. It seems one of the challenges facing public land states is to encourage the congress to modernize federal land laws. New legislation is needed for development of a watershed and range improvement program. The private and public sectors need to team up in a mammoth watershed and rangeland improvement program. If a constructive opportunity were provided, the many improvement projects on federal lands could be accomplished in a realistic period of time.

The watershed and range improvement question might correctly be stated: *Could more intensive management of federal and private land watersheds be justified on the basis of water yields, soil containment, flood control, improved forage for both game and domestic livestock, and general recreation benefits?* How? What would it cost? Where should the Colorado Basin States begin?

There are also important national water policy questions that will have far-reaching impacts on environmental development in the Colorado River Basin. Among these are the following:

RESERVATION AND INDIAN WATER CLAIMS

The majority of water resources in the Colorado River Basin arise on Federal lands. Can additional investment in the improvement and development of water resources be justified as long as the Reserve Water Doctrine and the Indian water claims remain unresolved? The Las Vegas "pupfish" case established that the Devil's Hole Reservation has a prior claim on groundwaters over long-recognized irrigation pump rights and therefore clearly establishes that the Reserve Water Doctrine applies to groundwater. While the "eagle case" in Colorado clarifies one aspect of the federal water claim, this issue remains a serious concern relative to additional water development in the Colorado River.

Many recommendations for the resolution of these two claims have been proposed. The two most recent proposals were by the Public Land Law Review Commission and the National Water Commission.

As long as these two claims remain unresolved, there is a cloud on the title of most established water rights in the Colorado River Basin.

NATIONAL WATER COMMISSION

The National Water Commission recommended that water resources allocated for irrigation could be substantially reduced by levying a use charge, against irrigators. The Commission proposed that a charge be made for the water resources which are appropriated by all users. This commission proposal violates the Appropriation Water Doctrine under which the Colorado River Basin water structures, transportation facilities, and water rights are based.

Some may conclude that the National Water Commission's recommendation to reduce irrigation would be a reasonable answer to the water-oriented environmental problems of the Colorado Basin. Because of increased and and fiber requirements, plus emerging problems created by a national and international energy shortage, the Colorado River Basin states must assess carefully the long-range implications of reduced irrigation in the Basin.

It seems very important that the water policy that this Commission recommends be resolved prior to consideration of other environmental management issues of the Basin.

APPROPRIATION DOCTRINE

Under the Appropriation Doctrine, irrigators who conserve water can lose it. This policy, in effect, penalizes those who save water by mangement or investments in more efficient systems. Should the Colorado River Basin states support the modification of the Appropriation Water Doctrines? A modification has been proposed that those water users who invest in irrigation equipment or application methods that conserve water should have a priority right to appropriate or to dispose of the amount of water conserved.

Providing a reliable supply of food and fiber demanded of the original settlers in this basin environmental management principles directed to the conservation of water resources. Twentieth Century developments have altered the emphasis, but the benefits from water conservation for food and fiber production must remain a vital factor in any consideration of an environmental management program for the Colorado River Basin.

BIBLIOGRAPHY

Wayne N. Aspinall, "Development Oriented Future with Emphasis on Water Development," August 1-3, 1973.

Victor R. Champlin, "A Future with Maximum Individual Freedom of Choice and Minimum Government Intervention in Land Development and Growth Patterns," Victor R. Champlin, Colorado Land Developer.

Roger P. Hansen, "An 'Environmental' Future for the West: The Light at the End of the Dark," August 1-3, 1973 (ROMCOE).

Victor A. Koelzer, "A Future of Population Growth in Accord with National Needs," July 27, 1973, Colorado State University.

Larry E. Moss, "A Future Stressing Preservation of Presently Un-populated Areas, with Strict Controls on Growth of Populated Areas," August 1-3, 1973, Sierra Club.

Eugene K. Peterson, "Ecology and the Economy, the Regional Carrying Capacity Scenario," August 1-3, 1973, Pacific Northwest River Basins Commission.

Clyde E. Stewart, "Economic Impacts of Water Quantity and Quality Constraints on Agriculture of the Colorado River Basin—An Inter-industry Projections Study," December, 1969, agricultural econo-mist.

Lower Colorado Region State-Federal Interagency Group for the Pacific Southwest Interagency Committee, "Comprehensive Framework Study of Water and Land Resources." June, 1971.

Thomas S. Clevenger, William N. Capener, and John D. Canady, "Po-tential for Agriculture and Forestry Development." New Mexico State University.

Summary conclusions and recommendations from the final report of the National Water Commission, "New Directions in U.S. Water Policy." 1973.

Letter, David P. Hale, Interstate Stream Engineer, September 6, 1973.

Letter, John W. Jackson, Water Resource Economist, August 31, 1973.

Letter, Wesley E. Steiner, Arizona Water Commission, September 27, 1973.

Letter, Laren D. Morrill, Colorado Water Conservation Board, August 31, 1973.

Adrian O. Hutchens, Economist, August 27, 1973.

Arizona Watershed Symposium Proceedings, 5th, 6th, 7th, 8th, 9th, 10th, 12th, 14th, 15th, and 16th Annual. (September 1961 through September, 1972.)

Ivan V. Goslin, report at Annual Meeting, Upper Colorado River Com-mission, September 17, 1973.

National Water Commission Report, "Water Policies for the Future. 1973.

Report of Public Land Law Review Commission, "One Third of the Nation's Land." June, 1970.

S. E. Reynolds, "New Mexico Water Planning." April 5, 1973.

S. E. Reynolds, statement on "Proposed Report of the National Water Commission." New Mexico State Engineer, February 5, 1973.

Clyde E. Stewart, USDA Economic Research Service, Logan, Utah, September 11, 1973.

John D. Hedlund, SCS Water Resources Work Group Member, July 31, 1969.

Daniel F. Lawrence, Division of Water Resources, State of Utah, August 31, 1973.

Governor Calvin L. Rampton, a report to the people on "The State of Utah Water." September, 1972.

LeMoyne Wilson, T. B. Hutchings, Paul Shafer, "Amable Land Resources of Utah." Utah State University, February, 1968.

Utah Board of Water Resources, "Water for Utah." April, 1973.

Colorado River Basin
Agriculture Workshop Summary

QUESTION: What are the major concerns or problems faced by agriculture in the Colorado River Basin?

CONSENSUS: Several problems were emphasized. While no solutions to them were proposed, there was general agreement as to their serious nature. The major issues facing agriculture in the Colorado River Basin are (1) the problem of ground water mining: water conservation could be best served by eliminating irrigation where ground water mining occurs, (2) the balance of payments problem and the high rate of agricultural export, (3) the problem of export from the basin and the fact that the people who live in the basin have little control over those exports, (4) the problem of increased salinity from increased water use (this is also an international concern), (5) the need or institutional cooperation and coordination to achieve recreational and fish and wildlife values, (6) the problem of certain non-reversable actions involved with ground water mining, (7) the need for solutions to problems surrounding Indian water rights and Indian trust lands, and (8) the need for agriculture in the Colorado River Basin to receive financial incentives, educational opportunities, and legislative action to increase efficiency in water and energy use and to promote land use planning.

QUESTION: Should some of the agriculture in the Colorado River Basin be moved elsewhere in the U.S.?

CONSENSUS: In general, agriculture in the basin would reject a move to other parts of the U.S. This need for change is the result of demands by other segments of society who can pay a higher price for basin water and who may pose lower environmental impacts.

The objections to moving are offered on the basis of prior rights to the water and on the belief that some environmental impacts posed by possible alternate users of the water might well be greater than the impacts caused by agriculture.

The question of social justice in any reallocation of water used by agriculture also needs to be examined. Agricultural interests regard water as a special right and essential for the utilization of the land resources of the Colorado River Basin.

CHAPTER XII

Fossil Fuels and Power Generation in the Colorado River Basin

Kimball T. Harper*

INTRODUCTION

The Colorado River Basin is richly endowed with large reserves of a variety of fossil fuel resources. Massive coal beds are widespread over much of the upper basin. In the Green River Basin of that area, one of the largest oil shale deposits on earth is situated. Energy reserves in the form of oil and gas are far less extensive than either coal or shale, but are nonetheless locally abundant and of great importance to the regional economy.

Of these vast resources, only coal has been exploited in the Colorado River Basin for any significant length of time. Production climbed steadily from settlement to almost the midpoint of this century. A brief decline in local production following World War II is traceable to increased use of natural gas, a more convenient and cleaner fuel, for domestic heating and many industrial chores. That decline has now been arrested and a variety of causes seem to promise that coal production will soon climb to unprecedented heights.

INCREASED EMPHASIS ON COAL

The cause of this return to coal is related to many factors in our society. Of primary significance is the rapid depletion of United

*Department of Botany and Range Science, Brigham Young University, Provo, Utah

States oil and gas reserves. At current rates of use, the proven domestic supply of these fuels are sufficient for only slightly more than a decade. (*Newsweek,* Jan. 22, 1973). Electrical power demands with a doubling rate of about 10 years (Hammond, 1972) have long since outstripped the capacity of existing hydroelectric and nuclear generating facilities and placed an ever increasing burden on fossil fuels. Only coal is present in sufficient quantities and at competitive prices to satisfy the large energy needs for power generation.

Foreign sources of petroleum and natural gas are, of course, available in the Middle East and elsewhere. In fact, a full third of our petroleum products are now imported bearing a price tag of about $9 billion annually (Abelson, 1973). This flood of imported energy will almost certainly increase for several years. Meanwhile, competition from other petroleum importing nations such as Great Britain, West Germany, and Japan will undoubtedly make the product increasingly more expensive. It seems apparent that the independence of this nation cannot be great, if we are to continue to depend so heavily on foreign fuels. For that reason alone, if for no other, pressures to develop internal energy sources will be immense in the next decade. In this respect, it should be noted that in his energy message of June 29, 1973, President Richard M. Nixon called for over $5 billion to be spent on coal research in the next decade.

Considering the internal energy resources available, the massive and readily exploitable reserves of cheap, low sulfur coal in the Colorado River Basin are competitively superior to most domestic sources and are certain to be developed quickly. Furthermore, large coal fueled power generating plants have been an operational reality for decades. On the other hand, energy from the oil shale has never been commercially developed and will apparently be more costly than that from coal for at least the foreseeable future. Our oil and gas reserves are too much in demand for petroleum products and home heating to be considered for power generation.

The foregoing considerations in combination account for the fact that 44 percent of the electricity now used in the United States is generated by coal burning plants (Henrie, 1973). That percentage is likely to increase in the future with a disproportionate amount of the increase occurring in the Colorado River Basin, since the bulk of eastern United State's coal has a high sulfur content.

COAL AND THE ENVIRONMENT

The environmental impacts associated with coal fueled power generating plants will be diverse. Disruptions can be expected in connection with the mining operation, transportation of fuel to plant sites, the power generating operation itself, conveyance of power to consumers, and associated but indirect developments. The magnitude of any one of these impacts will depend upon the size of the power generating industry in the Basin, the attention given to impact mitigating practices, and unforeseen technological advances. Possible size of the industry will be discussed at a later point in this paper. Attention given to impact mitigating practices should be monitored by appropriate governmental agencies. Selected areas in need of technological innovation will be identified in the concluding section of this paper. In the following paragraphs, I will list and briefly discuss some of the more obvious impacts associated with each of the five major areas listed above.

Mining. As currently designed plants in the Colorado River Basin demonstrate, coal will be mined by both underground and strip processes. Surface disruptions will be greatest where stripping procedures are employed, but danger to human life has proven to be greatest in underground mines (Council on Environmental Quality, 1973).

Possible impacts associated with mining include altered life ways of local people, destruction of the local habitat and its biota, altered surface water relations, reduced soil stability, aesthetic losses, and increase in atmospheric particulates. Direct influences on the affairs of local peoples are anticipated primarily in the case of strip mining on Indan Reservation lands used for grazing. Stripping operations anywhere in our area will have long term and profound effects on the natural ecosystems. Obviously, the impacts of underground mines will be less severe in most of the categories noted above. Off site impacts for both types of mining will probably be most serious in respect to altered surface water relations. Water tapped in underground mines may become acidified flowing through rubble on its way to the outside. Channeling such waters into surface streams could significantly alter biotic relations of the streams. Such waters may also trigger severe channel erosion as they cut new courses or enlarge the flow in existing channels. Several mitigating practices could be applied to these problems, however.

Strip mines are not likely to generate new water in the Colorado River Basin. On the contrary, these operations will probably demand outside water for dust abatement and revegetation operations. In the arid region in question, new water demands will be difficult to accommodate and will have the potential of engendering bitter social responses.

Transportation. For economic reasons, mines and generating plants will always occur as close together as is feasible, but topographic considerations and the immense tonnages of coal required (the 2,000 megawatt Four-Corners Plant consumes 2,500,000 tons annually) will always insure that some transportation system is needed. Strip mines will probably rely on large trucks which raise some dust and offer some safety hazards. The new Huntington Canyon Plant will utilize a large belt conveyor. The impacts in either of the foregoing operations will be minimal.

In other cases, however, transportation is a more significant portion of the total operation. Both the Mojave and the Navajo Plants, for instance, will burn coal from the moderately distant Black Mesa in Arizona (275 and 80 miles respectively). The Mojave Plant is fed pulverized coal via a slurry pipeline which requires over 10 percent as much water as the power plant itself (3,200 acre feet per year for the pipeline and 30,000 acre feet for the 1580 megawatt plant). The Navajo Plant will receive coal via an 80 mile railroad.

Power Generation. Although most of the objections of the environmentalist lobby to coal powered electrical generating plants in the Colorado River Basin have centered on stack effluents, there is good reason to believe that these will not prove to be a significant problem to the region. Certainly their efforts will be minor compared to the long term effects of the strip mines associated with these plants.

Unfortunately, many environmentalists have accepted as valid, reports now known to be grossly in error. One such report held that the Four-Corners plant alone produced more flyash than all stationary sources in New York City and Los Angeles combined (Josephy, 1971). Others conceded that all the plants now under construction in the Colorado River Basin would be required to top the flyash production of New York or Los Angeles. In point of fact, a study by Western Energy and Supply Transmission Associates demonstrates that these two cities produce 4.4 times more flyash than would all the operating and planned power plants in the Colorado River Basin, even without new emission control devices (*Deseret News,* Nov. 29, 1971). Currently equipment at the Four-Corners Plant is removing 99.2 percent of the flyash from three of their five units. Older control equipment removed only 78% of the ash from the gaseous effluents (*Deseret News,* Sept. 25, 1973).

Another oft repeated tale concerns a 1966 photo taken from 170 miles out in space by Gemini 12. That photo purportedly showed but one man-made object in the Four-Corners area of the Colorado River Basin: a 50 mile smoke plume from the Four-Corners Powerplant (Chaney, 1971). Subsequent research by Loren Crow (1971) demonstrated the photo interpretation to be faulty and forced NASA to retract their published interpretation of the line of haze as a plume from the powerplant. The object was apparently a condensation trail from jet aircraft!

In theory, the power generating process could have important impacts in each of the following areas: aesthetics (flyash), toxic gaseous effluents, solid waste disposal (ashes), water requirements, water quality. It is a fact to be deplored, I think, that despite the heated debates concerning the impact of flyash on aesthetics in the Colorado River Basin, no really comprehensive studies have ever been made of the relative impact of flyash on visability in the region. Certainly there is a need for such a study! Natural interferences to visability have always existed in this region. Beyond the range of the obvious plume, what is the relative impact of ash on visability?

The demands for Colorado River Basin water in power generation are sizeable but not prohibitive at the present time. Water requirements for power generation are compared with demands imposed by other competing energy industries in table 1.

TABLE 1. *Water requirements for selected energy industries that have economic potential in the CRB.*

Industry	Annual Water Requirements	Source of Information
Coal fueled powerplants	16-20 acre feet/year/megawatt capacity	Josephy, 1971 Finlayson, 1973
Coal gasification	10±20 acre feet/year/250,000 ft³ gas daily capacity	Henrie, 1973 Gillette, 1973
Oil shale extraction	79-145 acre feet/year/1000 barrels oil daily capacity	Hansen, 1972 *Deseret News,* 1973

Published plans for the seven large coal powered plants now envisioned for the Colorado River Basin (Four-corners, Mojave, San Juan, Navajo, Huntington, Kaiparowitz, and Bridger) call for a generating capacity of over 16,000 megawatts. By 1985, the power generating capacity of coal fuel plants in this region may well soar to 36,000 megawatts (Josephy, 1971). At that level of activity, the plants would use as much as 720,000 acre feet of water annually. The Center Utah Project of the U.S. Bureau of Reclamation, by comparison, will demand 135,000 acre feet per year. This CUP project would put 28,540 acres under irrigation and supply supplemental water to an additional 131,700 acres (U.S. Department of Interior, 1964).

By 1985, the Department of Interior anticipates an oil shale industry producing one million barrels of oil per day. Total water demands for such an operation could run to 145,000 acre feet per year. Six coal gasification plants each producing 250 million cubic feet of gas per day are probably not an unrealistic expectation for the Colorado River Basin by 1985, since U.S. Bureau of Mines personnel predict that 36 such plants will be in operation in the United States by then (Henrie, 1973a). Six plants would require 120,000 acre feet of water per year. Should these industries all materialize (and prospects are good that they will), the CRB will have need for over a million acre feet of new water per year. Add to these demands the increased urban needs, increased agricultural needs, and projected needs for strip mine reclamation that will exist in the year 2000 (population may then be twice as large as at the present) and water requirements become unmanageable in this arid region. Expensive and politically explosive water imports will be required if even the modest developments envisioned above are to become a reality.

Possible adverse effects of toxic compounds (e.g., SO_2 NO_x and mercury) from powerplant stacks have been much discussed by both laymen and professionals. Available data overwhelmingly support the position, however, that stack effluents have never exceeded state or federal standards for any significant period and clearly have not presented a health problem to either plants or animals (including man) in the vicinity of existing plants in the Colorado River Basin (*Utah Engineering Experiment Station*, 1971a, and 1971b; and *Deseret News*, Nov. 18, 1971). Furthermore, with the installations of more efifcient pollution control equipment now in progress or planned for the major coal burning plants in the Basin, the possibility of damage becomes progressively less likely.

Unusual resistance of desert plants to atmospheric toxins such as SO_2 provides an additional assurance that stack effluents are unlikely to cause damage to the region's plant cover. Mesophytic plants are often visually marked by SO_2 concentrations of less than 0.5 ppm (Treshow, 1970). In contrast, recent fumigation trials by Hill et al (1973) show that few desert species show visible injury even at 2.0 ppm for two hours. Part of the apparent tolerance is probably attributable to chronically dry soils and resultant closure of stomates, but Hill et al (1973) were unable to mark most desert species at concentrations below 2.0 ppm even when plants were irrigated. Hill et al also failed to find evidence of synergism between SO_2 and NO_2.

Solid waste disposal does present some environmental problems for coal burning plants, since the fuel will run from 3-10% ash. Under current emission standards, almost the entirety of the ash will remain in the furnace and must be disposed of. Where the fuel is stripped, a major part of the waste can be returned directly to the mine itself. Underground mines present a more difficult disposal problem. At Huntington Canyon, the ash will be moistened and trucked to retaining ponds in nearby, dry canyons. This method of disposal is expensive and produces a long term erosional and water quality hazard. These hazards are fortunately controllable, however.

Power Transmission. Although there has been much talk of buried transmission lines, we can expect that almost all lines will remain above ground. Economic considerations dictate this course, since buried cables cost from 10-40 times as much as comparable overhead lines.

Overhead lines can produce aesthetic and electronic communication impacts that are highly undesirable and difficult to remedy. In other cases, tower placement may trigger soil erosion and stream siltation. Occasionally lines are constructed across remote regions, and the construction roads continue to invite traffic long after construction is complete. Increased traffic may cause chronic erosion and disrupt normal activities of native animals. In most cases, however, judicious planning can circumvent the vast majority of the serious impacts associated with transmission lines.

RESEARCH NEEDS

There is an urgent need to develop better methods of strip mining and mine rehabilitation. The steep, unstable waste heaps are an ever present erosional hazard capable of seriously disrupting the ecology and destroying the quality of regional water resources. Techniques for preserving surface soil for subsequent spreading over inactivated mines need to be developed. Although surface soils are usually poorly developed in the predominantly aird Colorado River Basin, they are nonetheless superior to subsoils for plant growth.

To date, no attempts to revegetate stripped areas have shown much promise. The minor successes that have occurred have demanded large expenditures of water. Not only are such procedures expensive in terms of water, but the vegetation is likely not to persist in the absence of supplemental water. We may thus be breeding long term demands for water that could be more profitably used elsewhere. Vegetative stabilization of the heaps is, of course, highly desirable for environmental quality, aesthetic, and economic reasons, but reclamation operations that require little or no imported water are to be preferred.

The social readjustments occasioned by development and abandonment of strip mine-powerplant complexes are and will continue to be painful. The average operational life of such a complex will probably average between 30 and 40 years. Especially on Indian Reservations, the operations will completely displace some herdsmen and force total professional reorientation. Should the affected parties select employment with the industry, they will eventually be forced to move to new locations as the local coal reserves are exhausted or to again retrain themselves. Such social dilemmas demand sympathetic remedial research.

Finally there is a genuine need to assess the ultimate cost to consumers of the plethora of pollution control and environmetal quality constraints now being imposed on the power industry. Certainly I do not intend this to be a plea for return to practices that degrade the carrying capacity of the environment. I simply believe that the cost-benefit ratios of many of the control practices now being imposed are far greater than unity. We cannot morally pass such costs on to the consumers nor can we hope to maintain a viable economy by demanding complaince with economically unsound practices.

REFERENCES CITED

Abelson, Philip H. 1973. Importation of petroleum. *Science* 180:4091.

Chaney, Ed. 1971. On a clear day you can see Grand Canyon. *Conservation News* 36(9):3-4.

Council on Environmental Quality. 1973. *Energy and the environment*: electric power. U.S. Government Printing Office, Washington, D.C. 58 p.

Crow, Loren. 1971. Analysis of Gemini 12 satellite photo taken November 13, 1966. Report No. 93 to Public Service Company of New Mexico (Report dated 14 June 1971).

Deseret News, 1971. EPA reports 'no danger.' *Deseret News* (Nov. 18, 1971), p. B3. Salt Lake City, Utah.

Deseret News. 1971. Study denies claim on plant pollution. *Deseret News* (Nov. 29, 1971), p. B3. Salt Lake City, Utah.

Deseret News. 1973. Water essential to make Utah oil boom. *Deseret News* (April 7, 1973), p. A5. Salt Lake City, Utah.

Deseret News. 1973. Fans scrub smoke at 4-Corners power unit. *Deseret News* (Sept. 25, 1973), p. B1. Salt Lake City, Utah.

Finlayson, Val A. 1973. Power generation and the Colorado River Basin. Paper presented at the Colorado River Basin Environmental Management Conference, Salt Lake City, Oct. 15-16, 1973. 27 p.

Gillette, Robert. 1973. NAS: Water scarcity may limit use of western coal. *Science* 181:525.

Hammond, Allen L. 1972. Energy needs: Projected demands and how to reduce them. *Science* 178:1186-1188.

Hansen, Roger P. 1972. *A Critical Review of Draft Environmental Statement for the Proposed Prototype Oil Shale Leasing Program of the U.S. Department of the Interior*. Rocky Mountain Center on Environment, Denver, Colorado. 15 p.

Henrie, Thomas A. 1973a. Some consideration on the impact of coal gasification. Paper delivered Aug. 21, 1973, at the Coal Seminar, Price, Utah. 7p.

Henrie, Thomas A. 1973b. Status of the U.S. mineral industry. Seminar delivered Oct. 4, 1973, at Brigham Young University, Provo, Utah.

Hill, A. Clyde, Thomas W. Barrett, S. Hill and C. Lamb. 1973. Sensitivity of native desert vegetation to SO_2 and SO_2 + NO_2. Paper presented June 1973 to the Air Pollution Control Association meetings, Chicago, Ill. 21 p.

Josephy, Alvin M., Jr. 1971. The murder of the Southwest. *Audubon* 73(4):52-67.

Newsweek. 1973. America's energy crisis. *Newsweek* Vol. LXXXI (Jan. 22, 1973): 52-54, 59-60.

Treshow, Michael. 1970. *Environment and Plant Response.* McGraw-Hill Book Co., New York, New York. 422 p.

U.S. Department of Interior, 1964. *Colorado River Storage Project.* Brochure 0-747-907. U.S. Government Printing Office, Washington, D.C.

Utah Engineering Experiment Station. 1971a. Air pollution investigations in the vicinity of the Huntington Canyon Power Plant: progress report. Utah Engineering Experiment Station, University of Utah, Salt Lake City. 129 p.

Utah Engineering Experiment Station. 1971b. Air pollution investigations in the vicinity of the Four Corners and San Juan Power Plants. Utah Engineering Experiment Station, University of Utah, Salt Lake City. 111 p.

CHAPTER XIII

Power Generation and the Colorado River Basin

Val A. Finlayson*

THE DEMAND FOR ENERGY

The Colorado River Basin will play a most significant role in the future of the western United States because within or adjacent to the Basin lies one of the Nation's largest storehouses of energy resources. Until recent years most of the wildlands of the Colorado River Basin have been the domain of the livestock man, a few rugged recreationists, and the occasional prospector. Today, many studies are being conducted by the U.S. Geological Survey, the Utah Geolgical and Mineral Survey, the U.S. Bureau of Reclamation, the Utah Division of Water Resources, and Utah Power & Light Company to inventory the large variety of energy resources in the Colorado River Basin including water, coal, oil, gas, uranium, and the nation's oil shale and tar sand deposits.

There will, no doubt, be competing areas of development between energy, recreation, agriculture and urbanism. Without the modern energy systems, there would be no freedom from backbreaking toil which gives Americans time to pursue education and recreation programs. It is the purpose of this paper to outline the energy requirements of the Utah Power & Light Company System and indicate the sources of energy we are looking at for supplying these needs for the next decades.

*Utah Power & Light Company

It is believed that intelligent men with planning responsiblities will be able to see through the ignorance surrounding the "energy crisis" and achieve a prudent balance between the energy, social, economic and environmental needs of our area. The energy crisis is growing. Last year the Minerals, Materials, and Fuels Subcommittee of the Senate Interior Committee, chaired by Senator Frank E. Moss, concluded that the energy crisis does exist. While some still claim it is an attempt to sell more power, and while the Government has continued in a state of indecision, industry faces major delays in constructing the needed new facilities either because extreme regulations have been set to protect health, although no scientific or medical evidence indicates a need; or environmental reports are required to be written by Government Agencies (although provision is made to provide the manpower or funds necessary to produce those reports).

Meanwhile, the demand for electrical energy increases. In 1920, 10 per cent of all energy resources were used to produce electricity while today over 25 percent is so used. It is estimated by the year 2000, 40 percent of all energy resources will be used for electrical production.[1]

Utah Power & Light Company's present capability is about 1658 MW (megawatts) of which approximately 10 percent is generated by hydroelectric units and the remainder mainly from coal-fired steam plants. Figure 1 shows our expected peak loads through 1982 and our resource picture to match these loads. The lower sixty minute firm peak load line shows a summer peak about 100 MW more than the previous winter peak load, except for this last year when the severe winter, together with an above average increase in the number of customers, caused an increase in the winter peak. Electrical power projections through the next twenty years call for an additional 4000 MW of capacity most of which must come from the region's coal deposits with some supplemental power possibly from geothermal or nuclear plants.

Some economists project a leveling of growth rate in the future. This is not to be expected in this area. Instead the following conditions in this region will result in greater demand for electrical energy:

---

[1]*Energy and the Environment—Electric Power* (Washington, D.C.: Council on Environmental Quality, U.S. Government Printing Office, August 1973), p. 1.

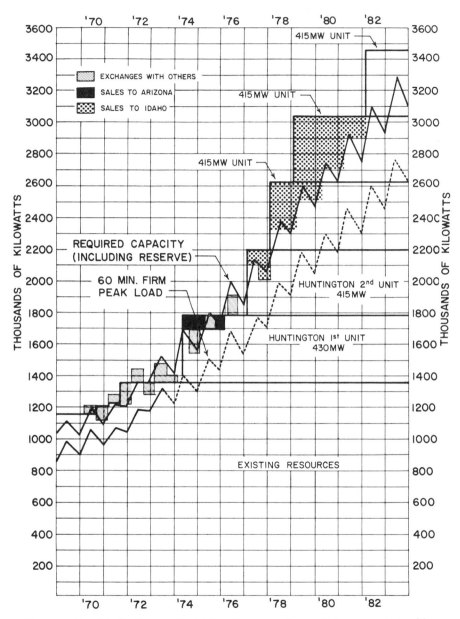

FIGURE 1. *Utah Power & Light Company's peak load and peaking capability through 1982 is shown. The Company's predictions have always fallen under the actual demands and this forecast is under continual revision.*

1.   The population growth in the Intermountain Region ranks
the four states served by the Company in the top thirteen in
the nation; Colorado is fifth, Utah is sixth, Idaho is seventh and
Wyoming is thirteenth.[2]

2.   During the next twelve year period, 25 to 30 percent of the
population will be in the twenty to thirty-five year age group—
the time when new families and homes demand an increase in
energy.[3]

3.   The supplies of the major fuels, oil and gas, are dwindling
and must be replaced by other fuels. The estimated lifetime of
the world fuel supplies is shown in table 1.

TABLE 1—*World Fuel Supplies in Years*

	USAEC[4]	HOLDREN[5]	HUBBERT[6]	NAS[7]
Gas	27	22	- 49	50
Oil	30	38	70-80	50
Coal	200	122	100-400	300
Oil Shale		6000	10-100,000	
U-235	30			
(Breeder)	2000			
D_2	2 Billion			

One result of the shortage of oil and gas has been the demand for
electric heat which has increased in Utah from 5 percent of the new
dwellings in 1965 to 25 percent this year. Contrary to the common
belief that electric heat is wasteful of natural resources, recent studies[8] [9]

[2]*Statistical Review of Government in Utah,* (Salt Lake City, Utah Foundation: 1973).

[3]J. G. Winger, et al., *Outlook for Energy in the United States to 1985* (New York: The Chase Manhattan Bank, 1972).

[4]T. Thompson, United States Atomic Energy Commissioner, remarks before the Annual Meeting of the Division of Plasma Physics, American Physical Society, Washington, D.C., November 5, 1970.

[5]J. Holdren and P. Herrera, *Energy,* (San Francisco: Sierra Club, 1971).

[6]M. K. Hubbert, *Resources and Man* (San Francisco: W. H. Freeman and Company, 1969), p. 157.

[7]*Science Digest* 70, 15 (1971).

[8]H. B. Hansteen and J. Krikawa, in *Proceedings of the American Society of Mechanical Engineers,* (New York: ASME, 1969), 68-WA/PEM-3.

[9]C. C. Burwell, *State-of-the-Art of Energy Conversion—Today and Tomorrow,* Oak Ridge National Laboratory Report (1973).

at national laboratories and actual metered data[10] show that electric heat either uses the same quantity of raw fuel or actually conserves natural resources. The application of the electrical heat pump to commercial buildings is greatly reducing the demand on natural resources. For example, the new thirty story Church Office Building in Salt Lake City is utilizing heat recovery within the building and uses an electrical heat pump to transfer heat from underground wells to the building with a co-efficient of performance of five. Hence, this building consumes less than 30 percent of the raw fuel utilizing the heat pump as compared to using conventional heating systems.

If one takes a long range look, it is clear to see that the fossil-fuel age is a "slender spike" in history (see figure 2), and we must find a replacement for this depletable resource.[11]

4. The Nation is entering a "minerals crisis" which will place an additional demand on Colorado River Basin energy resources to supply electrical energy for processing and smelting the ores located in the rich mineral belts surrounding the River Basin.[12]

How does Utah Power & Light Company plan to meet the growth in its service territory? We can either build our own generating facilities or buy power from neighboring utilities and transport the power on interconnecting transmission lines. For this decade, or until 1980, there is no power available from neighboring utilities. Hence, Utah must look in its own backyard coal deposits to supply its energy requirements which will call for the building of new power plants during the next five years whose cost will equal that invested by Utah Power & Light Company over the past seventy years.

COAL AND ENVIRONMENTAL QUALITY

Since there is little oil or gas available for future power plants in this area and nuclear power plants have lead times from conception to operation in excess of ten years due to licensing, engineering, and environmental considerations, only coal is available for electrical generation in the next decade. Within the Utah portion of the Colorado River Basin there is a total coal reserve of 24.3 billion tons and a

---

[10]"Does Electric Heating Waste Energy" (Oklahoma Gas and Electric Company Report), *Electrical World* (May 1973), p. 66.

[11]M. K. Hubbert, *Resources and Man.*

[12]Department of the Interior, *U.S. Geological Survey News Release,* May 8, 1973.

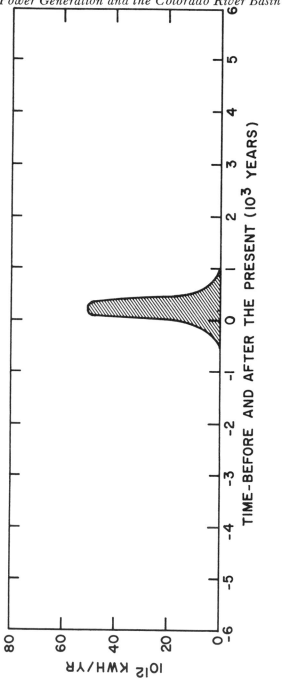

FIGURE 2. *The entire fossil-fuel age is short on the historical timetable.*

recoverable reserve of 7.8 billion tons[13] and a recoverable reserve of 7.8 billion tons.[13] The recoverable reserve of coal is more than adequate, by an order-of-magnitude, to supply Utah's electrical needs through the thirty-five year lifetimes of those plants to be built during the next two decades.

What is the impact on the environment of operating coal-burning plants? An analysis of the operation of the new 430 MW Huntington Plant First Unit will serve as a good example. In early 1974 the First Unit will begin operation with an annual fuel consumption at 80 percent load factor of 1.2 million tons and a consumptive use of water mainly for cooling of about 7,000 acre-ft./yr. A coal analysis at Huntington shows 6.6 percent ash, 0.5 percent sulfur, and a heat content of 12,200 Btu/lb. In order to determine the effect of stack emissions on the environment, comprehensive studies have been conducted during the past three years and are continuing as follows:

1. Brigham Young University is defining the base line parameters of existing aquatic conditions and the effects of construction and future operation of the Huntington Generating Station and the Electric Lake Dam on the aquatic environment.

2. University of Utah is evaluating the atmospheric, vegetation, animal and general ecological conditions.

3. Utah State Division of Wildlife Resources is conducting physiological studies of large mammals.

4. North American Weather Consultants is collecting meteorological information.

The expected stack emissions and their effect on the environment is as follows:

PARTICULATE

An electrostatic precipitator with a collection efficiency of 99.5 percent will be installed on the First Unit. The resultant stack emission of ash will be aboutt 1.0 tons per day. During 1970 and 1971, the ambient average concentrations of suspended particulates in the town of Huntington was sixty to seventy-two micro-

---

[13]H. H. Doeling and R. L. Graham, Utah Geological and Mineral Survey Monograph Series 1, 2, and 3 (UGMS, Salt Lake City, Utah, 1972).

grams per cubic meter resulting primarily from wind-generated dust. Based on a 99.5 percent collection efficiency for the precipitator, the maximum annual average increase in particulate concentration in Huntington with one unit will be approximately 0.2 micrograms per cubic meter or an incremental increase of 0.35 percent.[14]

Consultants of the highest technical competence have studied visible impact of the emissions. Dr. W. O. Ursenbach of the Utah Engineering Experiment Station found in his studies that the effects of meteorological conditions and fly ash on visual range will not be noticeable over background dusts.[15] It is anticipated that visual effects on the backround will not be noticable for either the First or Second Unit at Huntington. The stack plumes at the plant will be essentially clear.

Sulfur Dioxide

SO₂ removal equipment is not necessary on the First Unit to meet applicable standards and has, therefore, not been specified, although room has been provided for later addition of SO₂ equipment should it be required.

Extensive studies have been conducted in the Huntington area to provide a quantitative evaluation of SO₂ emission impact for the Huntington Plant. Since there have been many questions raised during the past year concerning this SO₂ impact, the recent conclusion of the extensive North American Weather Consultants' studies is quoted here.[16]

The results of these studies again confirm the earlier findings that the impact of the SO₂ emission from one 430 MW unit in Huntington Canyon operating without sulfur

---

[14]F. N. Davis, *Environmental Considerations in the Design of the Huntington Steam Electric Station,* presented at the Thirteenth Annual Engineering Symposium, Brigham Young University, 1972.

[15]W. O. Ursenbach, "Contribution of Fly Ash to Light Scattering and Visibility in the Vicinity of the Huntington Plant," (Prepared for Utah Power & Light Company by the Utah Engineering Company by the Utah Engineering Experiment Station, February 1972).

[16]E. L. Hovind, R. D. Elliott and R. L. Petersen, *A Reevaluation of Plume Tracer Simulation Studies in Huntington Canyon, Emery County, Utah,* North American Weather Consultants Report 729-A, July 1973.

removal control will be well below existing State and Federal ambient air quality standards. For two 430 MW units operating without sulfur removal control, the studies to date indicate that the SO_2 impact will be within existing Federal Standards, including the three hour secondary standard.

However, present Utah State regulations require that 80 percent of the SO_2 be removed from the stacks of future plants including the Second Unit of Huntington. SO_2 equipment is not presently available on a commercial operating basis. In fact, most present systems being studied are just moving from the pilot plant stage to the demonstration phase. Utah Power & Light Company is actively supporting SO_2 research projects, one of which is being jointly studied with Envirotech Corporation at the Gadsby Plant in Salt Lake City. Present studies show that SO_2 equipment, if available, would cost about twenty-two million dollars for each unit and the total annual cost of the sulfur dioxide removal equipment (capital plus operating) will be about six million dollars per year.

Using the best available information, Dr. Noel de Nevers of the Chemical Engineering Department, University of Utah, has begun cost benefit studies for power plant pollution controls. The study assesses the cost and operation of the equipment versus the benefits to human health, property, and loss of scenic and recreational value. Preliminary results of the study show that costs of sulfur dioxide removal at Huntington exceed the benefits by a factor of approximately *forty*. If the standard methods of cost benefit analysis are used to decide whether or not to install that equipment, then the decision would clearly be not to install sulfur dioxide control equipment. However, Utah Power & Light Company must comply with applicable State regulations regarding installation of SO_2 equipment on additional units at the Huntington site.

NITROGEN OXIDES

The boiler manufacturer has employed the best engineering design to reduce nitrogen oxide emissions. The present ambient Federal regulation for NO_x is .05 ppm on an annual basis so that even with two units at Huntington, the annual average maximum concentration will be approximately one-quarter of the standard. The visible contribution from nitrogen oxides and sulfur dioxide will not be discernible.[17]

Water utilization by thermal plants is an important environmental consideration. If the entire 4000 MW of additional capacity for Utah Power & Light Company over the next twenty years is to be supported by the Colorado River Basin of Utah and Wyoming, approximately 60,000 acre-ft. annually will be required. There are adequate water resources if the states permit use for this purpose.

The Huntington Plant will have zero waste water discharge into Huntington Creek and will make use of all waters coming from the coal mine for plant use. Extensive design studies were conducted to make the plant fit in with the surroundings to increase the aesthetic appearance in the facility.

The Company is also installing new precipitators with a minimum of 98 percent removal efficiencies on its plants near Castle Gate, Utah, and Kemmerer, Wyoming.

EMERGING ELECTRIC POWER ALTERNATIVES

What are the possibilities of finding alternatives to the use of coal-fired generation and what would be their resultant impact on the Colorado River Basin directly or indirectly? Research on many alternative methods is being supported by the Company as follows:

GEOTHERMAL

A study last year by the Department of Interior estimated 1 percent recovery of the geothermal resource of the United States would equal the recoverable coal, oil and natural gas resources.[18] Geothermal power plants which utilize natural heat derived from batholiths within the earth were introduced in 1904 in Larderello, Italy and the present extent of the world electrical generation is shown in table 2.

---

[17]Letter from Wayne O. Ursenbach, Utah Engineering Experiment Station, Center for Environmental Studies, March 14, 1972.

[18]*Newsweek,* April 13, 1972, p. 13.

TABLE 2—1973 *World Geothermal Power Production*

		Operating	Under Construction
		\multicolumn{2}{c}{Electric Capacity, Megawatts}	
Italy	Larderello	358.6	
	Mt. Amiato	25.5	
USA	The Geysers	300	110
New Zealand	Wairakei	160	
	Kawerau	10	
Japan	Matsukawa	20	
	Otake	13	
Mexico	Pathe	3.5	75
USSR	Pauzhetka	5	
	Paratunka	.7	
Iceland	Namafjall	2.5	
		898.8	185

The U.S. Geological Survey has classified 4.5 million acres as having prospective geothermal value in Utah[19] (see figure 3). Extensive geology, geophysical and geochemical surveys have been made in Utah during the past two years and leasing of land for geothermal development is continuing by interested firms at the present. Letters of Intent to purchase steam have been signed between Utah Power & Light Company and two firms, Geothermal Kinetics, Inc. and Thermal Power Company of Utah. The drilling of experimental wells is expected early in 1974. If commercial steam deposits are found in Utah, construction of a demonstration geothermal plant could follow in the early 80's. Data on the reservoir must be collected and evaluated as the development of the steam field proceeds and the evaluation require a much longer time than is needed for the design and construction of the generating facilities.

[19]L. H. Godwin et al., *Classification of Public Lands Valuable for Geothermal Steam and Association Geothermal Resources*, U.S. Geological Survey Circular 647 (Washington, D.C.: U.S. Department of Interior, 1971).

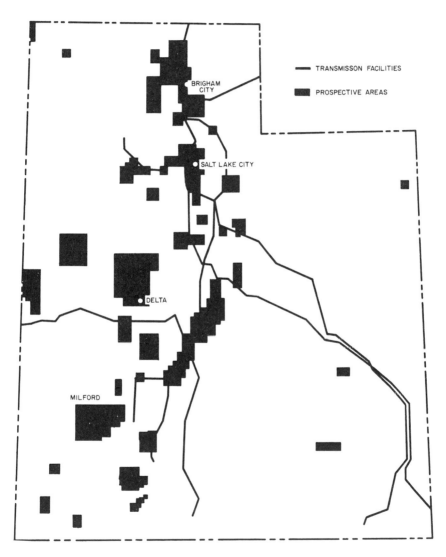

FIGURE 3. *The USGS has classified 4.5 million acres as having prospective geothermal value in Utah.*

Since most geothermal areas are outside the Colorado River basin and are expected to supply their own source of water for cooling, there would be no direct impact on the Basin.

NUCLEAR

It was recently reported by General Atomic that in 1985 the High Temperature Gas Cooled Reactor with a gas turbine cycle should be available. The significance of the announcement is that the Brayton Cycle used by the gas turbine will allow rejection of waste heat to begin at 440°F instead of 130°F temperature of the condensing steam cycle plants. This reduces the physical size of cooling towers and permits economical use of dry cooling towers which would use air in place of water for cooling.

Nuclear power is definitely an alternative for the 1980's, but economics, reliability, and nuclear safety will determine its introduction into the Utah Power & Light Company System.

COAL CONVERSION

Research continues to determine which method of environmental. control will be most economical for electrical production; stack gas scrubbing for SO_2 or low Btu gasification of coal with sulfur removal before burning of the gas. High Btu coal gasification will require significant quantities of water, as much as two pounds of water per pound of coal, of which about one-third of the water is consumed in the methanation process and the remainder is used in evaporating cooling. Therefore, coal gasification is expected to make great demands on the Colorado River Basin water supplies.

OIL SHALE

Many studies have been made on the recoverable reserves of oil shale within the Colorado River Basin. M. King Hubbert of the USGS estimates the recoverable oil from shale to be thirty billion barrels from shale with 10-100 gallons/ton. New technology will be required to release the 100,000 billion barrels from shale having 5-10 gallons/ton.

Shale oil differs from crude oil in that it is high in nitrogen and low in hydrogen. Therefore, the nitrogen must be removed and hydrogen added. The adding of hydrogen will demand water which will be the controlling factor in its development.

TAR SANDS

Ninety-five percent of the Nation's reserves of tar sands or twenty to twenty-five billion barrels of oil lie within the Colorado River Basin. Hot water extraction of the oil, a method used in Canada, could demand large quantities of water, but research is being conducted on the use of hot air which, if it works, would reduce the water requirements for tar sand development.

LONG RANGE ALTERNATIVES

To insure that we have adequate supplies of electricity in the future, the Nation's electrical utilities, both private and public, organized the Electric Power Research Institute (EPRI) in March of 1972. The president of the new institute is Dr. Chauncey Starr, who was Dean of Engineering at UCLA. The research budget for 1973 is $86,000,000 and for 1974 is $137,000,000. Expenditures are expected to increase steadily through the year 2000. Utah Power & Light Company is supporting the program according to a prescribed formula with $354,000 in 1973 and $570,000 in 1974. Some seventy-seven projects originally under the Edison Electric Institute (EEI) have been absorbed into the new program. A description of major energy projects supported and the timetable for expected commercial use follows:

Breeder Reactor is expected to be in commercial production in the 90's and would extend the lifetime of present nuclear fuels from thirty years to more than 1000 years.

Fusion or the reaction by which the sun and stars generate energy is expected after the year 2000 and will have a two billion year fuel supply.

Magnetohydrodynamics will have higher efficiencies of 55 to 60 percent but will still require water and coal and will not be available before the late 90's.

Solar energy has many options as shown by table 3.[20]

TABLE 3—SOLAR ENERGY OPTIONS

	Actual	*Theor.*
Direct Conversion (Solar Cells)	5 to 11%	18%
Biological (Algae/Methane)	1 to 2.5%	3%
Biological (Grain/Alcohol)	1%	1%
Biological (Animal/Methane)	1%	1%
Sea Thermal Gradients	1%	2%
Thermocouple	2 to 4%	7%
Thermal (Hydrogen Dissociation)	1%	?
Thermal (Thermodynamic Cycle)	2 to 4%	30%

The thermal cycle utilizing a reflecting surface to focus the sun's rays on a pipe containing a working fluid and the extraction of energy with conventional turbines appears the most promising and the most ardent supporters have a time-table for commercial production near the year 2000.[21]

Colorado River Basin
Fossil Fuels and Power Workshop
Summary

QUESTION: What should be the major facets of a national energy policy?

CONSENSUS: A national long range energy policy should take into account regional policies and objectives; it is important that the affected people in the energy producing areas be involved in the decision

---

[20]A. B. Meinel and M. P. Meinel, A Briefing on Solar Power Farms to the Task Force on Energy of the House of Representatives Committee on Science and Astronautics (Washington, D.C., 1972).

[21]E. L. Ralph, *Solar Energy* 14:11 (1972).

making processes concerning their region and that the effects of energy production be fully understood by the people to whom they accrue. International policies and concerns should also be taken into account.

A national energy policy should be tied to land use policy and should address itself to environmental planning and transportation planning.

QUESTION: To what extent should a national energy policy seek to internalize the social and environmental costs of energy production?

CONSENSUS: There was little consensus regarding the internalization of costs. The position paper authors indicated that economic costs of pollution control beyond federal and state standards would exceed the economic benefits of such control. There was disagreement regarding the degree to which environmental costs of energy production should be reflected in the cost to the consumer.

RECOMMENDATION: A well funded effort should be made in energy research and development. The research should address itself to energy saving techniques and materials as well as energy production and utilization. High priority should be placed on energy conservation at all levels of production and use.

CHAPTER XIV

Transportation and Regional Environmental Management

Dwight M. Blood*

The purpose of this paper is to consider the relationships between transportation and the environment. The discussion focuses on conceptual issues and institutional bottlenecks which must be resolved prior to formulating effective transportation components of regional environmental plans or strategies. Emphasis is necessarily on identifying problem areas and on discussing possible avenues to solutions. The current state of the analytical art has not yet produced, in most instances, highly credible results; rather, progress to date has come largely through considering a wider range of social, economic, and environmental effects in reaching public and private investment decisions than was the case historically. While the use of expanded criteria check-off lists has obviously altered the outcomes of numerous decisions, such as the stoppage of the Cross-Florida Barge Canal and the delays in building the Alaska Pipeline, much is yet to be done in improving the analytical and institutional basis for making decisions affecting transportation and the environment.

Numerous questions remain to be answered before transportation effects can be plugged neatly into socioeconomic-environmental planning frameworks, such as: How can the social, economic and environmental effects of transportation be identified and objectively determined? How can the tradeoffs among these effects be assessed

*Department of Economics and Division of Business and Economic Research, University of Wyoming, Laramie, Wyoming.

and weighted in a multi-dimensional framework for decision-making? What analytical and data deficiencies must be remedied before substantive and reliable results can be obtained from models designed to assess multi-dimensional tradeoffs? What institutional bottlenecks exist that would hinder the process of effective transport policy formulation within an environmental framework?

In attempting to provide some insight into the range of possible answers to these questions, the discussion in this paper will proceed as follows: (1) first, it is necessary to determine what is meant by "transportation" and to set forth the institutional framework within which transportation systems and intermodal networks have been developed; (2) the ways in which transport systems interact with and affect social, economic, and environmental characteristics of regions will be discussed; (3) conceptual issues in developing a multidimensional framework for assessing tradeoffs among diverse kinds of transport effects will be developed; and (4) conclusions will be reached concerning needed reasearch for remedying analytical deficiencies in relating transportation to the environment.

THE NATURE AND DEVELOPMENT OF TRANSPORT SYSTEMS

It is first necessary to clarify what is meant by transportation, and to elaborate on the nature of transportation modes and systems, the effects of which are to be incorporated into a framework for regional environmental management. Also, it is essential to review the real world of transportation institutions within which existing transport modes have developed and within which public policy decisions affecting future transport development will likely be made.

The term "transport system" is actually a euphemism for what, in reality, is a collection of disparate transport modes, each possessing dissimlar physical and economic characteristics. Thus, there is not so much a transportation system as there is a variety of alternative transport modes, each possessing a unique configuration of transportation supply and demand characteristics. While it makes sense to consider an abstract representation of total transport capacity through a total transport system, the principal value of such a concept is to provide a basis for disaggregating total transportation demand into modal requirements. In the last analysis, passengers and commodities move by air, rail and highway in the Colorado River Basin, and transport policy decisions ordinarily relate to specific transport modes.

The existence of a transport system composed of separate modes would not, in and of itself, present major difficulties in policy formation if transport policies affecting separate modes were channeled through a central clearinghouse for transport policy. In such a system, the tradeoffs among modes in attaining central goals of transportation policy would be determined and optimal public investments made. In the real world, transportation policy formulation does not take place in this way, except to a very limited extent.

Thus, the first major conceptual issue in analyzing transportation effects stems from the fact that no unified transportation system exists in reality, and that intermodal transportation tradeoffs have traditionally been given only cursory attention. This gap between a normative transport policy framework, in which intermodal considerations enter into the attainment of major transport goals, and reality, in which policy is made for separate modes, is the source of serious problems in generating data, in establishing policy, and in estimating transportation effects.

Since the preceding observation is central to most of the discussion which follows, a few comments are in order about how the current institutional framework for transportation evolved. This brief summary is intended to help illuminate the institutional deficiencies in transportation decisionmaking, and to help explain why more progress has not been made in considering aggregate transportation systems.

National transportation policy from the 1830's until well after the turn of the Twentieth Century was national railroad policy. Only when forced by the exigencies of technological development stemming from the internal combustion engine, leading first to highways and then to air transportation, did national transportation policy evolve into a multimodal framework. True, water transportation, both deep and shallow draft, was a crucial transport component for much of the nation, and inland and deep-sea water transportation preceded rail transport in the U.S. for many decades.

With national railroad policy predominating the development of national transportation policy, and since rails predated highways and air transport, highway and air transportation policy became national railroad policy once-warmed-over, with most of the regulatory drawbacks of rail policy served up once more for highway and air transportation. Most of Locklin's classic text on transportation economics is concerned with railroad transportation, with only limited space toward the end given to other modes, because the basic structure of rail regulation was reapplied to the other modes—much as a state legislature confronted with a need for a new bill often clips and pastes from other statutes.[1]

Not only was national transportation policy pre-eminently railroad policy for a lengthy period, but also the focus on early transport development was primarily at the state and local government level rather than at the federal level. Though concern for national benefits of transportation development began with the Gallatin Report in 1808,[2] intergovernmental disputes over primary jurisdiction in transport development were fought on constitutional grounds during much of the early 19th century and delayed development of transportation projects. State and local governments inaugurated many projects during this period with results that were for the most part disastrous.[3] After numerous states met with financial disaster in paying for local improvement projects during the financial collapse of the 1830's, the pendulum swung once more to federal development of such projects.

As state and local government domination of transport development gave way to federal government domination, and as transportation policy extended from the railroads to the highways and the air, an important pattern of modal separatism emerged—a pattern that ultimately has become crucial to the rational consideration of aggregate transportation policy within a unified transportation framework.

The origin of modal separatism, in which individual transport modes are administratively separated in the bureaucratic framework, can be traced back ultimately to the budgetary process. Individual projects have traditionally been funded on an individual, fragmented

[1]D. Philip Locklin. *Economics of Transportation.* Homewood, Illinois: Richard D. Irwin, Inc., 1972, 913 p.

[2]Albert Gallatin. "Roads and Canals," reprinted in *Senate Documents.* "Preliminary Report of the Inland Waterways Commission." 60th Cong., 1st sess., February 3, 1908, Document No. 325, pp. 536-581.

[3]Mid-Continent Research and Development Council. "Transportation Systems for State Growth Policy." *Proceedings 18th Annual Conference,* (Rapid City, S.D., 1971), pp. 25-37.

basis without reference to total national or regional transportation requirements. Not only did the appropriations process in Congress foster modal separatism, but separate administrative agencies were established in the Executive Branch of the federal government, precluding intermodal coordination in any but the broadest sense. Thus, each mode generated its own constituencies, its own administrative procedures, its own project review and project justification procedures, and its own advocacy procedures.

As highway construction dominated intrastate transportation development, parallel fragmentation of transport modal agencies was transplanted in the states. On the surface, it appeared that the intent of the act to create a Department of Transportation, passed in 1966, was to consolidate all transportation functions. Instead, the current Department of Transportation is more nearly a loose confederation of separate transportation fiefdoms, each of which behaves in approximately the same way it did before the DOT consolidation.

More serious as far as the present discussion is concerned is the observation that parallel planning and research programs do not exist for the separate modes. While the Federal Highway Administration and the Federal Aviation Administration are primarily construction and planning agencies, the Federal Railroad Administration is primarily a safety agency, with major attention on railroad economic policy centered in the Interstate Commerce Commission. Pipelines, the nation's "hidden" transport system, are totally outside the purview of DOT, with natural gas pipelines regulated by the Federal Power ing this period with results that were, for the most part, uniformly dis- Commission and Petroleum Pipelines regulated by the Interstate Commerce Commission. Thus, pipeline transportation does not enter into a cohesive national transportation system either in terms of planning or in terms of administrative structure. This omission is unfortunate: in Wyoming, for example, total physical investment in plant and equipment in pipelines equals total capital outlays on the Wyoming interstate highway system since 1956. Economic regulation of all modes is outside the Department of Transportation.[4]

Although several states have emulated the federal pattern in developing state departments of transportation, the net result at the

[4]Curtis A. Cramer. "Pipeline Transportation in Wyoming" Division of Business and Economic Research, University of Wyoming, 1973. Unpublished manuscript submittted for review to Wyoming State Highway Department.

state level has been approximately the same; because of unique modal funding patterns and planning requirements at the federal level, states can do little more than follow the federal pattern except with discretionary state funds.

The results of programs of modal separatism in funding and administering transportation elements include the following: (1) transportation policy formation has been fragmented as separate modes have vied for funding laurels; (2) planning and data requirements have varied substantially among modes, so that intermodal comparisons are either difficult or impossible. The last state-to-state commodity flow data for railroads, for example, were published by the I.C.C. in 1966. With the responsibility for commodity-flow data turned over to DOT shortly thereafter, DOT has delayed issuing such data for railroads until similar data can also be issued for other modes, to prevent a competitive disadvantage among the modes. Meanwhile, seven years have elapsed, and there are no state-to-state commodity flow data for any mode, let alone railroads; (3) the enabling legislation creating the Department of Transportation in subsection 7(a) of S.3010, as originally introduced, would have required the Secretary of Transportation to develop standards and criteria for the formulation and economic evaluation of all proposals for the investment of federal funds in transportation, with certain exceptions. In subsequent debate, concern expressed over traditional procedures with respect to inland waterways led to the exclusion of inland waterway transportation from the list of transport modes for which the Secretary of Transportation could develop investment standards and criteria. Thus, no true intermodal transport evaluation framework exists.

The implication of bureaucratic transport modal separatism for this discussion is that it is difficult, if not impossible, to consider the net impacts of an integrated transportation system, either regionally or nationally. Thus, the estimation of transportation impacts on a comparable basis among all modes of transportation has not been accomplished. This deficiency not only makes it difficult to incorporate transportation effects into economic development frameworks, but also makes the problem of incorporating environmental effects into a multi-dimensional evaluation framework involving a wide variety of economic, social, and environmental criteria even more difficult to solve.

As the authors of the Mueller Report on Federal Transportation Policy stated in 1960:

> National transportation is presently out of balance. It is less a national system than a loose grouping of individual industries. We have built a vast network of highways, railways, inland waterways and seaports, airways and airports, and pipelines, with little attention to conflict among these expanding networks. Economic regulation has been administered in rigid compartments although many basic problems are common to many areas of transportation. Total capacity is not closely geared to total need.[5]
>
> We do not know either the total volume of traffic handled or its composition by commodities and type, nor do we know over what distances the various elements of traffic move, the types of transportation performed, the reasons for choice under the present set of arrangements and the rates under which or the costs at which the movements are performed. . . . Hence a quantitative appraisal of the extent of imbalance as compared with a standard of economic efficiency and a measure of the significance to the nation of that imbalance is impossible.[6]

Thus, although the logic of considering transportation as a total system is inescapable in a normative sense, the real world of transport modal administration with its fragmentation and lack of cohesive interrelationships among modes exhibits substantive barriers to making inter-modal transport policy decisions in support of a well-enunciated, operational, national transporation policy.

SOCIAL, ECONOMIC, AND ENVIRONMENTAL EFFECTS OF TRANSPORTATION MODES OF REGIONS

Before considering the task of assessing the interrelationships between transportation and the environment in a multi-dimensional policy framework, it is necessary to consider briefly the range of effects of transportation networks on regions such as the Colorado River Basin.

---

[5]U.S. Dept. of Commerce, *Federal Transportation Policy and Program,* 1960, p. 3.

[6]Ernest W. Williams, Jr. and D. W. Bluestone, *Rationale of Federal Transportation Policy. Appendix to Federal Transportation Policy and Program,* Washington, D.C., U.S. Dept. of Commerce, April 1960, p. 4.

A preliminary observation to be made is that regions defined for one purpose need not necessarily provide a rational geographic boundary for evaluating another economic activity. Thus, the Colorado River Basin, defined along geographic boundaries delimited by the drainage area of the Basin, does not necessarily provide a parallel region in which transportation policy can be formulated.

The development of transportation facilities and demand for those facilities in moving passengers and commodities is linked directly to the location of economic trade areas. A comparison of the drainage area of the Colorado River Basin with the functional economic areas delineated by the Office of Business Economics, shows, for example, that of the entire Basin area, only Arizona and Colorado's Western Slope exhibit the basic qualifications to be classified as self-contained economic trade areas. Much of eastern Utah, in addition to south-western Wyoming, is linked to the Ogden-Salt Lake City-Provo trade area, while the western portions of New Mexico, except for north-western New Mexico, are linked to New Mexico trade areas extending across the rest of New Mexico. Thus, transportation goals for uniquely defined geographic areas such as river basins or flood plains may not be specified in the same way as transportation goals for entire functional economic trade areas.

The effects of transportation networks on social and economic affairs as well as on the environment are diverse, interdependent, and overlapping. For that reason, it is difficult, in most instances, to isolate and categorize sets of effects and view them from a single vantage point. For example, the combined major effect of modern transport systems is urbanization, which embodies and represents simultaneously complex social, economic, and environmental effects. For purposes of discussion, however, it is useful to segment the three categories of effects.

SOCIAL EFFECTS OF TRANSPORTATION

Perhaps the most obvious and direct social effect of transportation comes from changes in mobility patterns, as indicated by choice of residence, work location, and travel patterns. As indicated above, the principal manifestation of transportation is urbanization in all of its diverse forms and patterns. For sparsely populated areas, such as the Colorado River Basin, changes in transportation facilities have had

profound impacts on social and community structure in sparsely populated areas and in the growth and decline of community institutions
and community population concentrations.

The two fundamental choices that people usually make in life
are where they work and where they live. Sometimes the work choice
predominates; other times the work choice is dependent on choice of
residence. To the extent that transportation developments have influenced the work-residence tradeoffs, then, social institutions have necessarily changed to accommodate changing residential location patterns.

At the same time, changes in work-residence patterns have had
profound impacts on the environment. Shifts in neighborhood location; spatial shrinkage through more efficient transport modes; congestion; a continued transition toward increased specialization and
decreased span of working years for those in the labor force—these and
other similar factors have resulted in a wide range of changing impacts
on the physical and biological environments within which people
live. To argue that the impacts are environmental or social, or
whether they were induced by economic forces or by transport accessibility are chicken-and-egg arguments. The important point is that
the spectrum of social-economic-environmental effects are often joint
products of a complex system of social change.

ECONOMIC EFFECTS OF TRANSPORTATION

Senator Herman E. Talmadge (Georgia) stated, in reaction to
new standards for water resource development recently issued by
the Water Resources Council:

> I am well aware that just as the Department of Transportation
> now contends that roads do nothing to contribute toward regional
> development, it is also being contended that water resources de-
> velopment does not truly contribute to regional development. How-
> ever, purely empirical evidence to be found in the Arkansas River
> Basin and the Interstate Highway System indicate that these allega-
> tions are made by theoretical dreamers who have never watched a
> town die because it was cut off from the Interstate system, or
> watched a town like Pine Bluff, Arkansas, flourish because it was
> on a navigable waterway. The regional ripple effect from such
> development is also a physical thing that is quantifiable by even
> a first-year economics student.[7]

_____

[7]Senator Herman E. Talmadge. Quoted in *Criteria News,* National Waterways Conference, September 28, 1973, p. 14.

Senator Talmadge's position well represents widely-held views that the presence of favorable effects represents sufficient justification for project development. While even the most uninspired first-year economics student can obviously observe regional ripple effects, first-year economics students are also taught to evaluate any given economic proposition with the words, "compared to what?" Similarly, first-year economics students are indoctrinated with the concept of opportunity cost; i.e., the cost of any given economic alternative is measured not by the cash outlay on the alternative, but by the value of what was given up by not spending on the next best alternative.

Thus, regional economic effects of given transportation investments may very well produce positive economic benefits for the region, but what is often not clear is whether a particular investment represents the best use of economic resources in terms of optimal payoff to achieve specified economic objectives. Moreover, gains to the region often end up being regional transfers of income under conditions of full employment, and cannot be viewed as net increments to national income. Failure to account for the full range of opportunity costs in terms of returns from alternative investments may result in erroneous conclusions about payoffs from public investments in alternative transport projects. The show-and-tell-type logic in supporting specific projects often fails when comparative returns among alternative projects designed to attain the same end are compared.

Hurter and Moses have concluded:

> Investment in transportation facilities can have a critical effect on the economic fortunes of different regions by stimulating growth in some while retarding others. A rational investment choice must consequently take into account the differential economic effects of alternative proposals on a given system of regions.
>
> * * *
>
> . . . investment funds should always flow into the region and sector where capacity commands the largest imputed value. In reality, firms in one region and sector, with funds to invest, often are not attracted to another region and sector even when the latter's capacity has the highest imputed value. Firms tend to invest in sectors the same as or similiar to their own and in the same or nearby regions.[8]

---

[8]Arthur P. Hurter and Leon N. Moses. "Transportation Investment and Regional Development." *Journal of the American Institute of Planners.* XXX: 132-139, May 1964.

The logic of the foregoing argument hinges on testing the hypothesis that significant differences exist among regions with respect to the adequacy of transportation capacity and conditions of service that can be altered by differential levels of transport investment among regions. In this regard, Charles River Associates reached this conclusion:

> . . . transportation investment generally will not be a very significant stimulus to further regional growth in the United States. The conclusion cannot be entirely negative, however. In order to capitalize on the trend toward regionalization of industry, a region must have good intraregional transportation systems.[9]

While Charles River Associates also observes that "Failure to provide the necessary increases in the capacity of the transportation system will create a bottleneck and may eventually retard the region's growth," they emphasize that mangement of a region's transportation system, as opposed to net new investments, can ". . . aid or retard development."

For a well-developed regional transportation system, the basic problems in adjusting that system are usually incremental problems in resolving bottlenecks; e.g., movement of low-sulphur coal from Wyoming's Powder River Basin could well be facilitated by construction of a new Burlington Northern branch line from Gillette to Douglas. Similarly, transportation investments must be made to accommodate new towns, and to meet the needs of the poor, the elderly, and the isolated.[10,11] But once a transportation system is well developed, most alternatives to changing that system really involve only tinkering at the margin rather than constructing an entire new system.

Does transportation stimulate development or does development stimulate the need for transportation? Clearly, the effects move in both directions depending on the circumstances. The availability of

---

[9]Charles River Associates Incorporated. *The Role of Transportation in Regional Economic Development.* Prepared for U.S. Department of Commerce Office of Regional Economic Development. Cambridge, Massachusetts: Charles River Associates Incorporated. No date, p. iii.

[10]Resource Management Corporation. *The Transportation Needs of the Rural Poor.* Prepared for U.S. Department of Transportation Office of Research Development. Springfield, Virginia: Clearinghouse for Federal, Scientific and Technical Information, no date.

[11]American Academy of Arts and Sciences, *Conference on Poverty and Transportation,* June 7, 1968: Edited transcript (Springfield, Va. 1968).

better highways and air transportation has obviously contributed to spatial shrinkage throughout the Colorado River Basin, leading to longer trips for business, work, medical care, and shopping. Workers on the new Jim Bridger Power Plant near Rock Springs live as far away as Lyman, Evanston, and Kemmerer, while many Wyoming people commute regularly to the Wasatch Front Range in Utah.

The basic analytical task is to isolate and measure these economic impacts so that quantitative evidence is available concerning the inter-relationships between transportation and regional economics. Little attention has been paid to this general problem. Though the analytical models for estimating comprehensive economic impacts are available, the data are usually not sufficient for implementing them except for very large areas.

Many early transportation impact studies took the form of statistical compilations of all known economic characteristics of a community or region in which a new transportation facility such as a road or airport was to be located. While most of these studies improved public understanding of the basic descriptive characteristics of the community or region, they did precious little to pinpoint the inter-relationships between the transport facility or change in transport service and the economic structure of the area.

A new generation of analytical studies has attempted to consider the net eonomic impact of transportation facilities and services through estimation of changes in dollar flows for all affected segments of the economy by using input-output analysis,[12] while other studies have focused on benefit-cost analysis,[13] and still others have focused on ". . . a conceptual scheme for integrating into a common framework, all impact estimates at all area levels."[14] While progress is being made, there is a limitation to how far transportation flows can be simulated from knowledge of basic economic activity, and there are

---

[12]Karen R. Polenski. *The Study of Transportation Requirements Using National and Multi-Regional Input-Output Techniques.* Prepared for Department of Transportation Office of the Secretary by Harvard Economic Research Project. Cambridge, Massachusetts: Clearinghouse for Federal, Scientific and Technical Information, 71 p.

[13]Joseph D. Crumlish. *Notes on the State-of-the-Art of Benefit Cost Analysis as Related to Transportation Systems.* Springfield, Virginia: Clearinghouse for Federal, Scientific and Technical Information, November 1966.

[14]Richard A. Musgrave. "Cost-Benefit Analysis and the Theory of Public Finance," *Journal of Economic Literature.* VII(3):797-806, September 1969.

important limitations in using data obtained second or third hand from such simulation efforts. In short, it is questionable that regional transportation impact models can contribute a great deal in terms of new information without adequate state-to-state commodity flow data. While such data have been available in the past for the railroads, the unregulated character of much of the region's trucking industry makes it highly unlikely that detailed data on truck commodity flows will ever be made available on a continuing basis.

Economic effects of transportation can come in a variety of ways, including: (1) changes in transportation physical networks, such as roads, highways, railroads, and airports; (2) changes in transport equipment such as trucks, planes and railroad moving stock; (3) voluntary changes in terms of service within regulatory frameworks; (4) involuntary changes in terms of service, including changes in routes and rates, imposed by state or federal regulatory bodies. Thus, transport developments need not all be focused on new or bigger or better highways, airports, and railroads, which is where much of the attention is focused. Rather, increasing attention needs to be paid to the terms and circumstances which influence levels of service. Removal of less-than-truckload freight service from a small community, for example, can have a disastrous effect on retailer accessibility to small-lot shipments.

Considerable progress has been made in classifying the types of effects generated by all public investments, including transportation.[15] Yet, much public and private debate concerning transport investments or changes in regulatory provisions fails to account for differences between real and pecuniary benefits and costs, or between the actual, intended benefits or costs of a project or those benefits or costs induced by changes in the relative price level, such as higher wages or rents in booming communties. Much additional work remains to be done in classifying the range of total transport economic effects on regions and communities.

In summary, much progress has been made in the conceptual identification and estimation of transport economic effects, both nationally and locally. Originally, much effort was expended on non-

[15]U.S. Congress, Joint Ecnomic Committee. "Policy Analysis in Transportation Programs," by James R. Nelson. *The Analysis and Evalaution of Public Expenditures: The PPB System,* Volume 3. Joint Committee Print, 91st Cong., 1st sess., 1969, p. 1102.

analytical approaches to assessing vast quantities of often-unrelated data and information to attempt to see how a new transport project would fit into a community or region. The new generation of economic impact studies seeks to assess and quantitatively measure a wide range of interdependencies between transportation and the remainder of the economy.

ENVIRONMENTAL EFFECTS

The interrelationships between transportation and the environment have been well stated by Nelson:

> Investments in transportation facilities appear to be little different from other private and public investments in that they involve large-scale physical facilities, require valuable inputs, and produce output for long periods into the future. However, analysis of alternative investments in this area is especially complicated by the fact that a large portion of the output entails the saving of human time and reduction in the loss of human life. Both of these are notoriously hard outputs to value. More significantly, transportation facilities are intimately related to the environment in which they are placed—not only does the environment determine the demand for transportation services, but the existence of transportation facilities alters the environment and in turn, alters the demand for its own output. Finally, transportation policy in the United States is affected by many institutional and economic constraints which make policy analysis both highly important and most difficult.[16]

Basically, environmental effects from transportation may take the form of altered neighborhoods or living patterns; they may directly add noxious substances to the air, soil, or to living organisms; they may offend our sense of visual aesthetics; or they may appeal to our capacity to absorb noise. In each case, the effectiveness of the impact estimate depends on what is known about crisis levels of survival in relation to the existing levels of environmental alteration.

The tradeoffs between economics and the environment were well put, though inadvertently, by Congressman Robert L. F. Sikes of Florida at a recent annual meeting of the American Waterways Con-

---

[16]Isard, Walter et al. *Ecologic-Economic Analysis for Regional Development.* New York: The Free Press, 1972, p. 233.

ference in Tampa. At the outset of his remarks, the Congressman stated that we must not stop the business of our country just to make the environmentalists happy. (Cheers, applause, whistles). A few minutes later, he appealed to a sense of righteous indignation by indicating that we must preserve west Florida's white, sandy beaches—that Louisiana and Mississippi could drill for off-shore oil—if they wanted to, but Florida's beaches should be protected.

This apparent contradiction illustrates the fundamental rule of economics, to wit, you cannot have your cake and eat it too. Furthermore, unless you are very rich, you cannot afford to worry much about pollution or environmental impacts to begin with.

Analytical efforts to incorporate simultaneously the interrelationships between ecology and economics have only recently been initiated. The work of Isard[17] and Kneese[18] is exemplary.

Isard concludes:

> . . . the system of linkages governing natural and social phenomena is extremely complex. There are . . . few, if any, systems which are simple. We are operating in a world in which variables are all intricately interrelated. It is for this reason that there are some investigators who avoid empirical investigations because this approach cannot possibly portray accurately and comprehensively the independent web of real life.[19]

The confusion which prevails in the development of environmental impact studies illustrates the confusion over interrelationships between economic and environmental factors. While the argument is frequently made that decisions to be made outside the market for want of a pricing mechanism—i.e., decisions about pure social goods— must be relegated to the political mechanism for decision making by ballot votes instead of dollar votes, this route hardly solves the problem. Are politicians possessed of some omniscience not vested in ordinary mortals? The people's representatives, too, must make a decision, and it would help if objective evidence concerning these interrelationships were available to do so.

---

[17]Isard, *Ecologic-Economic Analysis.*

[18]Kneese, Allen V., Ayres, Robert U. and D'Arge, Ralph C. *Economics and the Environment: A Materials Balance Approach. Resources for the Future, Inc.* Baltimore: The John Hopkins Press, 1970, 120 p.

[19]Isard, *Ecologic-Economic Analysis.*

THE EVOLUTION OF MULTI-DIMENSIONAL CRITERIA
FOR PUBLIC DECISION MAKING

In the early days of public spending, when funds were plentiful and public projects limited largely to national defense, natural resources, and to running a bare-boned government bureaucracy, the question of estimating impacts of government projects was a moot question. The quest for objective criteria for appraising the desirability of public projects is a rather recent quest, fueled by the Presidential decree in the mid-1960's that something new and wonderful called PPBS—officially known as Planning and Programming Budgeting Systems; unofficially referred to as the Perfect Path to Budget Salvation—would bring us out of darkness and into light.

But many in the sanctuaries of Congress scoffed, and said lo, who are these scalawags in green eye shades who conjureth up benefit-cost ratios which thus removeth my pet project from the list of favored ones? And so there was rumbling and mumbling about this intrusion into time-honored political mechanisms for deciding who got what.

It was indeed unlikely that the advent of PPBS could resolve public spending problems overnight. Little attention had been paid to public expenditure analysis by public finance specialists and by the government. Public finance as a subject matter area meant taxes, ignoring the fact that the way in which tax money was spent could produce economic effects just as serious or just as beneficial as could removing the taxes from the private sector to begin with. The conclusion to be reached is not that PPBS has produced incontrovertible results; rather, the appropriate conclusion is that there has emerged a vast search for higher standards of objectivity and rationality in apportioning out a limited supply of public funds to a proliferating shopping list of potential public activities.

The basic question in this debate is, what criteria shall be used to judge the worthiness of public projects? Beginning with the Flood Control Act of 1936, emphasis in funding water projects was placed on benefits and costs ". . . to whomsoever they accrue." Translated this emphasis meant that economic efficiency criteria were to dominate water-resource funding discussions; i.e., if public investments in water resources resulted in net increments to national economic income, with a benefit-cost ratio of 1 or more, they could be ranked in a lineup of potential projects. This conclusion made sense to economists: if resources could be shuffled around to yield higher net returns to the nation, one of the basic canons of economic analysis would be justified.

Although efficiency criteria were applied to water and natural resource projects, little attempt was made to apply them to other categories of public spending. Beginning in the early 1960's, various analytical criteria were applied in the area of national defense. Thus, much of the early literature on benefit-cost analysis is focused either on water or on national defense.

As the economy has become wealthier, the basic focus of policy has shifted from basic survival to the process of learning to live with abundance. Although it has become apparent that not even rich societies can have everything they want, the range of possible alternatives broadens. Garbarge and trash, for example, are not much of a problem in poor societies since very little is not recycled by the poor. Questions about how rich societies can accommodate themselves to a new-found affluence inevitably lead to concern about appraising the effects of alternative investments or expenditures. This situation is paradoxical: it would appear that the richer societies become, the more obvious it would be as to where money should be spent to produce optimal results. The problem in our society, however, has been that the range of alternatives has expanded more rapidly than has the wealth to pay for them.

There are two major implications of the foregoing discussion: (1) increased wealth has permitted greater attention to be paid to investing in all forms of capital, including human capital, and has generated increasing recognition that intangible forms of capital, such as the results of research, can enhance our economic and social well-being just as constructively as in the case of bricks and mortar; and (2) the time span of public concern has lengthened. That is, increasing wealth has meant increasing attention can be paid to events further removed from today's crises.

One of the major developments that has occurred during the quest for methods to live with abundance has been an increasing awareness of the linkages among various kinds of economic, social, physical and biological events. No longer can single-dimensional analyses accommodate the growing range of individual and public concerns about social and economic change. No longer are provincial interests sufficient justification, in most instances, to warrant large public outlays simply because local benefits will be enhanced.

The problem to be resolved is, how can multi-dimensional effects be identified, estimated and weighted in reaching yes-no, where, and how much-type decisions? The recent experience of the Water Resources Council in promulgating planning principles and standards for water and related land projects is instructive in this regard.[20] Following several years of debate and pretesting, the Council published the new set of standards in the FEDERAL REGISTER on September 10, 1973. As originally published, the multiple objectives of the principles and standards included (1) national economic development, (2) environmetal quality, (3) social well-being, and (4) regional development. The methodology for assessing impacts consists primarily of developing a "... complete display or accounting of relevant beneficial and adverse effects on these . . . objectives."[21] As finally published, however, only the national economic development and environmental objectives survived the preliminary attempts to bring about objective rational analysis of all four original objectives. While development effects and social-well-being effects are to be displayed, regional and well-being goals did not survive the analytical and policy processes. As the author has stated elsewhere:

> Thus, the economic evaluation framework of a decade ago would not produce the range of answers being sought today. While economists devoted to a traditional efficiency framework would dispute this conclusion, it seems increasingly clear that the kinds of decisions being made in the public sector today are taking additional non-efficiency criteria into account. The question, then, is whether economists and social scientists will remain faithful to their strict efficiency framework, or whether they will lend their analytical skills to provide some objective rationale for incorporating multi-dimensional effects.[22]

In summary, one outgrowth of the transition to a wealthy society has been increasing concern about the range of diverse effects of public investment in justification of budgetary appropriations. The

---

[20]U.S. Water Resources Council, "Water and Related Land Resources: Establishment of Principles and Standards for Planning," *Federal Register*, XXXVIII, No. 174, pt. III, Sept. 10, 1973, 24778-24869.

[21]U.S. Water Resources Council, "Water and Related Land Resources."

[22]U.S. Water Resources Council, "Water and Related Land Resources."

pressure for appropriate multidimensional analysis has become intense at a period in which public expenditure analysis is still in its infancy. Yet, despite the crudeness of many preliminary answers, it seems clear that continued attempts to bring rationality to spending increasing sums of money on transportation as well as on dozens of other categories of public spending will intensify the need for analytical approaches to the kinds of problems discussed here.

SUMMARY AND CONCLUSIONS

In summary, the task of incorporating transportation considerations into a regional environmental management framework is complicated by the following factors:

(1)   Regions delineated for one purpose do not necessarily make ideal regions for analyzing other economic and social activities;

(2)   The task of making transportation decisions is made complicated because transport policy has not evolved as a cohesive body of clearly-articulated, operational goals; rather, transport policy proceeds in a fragmented framework of individual transport modes, each with overlapping and often-competitive goals. Thus, there is no integrated transport system, no integrated, cohesive transportation policy to serve as a benchmark against whcih the impacts of transportation improvements can be assessed.

(3)   Basic data for estimating the interrelationships between social, economic, and environmental effects of transportation are lacking. There are virtually no state-to-state commodity-flow data on an origin-destination basis, and information on highway traffic is of widely varying reliability. There is probably no area of massive public expenditure for which more is known about physical facilities, and about which less is known about the use made of those facilities, than in the case of highway transportation. There are few industry studies, particularly for the unregulated areas of common-carrier transportation. The competitive structure of much of the transport industries is such that there is no incentive to reveal cost-commodity data by individual carriers when not legally compelled to do so.

(4)   Transportation policy is tied closely to national land and water policy, thus making it impossible to consider transportation goals and policies in isolation from goals of national land and water policy.

(5)   The late advent of public expenditure analysis, including the areas of analysis in which multiple objectives are weighted and

assessed, has made it difficult to pinpoint data requirements sufficiently in advance of their need so that appropriate analytical techniques can be fully exploited in the solution of transportation investment problems.

Thus the tasks for resarch and analysis are monumental in resolving the issues posed by multiple effects of transportation on nations, regions, on the economy, on society and on the environment.
That we are belatedly aware of these multidimensional ties and of
their importance, and that we are sufficiently concerned about them
to attempt to advance the capacity of objective analysis to contribute
toward solutions to complex problems in these overlapping areas is
progress in itself. Increasing attempts must be made to develop cohesive regional and national transportation policies, and to remedy the
barriers to comprensive consideration of the total impact of transport
systems, as opposed to traditional methods of fostering growth of
separate modes, must be made. And positive attempts must be made
to remedy the basic data deficiencies which now retard the progress
that could otherwise be made in the objective analysis of transportation issues. No small resurgence is needed, also, in the areas of land
economics and transportation economics, areas of economic analysis
that took a back seat during the glamour days of weightier topics like
growth and stability, if trained people are to be available to tackle the
deficiencies and problems posed in this paper.

Perhaps the incentive to accomplish these tasks must grow from
within, from an inborn sense of responsibility toward the well-being of
mankind, and toward a heightened sense of responsibility concerning
the legacy we choose to leave for future generations. While tomorrow's
anthropologists may well have a field day in unearthing Barbie dolls
and electric wax-paper cutters from the Mount Trashmores of today,
one senses that the destiny of mankind hardly lies in these kinds of
consumption patterns. As Louis Mumford put it:

> Perhaps the first step toward regaining possession of our souls will be
> to repossess and replan the whole landscape. To turn away from
> the processes of life, growth, reproduction, to prefer the disinte-
> grated, the accidental, the random to organic form and order is to
> commit collective suicide; and by the same token, to create a coun-
> termovement to the irrationalities and threatened exterminations
> of our day, we must draw close once more to the healing order of
> nature, modified by human design.[23]

---

[23]Mumford, Lewis. *The Highway and the City.* New York: The New
American Library of World Literature, Inc., 1963, p. 226.

CHAPTER XV

Transportation in the Colorado River Basin

Stuart L. Hill*

It is customary to begin papers on transportation by reciting figures on annual expenditures for transportation, ton miles of goods carried, numbers of miles of highways, numbers of trips for recreation —some measure of the magnitude of the topic because it is immense.

Direct expenses for transportation represent nearly 20% of our gross national product. Since the end of World War II, we have spent $2.3 trillion on transportation. In 1970 Americans traveled over one trillion miles, domestic freight logged two trillion ton-miles, and over $200 billion was spent moving goods and people.

The magnitude of this activity and its impact on our daily lives is staggering. In fact, the magnitude is so great that the figures rarely mean anything to anyone—except those writing papers. There is no way to put those figures in perspective—they seem to permeate everything. And indeed they do. Our entire "way of life," our economy, our society, our environment, they are all enmeshed in transportation. Dependent upon it or interdependent with it.

Minute changes in a portion of the transportation system will have repercussions throughout the entire system by changing relationships on how we do things, how we earn a living and how we get where we want to go. This is particularly true in the Colorado River Basin.

Relative to land and environment, transportation is equivalent to access. The concept of "carrying capacity," one of the fundamental concepts of this conference, implies that a measure or an index can

---

*Boston Aschmann Associates, San Jose, California.

describe the capacity of the environment either to supply resources or to assimilate waste. In either event, while the actual capacity of the environment to endure human activity may be fixed and measureable, the actual rate of consumption or assimilation for many aspects of the environment is a function of man's access to the environment.

Thus, while it appears that sound environmental management will require some means of measuring carrying capacity, a means of relating transportation systems to the rate of consumption or assimilation is also necessary.

In the Colorado River Basin, while rail and air transportation are significant, roads and highways are the principal means of transportation. As a consequence this paper will deal primarily with highway transportation.

In 1965 six of the states in the Colorado River Basin had a total of 346,298 miles of roads. Of this amount, 324,300 miles were classed as rural. That is, 93.65 percent of the road mileage is rural.

There are thus two aspects to transportation: urban and non-urban. The overwhelming majority of road miles lies in rural areas, an equally overwhelming majority of vehicle trips occur in urban areas.

There are two fundamental alternatives for non-urban roads. Either all existing highways are adequate or improvements will be required to increase capacity or improve safety. The latter is most likely the case.

On the other hand, it is quite possible that the existing network of roads has sufficient capacity that if it were used for all potential social and economic purposes, then the Colorado River Basin might exceed its environmental "carrying capacity" in very short order.

While it is not likely that this will occur, it does make the task of evaluating the impact of road improvements very difficult.

In recent years the strongest demands, or warrants, for improvement of non-urban roads is related to recreation and the growth of recreation. Some of the most congested highways in the United States have been the two, three, and four lane roads leading to recreational areas less than one day's drive from urban areas, and those roads are most frequently crowded on Friday evening and Sunday evening. Highway 50, from San Francisco to Lake Tahoe is a classic example The average daily traffic on this road during peak month is from 13,000 to 20,000—seven to ten times what would be experienced on a comparable California highway without the recreational attraction. Similar highways with similar problems exist throughout the country. As this traffic increases, then so does the need to improve roads.

In the past, evaluation of the need for transportation system improvement was a fairly straight forward activity. Traffic counts were obtained and projected and related to highway capacity at existing design; special safety problems were noted and a variety of projects were all compared to determine which improvement project demonstrated the most need. Since improvements funds are limited, theoretically only those projects with the greatest need were developed. But while this means of evaluation was prevalent, traffic on highways increased at twice the predicted rate.

In the mid-60's it became obvious to nearly all transportation planners that chasing traffic growth with improvement projects was never going to achieve the desired end. The growth rate in the nation and the increasing use of automobiles make it nearly impossible to catch up with future needs as a criteria for transportation improvement.

As an example of what is happening, the State of California predicts that by 2020 nearly 40 million people—double the present population—will be living in California. That amounts to one in every seven Americans. This increase, if realized, will have a very significant impact on the Colorado River Basin and burden its transportation system beyond current improvement programs.

In the mid-60's transportation planners began to evaluate their projects in terms of other criteria.

Transportation planning is viewed by its critics as the most narrow form of single purpose planning, and, indeed, it appears to be. But nothing which affects such a large segment of our daily life and our economy can be truly single purpose. Since transportation so permeates a variety of human activities, transportation planners have operated on the assumption that the demand for improved transportation was in fact a manifestation of a need to fulfill other human social and economic goals. In the mid 60's, transportation planners, then, began to attempt to identify these goals as "non-user" or "community" benefits. A significant amount of research commenced and planning programs began to embark on a program to evaluate multiple objectives related to improvement projects and to weigh those objectives as part of a rationale for project improvement. In general, those objectives were development related—objectives which could assist in meeting other needs for services created by the tremendous population boom then, and now, on-going.

Examples of some of the projects and reports which stressed this approach are "Golden Gate Freeway," "Westside Freeway," and the "Century Freeway," all in California, the "Crosstown Freeway" in Chicago and the urban design team in Baltimore.

This approach did not get far, however, before it ran into NEPA —the National Environmental Policy Act. NEPA and its implementation put some constraints, or "thou shalt nots," on transportation planning, and multiple objectives soon were forgotten. The key to "successful" planning is now fundamentally negative since much of the criteria for project achievement lies in minimizing negative environmental effects—usually very specific, isolated effects.

In the absence of a rational management program for the Colorado River Basin, the current approach to transportation planning could create problems. The demand for improved roads will increase. As population densities increase, so does the demand for both urban and rural roads.

Table 1 tends to demonstrate this:

TABLE 1. Demand for Road Improvements

State	Population Density	Miles of Roads per Sq. Mile	Vehicles per Road Mile
Wyoming	3.4	.415	4.03
Nevada	4.4	.452	5.60
New Mexico	8.4	.555	6.91
Utah	12.9	.493	12.70
Arizona	15.6	.376	20.92
Colorado	21.3	.790	14.30
California	127.6	1.050	62.32

Control of access to land in the Colorado River Basin is a function of improved highways, but the demand and need for new highways is a function of the magnitude of the urban population in the Basin and, equally important, on its fringe. Any control agency which seeks to restrict the uses to which land can be devoted in the basin, or to restrict access must, then, take account of urban growth and urban development policies as they affect the Basin.

Transportation is an important component of our daily life, our industry and our recreation. Transportation policy should not be based upon crude assumptions and over simplification. Transportation, or access, or number of vehicles is probably one measure of the rate of consumption or the carrying capacity of the environment.

As urban populations increase, the rate of consumption will increase. Initial studies of the "carrying capacity" of the Colorado River Basin should therefore focus upon urban population growth and its impact on transportation facilities.

Colorado River Basin
Transportation Workshop Summary

QUESTION: In the future, what activities will impact significantly on transportation in the Colorado River Basin?

CONSENSUS: There will be heavy recreational demand on the transportation systems of the Colorado River Basin in the near future. Since there have been very few cost-benefit justifications for mass transit in rural recreation areas, and since many forms of recreation do not lend themselves to transportation by mass transit, most of this demand will be for private automobile transportation. This will place additional loading on the transportation systems because some recreational activities require great amounts of equipment and special vehicle to transport the equipment.

QUESTION: Instead of making transportation more available to a population, would it be a good strategy to make transportation less available and thereby effectively put a ceiling on the population?

CONSENSUS: The goal of most urban transportation planning is to place as many people as possible in mass transit rather than trying to constrain population by restricting mobility.

QUESTIONS   Would adoption of a regional transportation framework be favorable to the present national framework?

CONSENSUS: In general, a regional transportation framework would be superior to the present national framework because it would allow unique problems in the area to be solved by people in the region who are familiar with them.

There was some contention that the problems of regional transportation are primarily institutional problems complicated by a lack of funding for research; a possible solution is to obtain funds for training and research from the Department of Transportation directly out of the Secretary's office.

QUESTION: What impact will different transportation systems have on the environment and non-economic social consideration?

CONSENSUS: It was agreed that there is not enough information available to predict the social and environmental effects of different transportation systems. There is a general lack of data which indicate where expansion is needed in the transportation system and where portions of the system should be shut down. The problem is compounded, especially given the present national transportation planning framework, in that one cannot get public support or funding to collect this data unless one already has the information which proves that the data will be valuable. Such information comes only from the data. A regional approach to transportation planning may be a way to break this circle.

CHAPTER XVI

Urbanization in the Colorado River Basin

*Calvin W. Hübner**

INTRODUCTION

Generally the concept of carrying capacity has been applied to more or less natural ecological systems. It can, however, be applied quite logically to the man-built and man-dominated urban system. The concept generally refers to the capacity of an "environment to accommodate or absorb change without experiencing conditions of instability and attendant degradation."[1] When we see large urban areas covered with a pall of highly polluted and obviously unhealthy air, we wonder if the carrying capacity of the urban system has not been exceeded. This paper examines the recent urbanization process in the Colorado River Basin in some detail and then briefly relates the process of urbanization to the supportive resources of agriculture, recreation, transportation, and energy.

THE URBAN AREA OF THE BASIN

In order to discuss urbanization in the Colorado River Basin, two definitions are necessary: First, what is urbanization and second, where is the Colorado River Basin.

An urban area is obviously defined as a densely populated area. A standard concept of urban is the definition of the Census Bureau:

Associate Professor of Political Science, Utah State University, Logan, Utah.

[1] A. Bruce Bishop, et al., "The Concept of Carrying Capacity in a Regional Setting," (Logan, Utah: mimeo, 1973)

"all incorporated and unincorporated places of 2,500 or more."[2] Using this definition of urban, the seven states with jurisdiction over the drainage area of the Colorado River have their populations spatially distributed so that aggregate data show them to be highly urban states. Only New Mexico and Wyoming have less of their population living in urban areas than the national total of 73.4 percent urban. The more useful concept of urban is the census definition of Urbanized Areas (one or more cities of at least 50,000 and the densely populated surrounding areas).[3] Comparative data for the two recognized concept of urban that will be used in this paper as shown in table 1.

There are 25 Urbanized Areas within the seven states. There are two in Arizona (Phoenix and Tucson), 15 in California (Sacramento, Vallejo-Napa, San Francisco, Oakland, Stockton, San Jose, Fresno, Salinas-Monterey, Santa Barbara, Bakersfield, San Bernardino-Riverside-Ontario, Oxnard-Ventura, Los Angeles-Long Beach, Anaheim-Santa Ana-Garden Grove, and San Diego), two in Nevada (Reno and Las Vegas), three in Utah (Ogden, Salt Lake City and Provo-Orem), three in Colorado (Denver, Colorado Springs, and Pueblo), and one in New Mexico (Albuquerque). Wyoming contains no Urbanized Areas.

The second problem is to identify those counties within the seven states that actually fall within the water resource region. A total of 54 counties within the states were identified as falling within the region.[4] These are listed by state in Appendix A, and a map of county and state areas within the area are shown in Appendix B. The counties identified here make up about 30.5 percent of the land; 9.4 percent of the population of the seven states in the basin; and about 6.8 per-

---

[2]U.S. Bureau of the Census, 1970 *Census Users' Guide* (Washington, D.C.: U.S. Government Printing Office, 1970), p. 81.

[3]This area contains one or more cities of 50,000 or more population plus the surrounding closely settled areas. See *ibid.,* p. 82-83. Note that this concept differs from the Standard Metropolitan Statistical Area (SMSA) in that *no* rural population is included even though the rural population may reside in the county or counties of the SMSA.

[4]An outline map of the 22 Water Resource regions by county was prepared for the Select Committee on Natural Water Resources of the United States Senate by the Department of Agriculture. See U.S., Congress, Senate, Select Committee on National Water Resources of the United States, *Water Resource Activities in the United States: Estimated Water Requirements for Agricultural Purposes and their Effects on Water Supplies,* Committee Print No. 13, 86th Congress, 2nd Session, 1959, p. 25.

cent of the land area and 1.24 percent of the population of the 50 states in the nation.

The vast expanses of relatively unpopulated land in the western United States do not lead one to believe that they suffer from over-population. The detail of this is shown in table 2. The seven states contain only 24.2 people per square mile, while the nation as a whole contains 57.4 people per square mile. Those counties within the Colorado River Basin proper have an aggregate population of only 10.5 people per square mile.[5]

TABLE 1—*Percent of Population in Urbanized Areas in Colorado River Basin States: 1970*

State	Percent in Urban Areas[a]	Percent in Urbanized Areas[b]
Arizona	79.5	65.4
California	90.8	80.9
Colorado	78.5	64.5
Nevada	80.0	68.8
New Mexico	69.7	29.3
Utah	80.3	69.2
Wyoming	60.4	0
United States	73.4	58.3

[a]Urban area is a community (incorporated or unincorporated) with over 2,500 population.
[b]Urbanized area is one or more cities of 50,000 population and their densely populated fringes (incorporated and unincorporated).

[5]Data cited were calculated from U.S. Bureau of the Census sources.

TABLE 2—*1970 Population Density of Colorado River Basin: States and Selected Counties*

State	STATE TOTALS			COUNTIES WITHIN COLORDO RIVER BASIN		
	Area (Square Miles)	*1970 Population*	*Population Density*	*Area (Square Miles)*	*1970 Population*	*Population Density*
Arizona	113,563	1,770,900	15.59	113,563	1,770,900	15.59
California	156,537	19,593,134	125.67	4,241	74,492	17.56
Colorado	103,397	2,207,259	21.35	37,145	197,972	5.33
Nevada	109,889	488,738	4.45	7,874	275,954	35.05
New Mexico	121,445	1,016,000	8.37	21,304	102,657	4.82
Utah	82,381	1,059,273	12.86	39,958	78,457	1.96
Wyoming	97,281	332,416	3.42	15,324	22,146	1.44
Total CRB	784,493	26,827,720	34.20	239,409	2,522,578	10.54
United States	3,541,082	203,211,926	57.38			

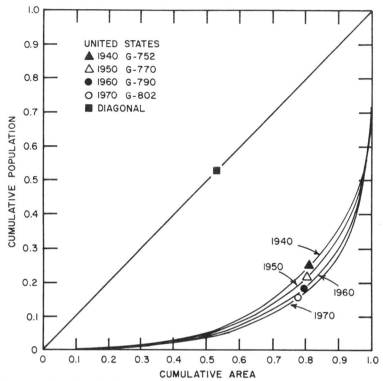

FIGURE 1—*Population Concentration, United States, 1940-1970*

Another method of looking at the urbanization process (population concentration) was used by Patterson and Bohm to show the extent to which the nation is concentrating population.[6] Data in the western states and the nation are shown in table 3. Their analysis used the Gini coefficient method to describe population concentration within states. In order to calculate the Gini coefficient, an ordered array of each state's counties was drawn on the basis of population density. Lorenz curves were then drawn which depicted the population concentration of the political area. The two axes for the points on the curve are the cumulative percent of the area and the cumulative population of the area to that point. Lorenz curves for the United States in 1940 to 1970 are shown in figure 1 by way of illustration.

[6]Robert A. Bohm and David A. Patterson, "An Analysis of Population Concentration and Dispersal in the United States, 1940-19770, *Civil Defense Research Project: Annual Progress Report, March* 1971-*March* 1972, (Oak Ridge Tennessee: Oak Ridge National-Laboratory, 1972), p. 10-15.

The Gini coefficient is simply the area between the diagonal and the Lorenz curve divided by the area of the entire triangle below the diagonal. The coefficients may vary from 0 to 1. The closer the coefficient is to unity, the greater is the concentration of population in just a few counties.[7] In order to simpilfy these coefficients, they have all been multiplied by 1000 in the data that follow.

In can be seen in table 3 that all of the Colorado River Basin States except Wyoming have most of their population concentrated in a very few counties and that the concentration has increased for every state in every decade since 1940. It should be noted that only the states of Arizona and to some extent Nevada have areas of concentrated population actually within the basin. In 1940 only Utah and California had highly concentrated populations, but by 1970 only Wyoming still maintained a decentralized population.

TABLE 3—*Population Concentration, Colorado River Basin States 1940-1970*

States	Gini Coefficients			
	1940	1950	1960	1970
Utah	769	802	834	854
Nevada	527	640	734	838
Colorado	650	706	774	806
California	788	791	796	797
Arizona/New Mexico[a]	473	567	646	676
Wyoming	354	388	434	419
United States	752	770	790	802

Source: Robert A. Bohm and David A. Patterson, "An Analysis of Population Concentration and Dispersal in the United States, 1940-1970, "*Civil Defense Research Project: Annual Progress Report, March 1971-March 1972.* Oak Ridge National Laboratory, Oak Ridge, Tenn., 1972, pp. 10-15.

[a]Counties in Arizona and New Mexico are combined because of the relatively small number of counties in Arizona.

[7]Bohm and Patterson, "An Analysis," pp. 10-11.

The extent of this population disparity can be seen in table 4. Of the 54 counties within the basin, 38 (70.4 percent) contain less than 20,000 people. Only one county, Maricopa (Phoenix), contained over 500,000 people, and only two other counties, Pima (Tucson) and Clark (Las Vegas) have over 75,000 people.

Table 5 shows population of place of residence. The Colorado River Basin residents choose urban places (over 2,500) to rural by a three to one margin (74.2 percent to 25.8 percent) which is about the same as the nation as a whole. The largest portion of these residents (38.5 percent) live in the three larger central cities of the Urbanized Areas—Phoenix, Tucson, and Las Vegas; and another 16.8 percent live in the suburbs (other Urbanized Areas) near these central cities. The small towns contain very few people and about one-fifth of the population lives in rural areas outside the jurisdiction of any community.

WHO LIVES IN THE BASIN

As there appear to be no demographic data published by water resource regions, the population by race was aggregated for use in this paper. This is shown in table 6. It can be seen that the population is mostly white, with the Indian population being concentrated mostly in the states of Arizona and New Mexico as expected because of the large tribal reservations in the Colorado River Basin portion of these states. Only 13.84 percent of this Indian population lives in the three urban counties of the region. The black population, on the other hand, is largely an urbanized population, with the urbanized counties of Arizona and Nevada containing almost 83 percent of the region's black population. There is also a sizeable minority of residents who claim Spanish as their mother tongue. A total of 396,481 residents in 1970 were in this group. This amounted to 15.72 percent of the total Colorado River Basin population or 17.51 percent of the white population (Spanish language speakers are generally included in the white population in table 6). The state of Arizona contains the largest number of this minority group with 322,701 or 18.22 percent of this state's 1970 population.

TABLE 4—*Counties by Population Group in Colorado River Basin 1970*

Population Group	Counties Number	Counties Percentage
Less than 999	2	3.7
1,000 to 4,999	14	25.9
5,000 to 9,999	9	16.7
10,000 to 19,999	13	24.1
20,000 to 49,999	7	13.0
50,000 to 74,999	6	11.1
75,000 to 249,999	0	0
250,000 to 499,999	2	3.7
Over 500,000	1	1.8
Total	54	100.0

TABLE 5—*Population by State and Race of Colorado River Basin 1970*

	Total Population	White Pop.	Indian Pop.	Black Pop.	Other and Unspecified
Arizona	1,770,900	1,604,948	95,812	53,344	16,796
California	74,492	68,806	889	2,586	2,211
Colorado	197,972	193,780	2,818	427	947
Nevada	275,954	247,061	1,269	24,761	2,863
New Mexico	102,657	56,378	44,976	737	566
Utah	78,457	71,391	6,685	79	302
Wyoming	22,146	21,677	54	236	179
Total CRB	2,522,578	2,264,041	152,503	82,170	23,864
Percent of Population	100.0%	89.7%	6.0%	3.3%	1.0%

Source: Calculated from data obtained from First Count Census tapes as reported in E. S. Lee, *et al., Demographic Profiles of the United States: The Mountain and Pacific States,* ORNL-HUD 24, Volume VIII, Oak Ridge, Tennessee, 1972.

TABLE 6—*Population by State and Place of Residence in Colorado River Basin: 1970*

State	Central City of Urbanized Area	Other Urbanized Area	Other Urban Population	Total Urban	Open Country	Less Than 1,000	1,000 to 2,500	Total Rural
Arizona	844,495	313,046	251,323	1,408,864	303,810	5,245	52,981	362,036
California	0	0	50,233	50,233	21,260	0	2,999	24,259
Colorado	0	0	69,787	69,787	88,533	22,347	17,305	128,185
Nevada	125,787	110,894	21,618	258,299	15,799	0	1,856	17,655
New Mexico	0	0	47,316	47,316	53,616	151	1,574	55,341
Utah	0	0	22,016	22,016	27,286	12,473	16,682	56,441
Wyoming	0	0	15,853	15,853	4,079	2,214	0	6,293
Total	970,282	423,940	478,146	1,872,368	514,383	42,430	93,397	650,210
Percent of Population	38.5%	16.8%	18.9%	74.2%	20.4%	1.7%	3.7%	25.8%

Source: Calculated from data obtained from First Count Census tapes as reported in E. S. Lee, *et al., Demographic Profiles of the United States: The Mountain and Pacific States,* ORNL-HUD 24, Volume VIII, Oak Ridge, Tennessee, 1972.

RECENT URBAN GROWTH

In 1960 the population of the 54 counties of the Colorado River Basin was 1,887,468, and in 1970 had increased to 2,522,578. This amounts to a population increase of 33.65 percent for the area in the decade. This overall growth has not only been very high; it has also been highly selective. The components of this population change are shown by state in table 7. Several generalizations may be made from the data shown here.

First, the growth of the Colorado River Basin has been primarily reflection of urban growth. The three urbanized counties of Maricopa (Phoenix) and Pima (Tucson), Arizona, and Clark (Las Vegas), Nevada account for over 84 percent of this change (536,291). A total of 20 counties (37 percent of the total) lost population in the decade. This is a continuation of the 1950-1960 decade when 18 counties lost population.

Second, the high fertility of the population accounted for a significant amount of the population increase. Over half (56.36 percent) of the population increase was a natural increase because of the excess of births over deaths. The extent of this high fertility can be seen in table 8. The fertility ratios for the states involved here are (except for California and Colorado) above the national figures. Also, the population of these states is heavily weighted toward those in child bearing years as indicated This can be seen by the generally high youth dependency ratios and the low aged dependency ratios. In short, the population is made up of a high percentage of those in the ages able to bear children—and they bear children more often than the average for the nation.

Third, migration is highly selective for each area. This statement can be deduced from the above discussions. The details, however, are much more startling. Aggregate data in table 7 show that only the Arizona and Nevada portion of the basin gained because of migration. In fact, 39 (72.2 percent) of the Basin counties had a net migration loss. In the decade 1950-1960, 35 Basin counties (64.8 percent) had a net loss due to migration. The selective nature is further seen by looking at migration data for the three urbanized counties in the Basin. These counties accounted for almost 124 percent (343,070) of the net migration gain of 277,162. Consequently, at least 65,908 people

TABLE 7—*Components of Population Change in Colorado River Basin*
1960-1970

Area	TOTAL STATE				COLORADO RIVER BASIN PORTION OF STATE			
	Births	Deaths	Net Migration	Net Change	Births	Deaths	Net Migration	Net Change
Arizona	364,685	122,117	226,171	468,739	364,685	122,117	226,171	468,739
California	3,634,254	1,511,403	2,113,079	4,235,930	18,993	5,701	-10,905	2,387
Colorado	400,812	162,991	215,491	453,312	37,975	17,661	-5,807	14,507
Nevada	91,030	31,303	143,733	203,460	51,895	13,989	108,492	146,398
New Mexico	262,808	68,140	-129,691	64,977	34,493	6,543	-23,542	4,408
Utah	244,926	65,322	-10,958	168,646	19,445	6,076	-15,146	-1,777
Wyoming	69,824	28,125	-39,349	2,350	4,548	1,999	-2,101	448
TOTAL	5,068,339	1,989,401	2,518,476	5,597,414	532,034	174,086	277,162	635,110

Source: U.S. Bureau of the Census, *Current Population Reports*, Series P. 25, No. 461, "Components of Population Change by County: 1960 to 1970," Washington, D.C., U.S. Government Printing Office, 1971.

TABLE 8—*Population, Fertility and Dependency Ratios for Colorado River Basin States*

State	Fertility[a] Ratio	Youth[b] Dependency Ratio	Aged[c] Dependency Ratio
Arizona	429	50.15	15.06
California	383	43.75	14.26
Colorado	384	46.85	13.06
Nevada	414	45.92	9.87
New Mexico	442	55.83	11.64
Utah	486	56.03	12.33
Wyoming	416	48.57	14.85
United States	404	46.25	16.01

[a]Number of children less than five years of age divided by total women aged 15-44 multiplied by 1000.
[b]Population less than age 15 divided by total population aged 15-64 multiplied by 100.
[c]Population over 65 years divided by total population aged 15-64 multiplied by 100.

Source: Calculated from data obtained from First Count Census tapes as reported in E. S. Lee, *et al., Demographic Profiles of the United States: The Mountain and Pacific States*, ORNL-HUD 24, Volume VIII, Oak Ridge, Tennessee, 1972.

moved from the non-urbanized portion of the basin to Phoenix, Tucson, and Las Vegas.

The magnitude of this migration can be seen in the data presented in Appendix C. This shows the gross migration flow between Maricopa County, Arizona (Phoenix) and the rest of the nation, taking residence in 1965 and in 1970 as reference points. The net migration gain for the county in this five year period was 69,750 people. In the period only nine states gained population from Maricopa county in the migrant exchange. Several states lost substantial numbers to the county as can be seen. New York lost 8,633; Illinois lost 11,079; and

Ohio lost 7,330 in exchange while California gained 10,249 from the county. The detail in the original data (not shown here because of the bulk involved) indicates that the majority of the migrants to Maricopa County were from urban areas. For example, the Chicago SMSA had a net loss of 7,799 migrants to the area in the five year period and New York City showed a net loss of 4,110 people.

FUTURE GROWTH TRENDS

By the year 2000 the population of the United States will increase substantially. Assuming a two child average family the population would be 271 million, if a three child average is assumed the population would reach 322 million.[8] Most of this growth will occur in urban areas—a continuation of present patterns. In 1970, 77 percent of the people in the nation lived on 17 percent of the land area, and in the year 2000 almost 84 percent of the population will live in this same land area.[9]

If the Colorado River Basin follows past trends, it too will be even more heavily urbanized. Pickard estimated that the urbanized population in the basin will grow significantly. His estimates for metropolitan growth areas in the seven basin states are shown in table 9. If these projections are correct, the Urbanized Areas of Arizona and Nevada that are within the basin will increase by 253 percent (1.7 to 4.3 million) in the thirty years between 1970 and 2000.

URBAN GOVERNMENTS

A great many of the problems caused by urbanization and the deterioration of environmental quality are handled by the state governments or their local governmental subdivisions. Within the basin there were 952 active local governments in 1967 plus the seven state governments involved. These are enumerated by type and state in table 10. Policy for these local governmental units is made by 4,615 elected officials.

---

[8]Commission on Population Growth and the American Future, *Population and the American Future,* (Washington, D.C.: U.S. Government Printing Office, 1972), p. 24.

[9]Jerome P. Pickard, "Growth of Urbanized Population in the United States: Past, Present, and Future," in D. W. Rasmussen and C. T. Haworth (eds.), *The Modern City: Readings in Urban Economics* (San Francisco: Harper and Row, 1973), p. 14.

TABLE 9—*Population of Future Urban Regions In the Colorado River Basin States*

Area	1970 Land Area (Square Miles)	Population (in millions)[a]	
		1970	2000
California Region	54,986	19.3	37.9
Colorado Piedmont	11,320	1.8	3.5
Metropolitan Arizona	12,677	1.4	3.2
Salt Lake Valley	4,721	0.9	1.6
El Paso - Ciudad - Juarez - South New Mexico[b]	3,457	0.4	0.7
Las Vegas	4,605	0.3	1.1

[a]Urban regions are as geographically defined in 2000. Population based on a United States total of 287 million (Series D).
[b]Includes United States population only.

Source: Jerome P. Pickard, "Growth of the Urbanized Population in the United States: Past, Present and Future," in D. W. Rasmussen and C. T. Haworth (eds.), *The Modern City: Readings in Urban Economics* (New York: Harper and Row, 1973).

Can this large number of governmental units agree on common policy that might help in solving the area's problems? Most likely the answer is no. If local governmental initiative is relied on to solve major problems, we should expect little basin-wide coordinated action.

Can the seven states agree on common policy and/or action? Again, the answer is most likely no, although it is not insignificant that the states are all members of an interstate compact that was aimed at attempting to solve some of the area's unique problems. What are the problems for state action?

The first problem involves the role of the governor in each state. He is elected at large in each state and acts for all of the people in the state. This is no problem in Arizona where all of the people live within the basin. In the rest of the seven states, however, the proportion of the population and land within the basin is a fraction of the total state land area and population. Can the Governor of Utah take action to benefit the basin residents that would be disadvantageous to the bulk of the state's population that do not live in the basin? An example of this might involve the burning of fossil fuels to generate energy. The energy is needed by the urban centers (outside of the basin) and is available within the basin. Where do you burn the fossil fuel (the proper question might be, where do you pollute the air)? The logical political answer is to burn it where there are the fewest people to be bothered by the effects of the activity—in the basin. The undesirable effects would be felt by people in other states where the Governor doesn't receive many votes.

The legislatures face similar problems. In 1964, the federal courts ruled that state legislatures should represent ". . . people, not trees or acres . . . voters, not farms or cities or economic interest . . ."[10] For many years prior to that time, as a result of population shifts without representational realignments, state legislatures were heavily weighted in favor of rural areas. The change that occurred between 1962 and 1968 can be seen from table 11. In 1962, 11 percent of the California voters from sparsely populated rural areas elected a majority to the California Assembly, but by 1968 the rule of "one man one vote" had been achieved. As was previously discussed, the portion of the basin states within the actual Colorado River Basin are basically rural in

TABLE 10—*Local Units of Government in Colorado River Basin:*
1967

State	Units of Government					
	Total	Counties	Municipal-ities	School Districts	Special Districts	Elected Officials [1]
Arizona	394	14	62	242	76	1949
California	52	1	7	17	27	255
Colorado	308	20	64	38	186	1462
Nevada	32	2	5	2	23	59
New Mexico	30	4	7	9	10	186
Utah	104	11	53	11	29	529
Wyoming	32	2	8	10	12	175
Total	952	54	206	329	363	4615

Source: U.S. Bureau of the Census, Census of Governments, 1967, Vol. 6, No. 1, *Popularly Elected Officials of State and Local Governments,* U.S. Government Printing Office, Washington, D.C., 1968.

nature. Consequently, their representation within the legislature is very limited. As in the case of the governor, a legislature that acts to help the basin population in ways that are looked upon as undesirable by the more urban portions of the state will not be popular.

Despite the above discussion, the future for state and local governmental involvement is not all bleak. Some policies (hopefully most) benefit most of the population independent of place of residence. Also, decision makers take actions and make policies that are temporarily unpopular with the electorate. Reason and informed decision making frequently take precedence over political opportunism. Finally, the spector of the power of the national government causes some things to happen because it is in the national interest. Many categorical grant-in-aid programs still exist, and if the "right" thing is not done, a state or locality can lose this valuable source of revenue.[11]

TABLE 11—*Changes in Representation Resulting from Reapportionment of Legislatures, 1962 and 1968 in Colorado River Basin States*

| | Minimum percentage of population that could elect a majority | | | |
| | Senate | | House | |
State	1962	1968	1962	1968
Arizona	13	52	NA	51
California	11	49	45	49
Colorado	30	50	32	54
Nevada	8	50	35	48
New Mexico	14	46	27	46
Utah	21	48	33	48
Wyoming	27	47	36	46

Source: Thomas R. Dye, "State Legislative Politics" in Herbert Jacob and Kenneth N. Viner (eds.), *Politics in the American States,* 2nd ed., Little, Brown and Co., Boston, 1971, p. 170.

[10]*Reynolds v. Sims,* 84 S. Ct. 1381 (1964)

[11]A more complete discussion of urbanization in most of the states under analysis here may be found in JeDon A. Emenhiser (ed.), *Rocky Mountain Urban Politics* (Logan, Utah: Utah State University, 1971). Also see Frank H. Jonas, *Politics in the American West,* (Salt Lake City, Utah: University of Utah Press, 1969).

THE EFFECT OR URBANIZATION ON OTHER ACTIVITY SECTORS

Urbanization is highly related to several other social indexes. There have been large cities for several thousand years in traditional societies, but the advent of the industrial revolution with its industrialization made urbanization imperative. Davis and Golden showed that this is a world-wide characteristic. They found:

> As of 1950, the (Pearsonian) correlation between degree of industrialization and degree of urbanization, as measured by our indices, was .86, taking countries and territories of the world as our unit.[12]

Urbanization also appears to be related to individual wealth, increased agricultural efficiency, increased literacy and education, more formal media communication, increased political participation, less social stratification, more political stability, and increased toleration. A second list of human behavioral characteristics that are usually not found desirable is also associated with urbanization. These include: more severe mental illness, more illegitimate births, higher divorce rate, more suicide, and higher crime rates.[13]

Urbanization and modern agriculture do not coexist well on the micro-level. This is true despite the fact that one of the correlates of urbanization is increased agricultural efficiency. Increased industrial pollution and higher land costs are two minor reasons, but agriculture in the Colorado River Basin is also highly dependent upon water resources of the area and these resources are already in short supply. In addition, water supplies are already deficient in the neighboring Southern California and Pecos-Upper Rio Grande water resource regions, and this will be the case in the Great Basin by 1980.[14] Most likely, some water now used for irrigated agriculture will be used for culinary purposes in the rapidly growing urban areas of the Mountain and Southwestern states in the future because it is doubtful that people

---

[12]Kingsley Davis and Hilda H. Golden, "Urbanization and the Development of Preindustrial Areas," *Economic Development and Cultural Change,* Vol. III, October, 1954, p. 8.

[13]See Bernard Berelson and Gary A. Steiner, *Human Behavior: An Inventory of Scientific Findings,* (New York: Harcourt, Brace and World, Inc., 1969), p. 605-607.

[14]Commission on Population Growth and the American Future, *op cit.,* p. 46.

and industries will move to where water is plentiful. There is some hope, however, as the recent Commission on Population Growth pointed out:

> . . . most water is used virtually free of cost or is distributed on a fee basis that provides no incentives for conservation; and free use of water bodies as waste dumping grounds is more the rule than the exception. If the cost of utilizing water for these purposes were raised to more appropriate levels, factories and power plants would install techniques of production that save water instead of wasting it; farmers would modify their irrigation practices or otherwise adjust it by changing location or shifting to crops using less water; and households would eventually adjust by reducing lawns and shrubbery.[15]

In short, agriculture will be affected severely by increasing urbanization.

Urbanization is related to increased wealth, which means that the urban residents will have more time for recreation and more money to spend on the activity. The author's recent personal experience with outdoor recreation in National Parks and U.S. Forest Service Campgrounds near urban areas is that the camping population density is higher than that of an ordinary suburb. "In the past 10 years, visiting to all national park facilities more than doubled, while the are of the parks increased by only one-fifth."[16] As the population and wealth of the area increase, pressure will be brought to bring more and more private land that has recreational potential under public ownership. It should be pointed out that the National Park, National Forest, and National Monument visitors are not all from the basin area and that "population" pressure would continue to be a problem even if urbanization of the basin terminated. Also, if increased congestion causes people to substitute organized sports, artistic, cultural, etc., activities that can use land more intensely without widespread environmental harm, then the effect of urbanization on recreational activities would not be severe, or at least would be manageable.

A modern urban population is a mobile population. Mobility in the low density western cities means that private automobile ownership is widespread and is an economic necessity. Air pollution and high

---

[15]*Ibid.,* p. 44.
[16]*Ibid.,* p. 47.

noise levels are largely caused by the widespread use of private automobiles. The obvious solution is mass transportation, but mass transportation (what little exists) is expensive per unit user and with patrons
limited to the poor and the old. A circular cause and effect problem
exists. There is no mass transportation because no one uses it and no
one uses mass transportation because it is not there. Masses of people
move every day in the urban centers, but the mass transportation system that they use is the freeway. Consequently, present urban transportation systems make urban areas less pleasant places in which to live
and work and they will, no doubt, be even less pleasant (more noise
and pollution) in the future. Technology can (and will) mitigate the
problem somewhat in the future as pollution control devices or a substitute for the present style of internal combustion engines is brought
into widespread use. In the end, however, lifestyles will have to
change—less reliance on personal transportation and more (some)
use of mass transportation.

Urbanization with its correlate industrialization means high
energy usage levels. The Colorado River Basin has enormous reserves
of energy in the form of fossil fuel—oil, gas, coal and oil shale. What
effect does urbanization within the basin have on fossil fuels and
power generation? In the short run the effects will be dramatic if
urbanization grows at the projected rates. In 1967 the per capita electricity consumption in Phoenix was 8,500 Kwhr and 6,936 in Tucson.[17]
The extraction of fossil fuels and the inefficient methods now used for
energy conversion and delivery will mean increased air and water
pollution as well as landscape changes from strip mining or mine
subsidence. Local energy sources will be used to support the energy
hunger of the urban areas because the transportation costs will be
less.

In the long run, however, it probably doesn't make much difference. The energy resources of the area will be used to provide energy
outside of the basin, hence where urbanization takes place matters
very little.

One mitigating factor could be the form in which energy is trans-
ported from the source to the ultimate consumer. Fossil fuel can be

---

[17]A. J. Miller, *et al., Use of Steam-Electric Power Plants to Provide Thermal Energy to Urban Areas,* ORNL-HUD-14 (Oak Ridge, Tennessee: Oak
Ridge National Laboratory, 1971), p. 23.

shipped in bulk to other areas where it can be converted to a useable form, or it can be converted at the extraction site. This could make a considerable difference on the relative pollution levels of remote areas in the basin. Also the efficiency of present energy systems could be improved in that normally about 65 percent of fuel energy is wasted in the generation of electricity. Potential efficiencies can be gained by producing electricity near the site where it will be used so that some of the energy now being wasted as thermal pollution can be recovered for space heating, airconditioning, water heating and chilling, and water and liquid waste treatment. In addition, urban solid wastes are potential sources of fuel.[18]

SUMMARY AND CONCLUSION

The Colorado River Basin is already highly urbanized and the forces are in motion to accelerate and intensify this process. The area has experienced a rapid growth rate in the past two decades. A large portion of this growth (43.7 percent) has been due to migration into the basin. The migration, however, has been highly selective for Urbanized Areas and many rural counties have lost population due to our migration. The area is not overpopulated by national standards and even the most highly Urbanized Areas have relatively low population densities. For example, it would take an additional 11.2 million more people living in the basin (1970 population was 2.5 million) before the average national population density of 57.38 persons per square mile was reached. It would, of course, be somewhat more unpleasant if all of the new population were added to Phoenix, Tucson, and Las Vegas—as present trends indicate would happen. A more likely situation will be the development of new communities for at least a portion of the population increase. For example, seven large developments or new communities have been completed or are under construction in Arizona since 1947. These seven developments (Kearny, Lake Havasu City, Litchfield Park, San Manuel, Sun City, and Tucson Green Valley) have a planned population of only 215 thousand people, but scores of other such developments are near term possibilities in other areas of the basin.[19]

---

[18]Gerald S. Leighton, "HUD Takes Total Energy Concept One Step Beyond," *Airconditioning and Refrigeration Business,* January, 1973.

Water and high quality land are scarce in the basin. Agriculture and the urbanization process are direct competitors for these limited resources. In addition, the water resources of the basin must be exported out of the basin proper to support the culinary water needs of urban areas adjacent to the river basin. These areas include metropolitan Colorado (Boulder to Pueblo), metropolitan Utah (Ogden to Provo), and the Southern California megalopolis. Consequently, the water and much of the high quality land available will be consumed by the rapidly urbanizing areas within the seven Colorado River Basin States.

The increased number of people in the area will also mean increased use of the outdoor recreational resources of the Basin. As these resources occur largely in public lands in the basin, the national government could protect and/or conserve them.

Transportation in the Colorado River Basin is almost synonymous with the private automobile. Mass transportation, except for long distance air travel, does not exist. Urbanization means more people which means more use of the automobile which means more air pollution. The absolute limits of automobile usage in urban areas without endangering lives are not yet known.

Where urbanization takes places may not be significant in the long run for the exploitation of the fossil fuel reserves of the area. These resources will be used as long as there are cold or hungry people. What matters is *where* the resources are converted from fossil fuel to other energy forms (electricity or gas). It might be attractive, in the short run, to use a relatively unpopulated and politically impotent area such as the Colorado River Basin as a *sink* for urban waste products.

Government and other organized groups can do some things to mitigate the more unpleasant effects of the urbanization process, although the powers for taking constructive action are diffuse and fractionalized into many power centers. The political power for preserving the environmental quality of the basin is not present in the basin proper. For example, lawmakers in Sacramento will make policy for the basin and only 38 percent of California's population lives within the basin. The Colorado lawmakers will make policy for the basin with only 9 percent of that state's population in the basin.

---

[19]Jerome P. Pickard, "Is Dispersal the Answer to Urban Overgrowth," *Urban Land, January,* 1970, p. 111-118.

Finally, it is important to note that only 1.24 percent of the national population lives in the Colorado River Basin.

No doubt, some political action to keep the area from exceeding its environmental carrying capacity is possible, and even probable. Political action would be more feasible if the answers to more questions about carrying capacity were known. What is its carrying capacity? If the capacity has to be exceeded, what would a future basin be like? Until the research community has an array of alternative solutions for the basin available, can we expect the political system to take positive action?

APPENDIX A

State	County		
Nevada (2)	Lincoln	California (1)	Imperial
	Clark	New Mexico (4)	San Juan
Arizona (14)	Yuma		McKinley
	Mohave		Catron
	Pima		Hidalgo
	Santa Cruz	Wyoming (2)	Sublette
	Cochise		Sweetwater
	Maricopa	Colorado (20)	Moffat
	Pinal		Rio Blanco
	Graham		Routt
	Greenlee		Grand
	Gila		Summitt
	Yavapai		Eagle
	Coconino		Garfield
	Navajo		Mesa
	Apache		Delta
Utah (11)	Washington		Pitkin
	Kane		Lake
	Garfield		Gunnison
	San Juan		Montrose
	Wayne		San Miguel
	Emery		Ouray
	Grand		Dolores
	Carbon		San Juan
	Duchesne		Montezuma
	Uintah		La Plata
	Daggett		Archuleta

APPENDIX B
COUNTIES IN COLORADO RIVER BASIN

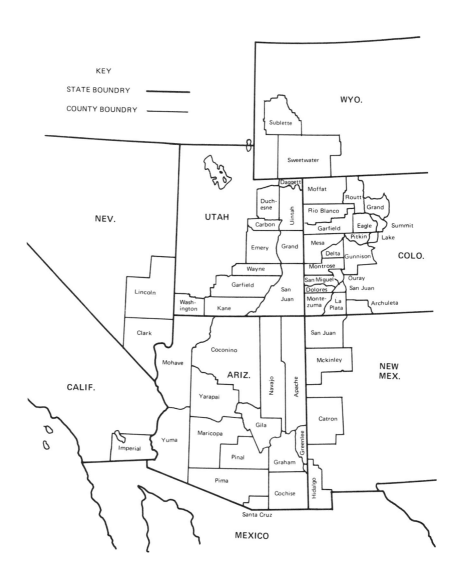

KEY

STATE BOUNDRY ————

COUNTY BOUNDRY ————

APPENDIX C

RESIDENCE IN 1970 BY RESIDENCE IN 1965 OF MIGRANTS
BETWEEN MARICOPA COUNTY, ARIZONA AND OTHER
STATES

State	In Migrants	Out Migrants	Net Migration
Maine	459	333	126
New Hampshire	435	275	160
Vermont	304	116	188
Massachusetts	2,236	1,066	1,170
Rhode Island	309	254	55
Connecticut	1,315	634	681
New York	10,822	2,189	8,633
New Jersey	3,664	1,212	2,452
Pennsylvania	5,380	1,744	3,636
Ohio	10,547	3,217	7,330
Indiana	5,954	2,552	3,402
Illinois	15,564	4,485	11,079
Michigan	8,828	3,017	5,811
Wisconsin	4,370	1,085	3,285
Minnesota	5,733	1,322	4,411
Iowa	5,231	1,306	3,925
Missouri	5,128	2,468	2,660
North Dakota	1,162	241	921
South Dakota	1,250	175	1,075
Nebraska	3,193	793	2,400
Kansas	4,030	1,482	2,548
Delaware	361	113	248
Maryland	1,404	1,083	321
Washington D.C.	365	112	253
Virginia	2,533	1,868	665
West Virginia	587	336	251

State	In Migrants	Out Migrants	Net Migration
North Carolina	1,026	938	88
South Carolina*	564	824	−260
Georgia*	1,206	1,277	−71
Florida	3,440	3,103	337
Kentucky*	950	962	−12
Tennessee	1,300	757	543
Alabama	1,111	633	478
Mississippi	497	393	104
Arkansas*	1,005	1,742	−737
Louisiana	825	763	62
Oklahoma	2,956	2,849	107
Texas*	9,503	9,518	−15
Montana	1,700	443	1,257
Idaho	1,731	1,061	670
Wyoming	1,537	557	980
Colorado	7,935	4,909	3,026
New Mexico	5,012	2,324	2,688
Balance of Arizona	22,916	21,530	1,386
Utah	4,069	2,079	1,990
Nevada*	2,280	2,375	−95
Washington*	3,578	4,265	−687
Oregon	2,925	2,685	240
California*	33,797	44,046	−10,249
Alaska	881	627	254
Hawaii*	797	917	−120
TOTAL	214,705	145,055	69,650

*Gained from Arizona

Source: U.S. Bureau of the Census, *Census of Population: 1970, Subject Reports, Final Report PC(2)-2E, Migration Between State Economic Areas* (U.S. Government Printing Office: Washington, D.C., 1972), pp. 115-322.

CHAPTER XVII

Urbanization With or Without Environmental Quality

Thomas A. MacCalla*

Urbanization is the process and environmental quality is the product. The issue to be raised is that the process may well become the product with or without the desired environmental quality to support it. Obviously the point is open to debate, but I would like to consider the proposition that man is the adaptable instrumentality of the human future. The question in the balance relates not only to the quality of man's future urban environment, but also to the challenge we have as planners, providers, and consumers of the present.

The rationale for this proposition is that urbanization, as a function of the unending dynamic of social change, is an irreversible process in the transformation of society and a determiner in the development of personhood and peoplehood in the world community. Moreover, when one considers urbanization in terms of both its physical and human dimensions and its press on our future human environment it becomes evident that the expectations of the world's privileged people will have to be compromised and the aspirations of the less fortunate will have to be accommodated. Our failure to respond to this inherent imperative of urbanization will mitigate against our efforts to achieve environmental quality and breed an acceptance for the lowest common denominator of environmental tolerance.

*Vice President, United States International University, San Diego, California.

At the 1967 conference of the American Institute of Planners, Pierre Bertraux made the provocative statement that "thinking about the future is not only the mightiest level of progress, but also the condition of survival." He also noted that "the future of a culture can be predicted by the power of its thinking about the future. No culture can maintain itself long without a positive and generally accepted image of the future."[1] It seems to me that although we possess great powers for predicting the future, we still do not have accurate enough tools or monitoring devices to accept the forecasts about our urban future. More specifically, we do not know enough about the contradictory nature of human behavior and its implications for social change to accept the promises of bliss or projections of gloom without registering a challenge in the name of caution or hope.

For this reason we need to reexamine our baseline information before we mislead those who listen to us. In focusing on the present and potential levels of urbanization, the required environmental support, the impact of urbanization on other kinds of development, and some of the indicators and strategies for shaping the urban future we need to reflect briefly on the disadvantaged position from which we contemplate the subject.

We are all products of our experiences and have the penchant for egocentrism and ethnocentrism. We who plan, provide, and consume, therefore, must possess humility and tolerance as well as knowledge and commitment to direct the urbanization process so as to approximate if not achieve our objective of environmental quality. Just as man assumes his right to rule over, to have dominion over, the earth we tend to assume our ability to explain the universe and to harness the elements. Although we have an abundance of data from which we can assess the probable and argue the possible, we invariably react to the unfamiliar and arrogantly defend the traditional and the popular. Against the backdrop of our computerized banks of knowledge, our professed awe of intellect in the Western tradition, our courtship with monetary and military power, and our various commitment to "the Good," "the Ideal," or "the State," we unfortunately tend to manipulate others to ensure our vested interests.

---

[1]William R. Ewald. "Reconnaissance of the Future (1920-1985-2000)," *Creating the Human Environment*. A Report of the American Institute of Architects. (Urbana, Illinois: University of Illinois Press, 1970), p. 10.

When we speak of man in the human predicament, we speak of all men, of persons with and without power. In the mirroring of our circumstance we should consider not only man privileged by the history of conquest but also universal man and culturally-diverse man. And when we speak of man in this sense, we need to remember that we, as men are not omniscient or objective as we profess. We are rational, irrational, extrarational, changeable beings. We are inherently ignorant and prejudiced, but also good and equal.

It may also be well to note that when we speak of the eviron- ment, we speak of an all-inclusive term. As we use it here, the environ- ment pertains to more than the conditions of land, air, water, energy, or silence. It includes man in the natural ecosystem and in the man- made surroundings, conditions, or influences of the world community. Since man is shaped by as well as shapes the environment, we should also view the environment as both a total system and a set of systems co-existing, competing and adapting or collapsing. As such, we can describe environmental quality in both its ecological sense which con- cerns the self-maintaining character of dynamic natural systems and its sociological sense which refers to an integrative state of human interaction and optimum quality of life. We then define it as a mutually supportive environment-man relationship. Lynton Caldwell sees the environment as an emerging social issue and argues that to be opera- tional, the concept of environmental quality "must be referenced to objective criteria by which the state of the environment can be meas- ured in relation to demonstrable human needs and preferences."[2] Jorge Arango refers to the study of the environment-man relationship as ambiology. He calls the discovery of the direct relationship between environment and social behavior and its impact on the sense of respon- sibility and happiness of the individual a new horizon of our time and probably the most important of present human tasks.[3]

PRESENT AND POTENTIAL LEVELS OF URBANIZATION

The United Nations report on Urbanization in the Second United Nations Development Decade states that throughout the

---

[2]Lynton Keith Caldwell, *Environment: A Challenge for Modern Society*. (New York: The Natural History Press, 1970), p. 27.

[3]Jorge Arango. *Urbanization of the Earth*. (Boston: Beacon Press, 1970), p. 98.

developing world the city is failing badly and stands as a warning of an imbalanced development process that could break down completely in the present decade.

> The city throughout the developing world is thus in some sense the sign and symbol of a development process that could run completely off the track in the coming decade. Their failures and frustrations, the shanty towns, the functional chaos, the environmental degredation and pollution, the unemployment, the hunger, the illiteracy, the general lack of skills—do not exist apart from the contradictions of the whole economy. The cities are where the evils come to a head in monstrously visible gatherings of human misery. Cities are symptoms of a wider distemper and their progress depends upon its cure.[4]

More recently, President Echeverria commented in his state of the union speech at the opening session of Mexico's 49th Congress that economic disorder has been brought about by a gap between the highly industrialized and poor nations. The world is deeply divided between the haves who are in the minority and the have-nots who are in the majority. The accumulation of wealth and the political power of the great power nations cause deep imbalances in international relations and are contrary to the expectations of the autonomous growth of lesser developed nations. Caldwell's warning also attests to the alarm over the pervasive nature of the urbanization process.

> . . . Unless rapid and effective action is taken to stop population growth, to reduce the threat of war and its costly burdens, and to prevent further destruction of the planetary biosphere and its living organisms, the early degradation of the human species is a certainty and its untimely extinction is a probability.[5]

Despite these well-founded concerns, the irreversible phenomenon is with us and its multifaceted by-products continue to outdistance our ability to arrest deterioration of the physical and social environment or correct economic imbalances much less achieve environmental

---

[4]United Nations. *Urbanization in the Second United Nations Development Decade.* (New York: United Nations, Department of Economic and Social Affairs, 1970.) p. 19.

[5]Caldwell, *Environment*, p. ix.

quality. As William Ewald points out in his study of social influences on the future of the physical environment, technology is converting us from a fear-of-failure society to a pleasure-seeking society but in the process nobody is happy.[6] Even more dramatic is the fact that nobody knows where were are going. The question that persists, therefore, is "Can man reverse his calamitous course, reshape himself by actualizing his potential, and commit himself to creating a pluralistic and humanistic future not only to sustain life, but also to enhance life?"

When considering the present and potential levels of urbanization it is important to recognize that the physical and socially supportive environment for desired urban growth defies order and control. As Simon Kuznets defines the process "urbanization embraces a whole complex of changes in which a large proportion of labor and population in non-agricultural pursuits results, for technical reasons, in the concentration of population in densely settled, relatively large aggregates with numerous consequences to the mode of life."[7] However defined, it is important to note that the process of urbanization involves both the rural area and the city, especially since the major increase in the urban population is a result of rural migration to the city and the sprawl to the semi-rural sector.

At the present urban growth rate in the United States we can estimate the following: (1) Blacks and other racial and ethnic minorities will dominate the central cites of thirteen metropolitan areas by 1985 plus the school systems of eleven more, (2) the working age population of 20-64 will increase from 106 million in 1970 to 136 million in 1985, (3) the biggest growth in the population during this same period (26 million) will be in apartment dwellers ages 25 to 54, who are subsequently the wave of future single-family dwellers, (4) those people over 65 will have more than doubled to 31 million, and (5) young people under 25 will constitute 45 percent of the population in 1985, although only 41 percent in the year 2000. Moreover, our lifestyles may be altered, if the projections hold true, by the 30 hour work week, rising incomes, greater interests and needs in recreation, travel, education, religion, medical care, new household furnishings and purchased transportation. As Ewald summarized it in his

---

[6]Ewald, *Reconnaissance*, p. 21.

[7]Inter-American Debelopment Bank. *Urban Development in Latin America.* Washington, D.C., 1969), p. 2.

"Reconnaissance of the Future" we have no operating, long-range conception of our nation's future or national conception of human and technological priorities or how they should all fit together.[8]

Apart from this profile and the all-too-familiar concerns over urban blight, overpopulation, water, air, land use pollution and the depletion of natural resources, we need to temper our haste to prescribe, we need to investigate the toll urbanization takes on man and community life, and we, as adaptable instrumentalities of the urbanization process, need to reorder our priorities.

The creating of an environmental conscience is mandatory for human survival. Equally imperative, however, is the fostering of a socially-supportive climate to ensure that man is consciously engaged in and shaping the urbanization process and not the victim of his own creation. It seems to me that we should begin by facing some basic social issues and direct our energies toward arresting counterproductive social behavior. Apart from abating the ecological crisis, we must contend with the issues of race and racism, persistent cultural value conflicts, and contradictory social habits in our multicultural and multiracial population centers. To take up the challenge we will need to gain insight into the variety of individual and collective orientations to the physical environment, the concept of cultural pluralism, and the nature and requirements of a humanistic future.

From the tenor of these remarks it should be clear that any success we may enjoy in approximating a desired quality of the environment or achieving the tolerable limits in the urban ecosystem will be difficult to achieve. In fact, the measure of success will be dependent largely upon our ability to comprehend the interrelatedness of socio-cultural, political and economic factors in the world and our ability to compromise in the spirit of being interdependent people.

We are a nation of planners, but Ernest Erber reminds us that the planning profession which aims to plan the future of cities, states, and nations, is not able to plan its own future.[9] It should be added that the "planning profession" as I use the term, would include all of the disciplines and the tribes of decision makers. Caldwell underscores the dilemma by observing that man's ability to plan his future depends

---

[8]Ewald, *Reconnaissance,* pp. 26-28.
[9]Ernest Erber, ed. *Urban Planning in Transition.* (New York: Grossman Publishers, 1970). p. xxviii.

largely upon his capacity for reason and that the quality of man himself must be improved before he can improve his environment. He also explains the callous threat to the ecological future of the nation by identifying our cultural orientations toward an uncritical bias for growth, a passive acceptance of technoeconomic determinism, a belief in the relativity of environmental choices, and a laissez-faire attitude toward the environmental rights of the individual.[10] Obviously these value orientations mitigate against environmental management and basic changes in our social structure. In addition to improving the quality of man, new institutional arrangements will have to be fashioned. The concept of boundaries will have to be reassessed and allegiances to traditional norms will have to be challenged. Community education will characterize the learning society, the building of trust and the acceptance of differences will undergird it.

To accomplish some of these ends we will have to begin at the pragmatic level. We could start with the concept and activity of community environmental planning and management and review some of the salient features of the recently published Community Environmental Management Prototype developed by the United States International University through its Center for Urban and Human Development.[11] The definition of community environmental management as used in the prototype parallels much of what has been said already. It is concerned with the totality of man's environment and involves an interdisciplinary exploration of human needs and the needs of a healthy natural environment. Moreover, the concept refers to the maximizing of physical and human resources in a coordinated and comprehensive way to improve environmental life quality. The effectiveness of the effort will depend, in part, on information, communication, education and maximum community participation and support. Communuity environmental management requires a present-future orientation and recognizes the role of creative tension in conflict resolution, noting that meaningful change should be worked for in a way that will be least disruptive to the community.

---

[10]Lynton Keith Caldwell. "Environment and the Shaping of Civilization," *Population, Environment, and Social Organization: Current Issues in Human Ecology.* ed. Michael Micklin. (Illinois: The Dryden Press, 1973), pp. 456-471.

[11]Thomas A. and Douglas G. MacCalla, *Community/University Prototype in Community Environmental Management.* San Diego, (California: United States International University, 1973).

In summary, the Community Environmental Management Project represents a collaborative university/federal-agency/regional community effort designed to create and field test in conjunction with the communities of Escondido and Calexico, California and Mexicali, Baja California, Mexico, a prototype training program for practitioners in the area of comprehensive community environmental management in urban growth areas. In addition to providing a university-based training model for other colleges, universities, educational institutions, and communities throughout the United States, the CEM Project is designed to prepare, through applied community research, new professional careerists or generalists in community environmental management. The need to prepare such careerists and to develop new structures and strategies for providing a better understanding of the relationships among the physical and human environmental factors is clearly evident. Decision makers and policy makers must be made aware of the environmental health and human welfare consequences. They also need to be made to realize that the new institutional arragements and strategies must be developed in conjunction with the community rather than for it. Equally important will be their understanding of the need for a holistic and interdisciplinary approach to theory and practice within the cooperative efforts of institutions, agencies, and consumers.

In short, the Community Environmental Management (CEM) Project stresses the need for general community improvement, an increased understanding of the ethnic and cultural context of a pluralistic society, the development of new types of local and regional community leadership, and the formulation of appropriate strategies

Such an activity as outlined by the CEM Prototype is transportable and could provide data on new institutional arrangements needed. Moreover, it would provide a profile on the availability of resources, consumption rates, human care services, the implications of technological advances, economic and political priorities, cross-cultural conflicts, and the range of tolerance for ecological balance and the limits of stress and social conflict. The kind of activity suggested for leadership training, applied community research, practitioner and community education, and the development of new institutional structurse and strategies also assume shared decision making.

Finally, when we emphasize the development planning aspect of urbanization as a collaborative, comprehensive, and continuous process, we attest to the significance of its action-oriented character and mutual trust base. We not only recognize the desired urban dynamic as including a sensitivity to the validity and completeness of baseline information, but also we acknowledge the interrelatedness of planning and shared decision making. Despite the size and complexity of the problems involved, we must undertake the task with hopeful enthusiasm. As David Godschalk pointed out in *Taming Megalopolis*, it should be possible and desirable to involve all participants (planners, providers, and consumers) regardless of race, influence or income in shaping urban policies and plans.[12] In his broad concept of collaborative planning he envisions bringing government planners face-to-face with citizens in a continuous, cooperative venture. Communication flows in two directions and respect is mutual. Community education receives new meaning as the education involves the community in planning and the planners in the community.

SOME SOCIAL AND BEHAVIORAL CONSTRAINTS OF URBANIZATION

The thesis advanced at the outset was that urbanization as a function of social change would probably persist with or without the desired quality of the environment. It is not a position of indifference to environmental quality but a profession of realism with hope. It is not the optimistic view of the future which Ely Chinoy[13] criticizes most sociologists of having in the face of disorder, decay, and distintegration. Essentially the position is rooted in a humanistic view of man as a creative and adaptable instrumentality for change. It merely challenges the all-things-being-equal arguments and the linear projections of chaos.

Since the question of survival is the one that is in the balance, we must be sensitive to our limitations and cautious with our optimism. As such, we must begin with man and examine urbanization as a reflection of man's conflict with himself and nature. We soon notice that as the urban environment is altered, social relationships are upset.

---

[12]David R. Godschalk, "The Circle of Urban Participation," in *Taming Megalopolis*, Vol. II, pp. 971-979.

[13]Ely Chinoy. "The Apocalyptic Future," in Ely Chinoy, ed. *The Urban Future*. (New York: Lieber-Atherton, 1973), p. 169.

We recognize that the seed of change is inherent in human societies and the existing strains in social systems assure the probability of change. We are painfully aware of the consequences of our arrogance toward nature and other men. We are awe struck by our nakedness in the dawning of consciousness about the future human environment. All of these are basic to our resolution to change.

As Edward Higbee points out, man is psychologically unprepared for urbanizatoin. The urbanization process as we have been describing it calls for a concentration of diverse culture groups within the confined spaces of cities. As technological integration weaves the world together into a common resource-generating network, it forces clashes between culture groups.[14] The United Nations report on urbanization[15] corroborates this concern and postulates that if large cities continue to grow (and there is every indication that they will) growth must be accommodated by better planning and organization. If the city is the place where man acquires his inheritance of literacy, equality and technical skill and where he is to play a role in the development process, urban strategies must involve not only a regional, national, and international plan for social and economic growth, but also a plan for the efficient use of men and resources. (See Appendix)

Urbanization is a value-laden dynamic. The inherent conflicts center on our view of man, the hierarchy of needs, contradictory social habits, the notion of fact versus convictions, cost versus choice, perceptions, preference, self-esteem, group identity, specialization in behavior, anonymous and impersonal relationships, and the consequences of value enhancement or deprivation. In short urbanization places its greatest limit or constraint on human development.

Too often the environmental concerns associated with urbanization are restricted to the physical context (air, water, noise, population density, etc.) in which man lives. The role of human behavior, organizational behavior, social order and conflict, and the concept of man as a valuing, creative and adaptive being is a parenthetical note to our study of the urban environment. We tend to minimize the significance of man interacting with the total environment, which includes other men. For this reason we need to recognize that our

[14]Edward Higbee, *A Question of Priorities, New Strategies for Our Urbanized World.* (New York: William Morrow and Company, Inc. 1970), p. 58.
[15]United Nations, *Urbanization,* p. 19.

ignorance of or indifference to the phenomenon of urban man impairs our research, planning, policy making, and management capability for ensuring environmental quality.

Understanding the human dimension of urbanization means understanding the environment-man relationship in the urbanization process. It requires identification of priority issues and researchable questions about man shaping, man willing, and man compromising in terms of his psychological and biological make-up. The accompanying diagram is designed to illustrate one configuration of that relationship. It is based on the premise that man's ability to enhance life and sustain life is directly related to his ability to control counter productive behavior and to arrest the deterioration and despoilation of his natural environment. As used here, man's ability to impose controls over his environment implies management rather than exploitation. It is viewed in terms of tolerable limits of stress and the natural limits for human survival. It seeks to foster through creative tension and humanistic inquiry the optimum climate for actualizing human potential as well as for developing a sense of community in which there is unity with diversity. It also seeks to engender in man a self-sustaining ecological conscience. The driving force behind this principle is that man will gain or approximate harmonious control of this environment and become less threatened by the stress and conflicts released when he comprehends that he is dependent upon the proper use and management of natural resources. It also suggests that man's purpose in life be affirmed as being the process of transforming society toward a world interculturistic future.

Two researchable questions worth stating at this point were considered by the Goals Task Force of the National Science Foundation, sponsor of the Urban Ecosystem Workshop held at Austin, Texas earlier this year.

1. *Identify social and behavioral constraints in the development and revitalization of selected human settlements through community-based research.* Such research should be conducted on neighborhood, barrio, larger community, supra-community or regional and binational scales. Analysis, synthesis, and validation of social and behavioral determiners and constraints should yield useable information on inter-personal and inter-group interaction with reference to (a)

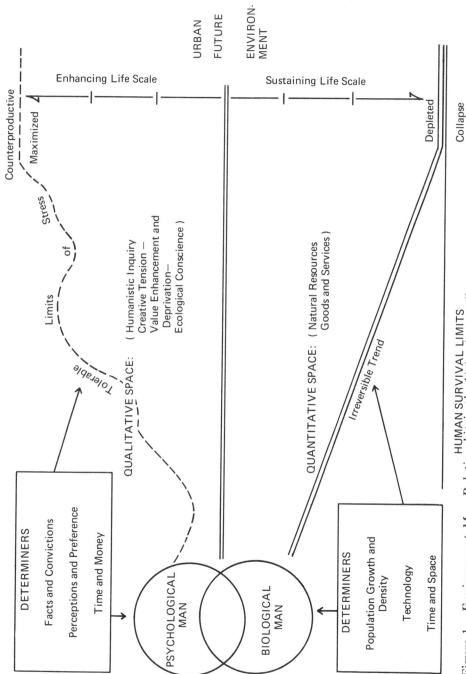

Figure 1—*Environment-Man Relationship in the Urbanization Process*

value orientations and value conflicts, (b) expectations and satisfaction, and (c) stimulation and stress.

2. *Identify and field-test communuity education and decision making prototypes for regional environmental management.* Such a study should provide data on new institutions (formal and informal) and institutional arrangements needed, including a profile on the availability of natural resources, consumption rates, implications of technological advances, economic and political priorities, and the ranges of tolerance for ecological balance and mental health.

Apart from its impact on human development, urbanization also places a constraint on social policy. As Lloyd Rodwin observed, one of the dominant beliefs of our time is that urban growth does not take place the way it should and that a policy designed to influence urban growth presupposes no particular philosophy or ideal development. The policy implication he cites calls for a national urban growth strategy in which a small, high level professional staff of policy and research specialists work in a national agency and in each of the major urban growth centers. It calls for new efforts in economic planning to put into perspective the location, scale, and impact of urban growth. Of even greater importance, however, is the need to identify researchable questions related to the aims of development and meaningful priorities and alternatives.[16]

Similarly, Jean Gottman alluded to the impact of urbanization on social policy when he remarked:

> . . . the most rapidly growing urban areas are the megalopolitan clusters and urban areas in parts of the country that resemble the Riviera in the opportunities they provide for leisure activities. Because, he argues, these trends reflect underlying tendencies that cannot really be controlled, the future shape of urban America will depend upon how public policy copes with the continuing movement of population into megalopolis and the Rivieras of the south, southwest, and west.[17]

---

[16]Lloyd Rodwin, *Nations and Cities, A Comparison of Strategies for Urban Growth.* (Boston: Houghton-Mifflin Company, 1970), p. 3.

[17]Jean Gottman. "The Rising Demand for Urban Amenities," in Ely Chinoy, ed., *The Urban Future.* (New York: Lieber-Atherton, 1973), p. 95.

A promising institutional arrangement for shaping regional social policies in the United States is the multiuniversity and local government collaborative research model on regional environmental management being field tested in San Diego, California. The main objective of this prototype is to establish concepts of the appropriate scope of regional university collaboration with local government and public agencies on environmental decision making. It is to be achieved by (1) an analysis of the content of regional decision making needs and the effectiveness of the unversity-government collaboration in assisting policy makers and (2) conducting a set of research projects which are focused on perceived governmental needs.

The research activities involved in this pilot effort sponsored by the National Science Foundation included (1) a study of coastal zone problems to match consumer and decision maker needs with available scientific information to determine need areas of research, (2) a study of various types of urban communities to discover how they were either protected from, or vulnerable to, specific types of environmental abuses. It was assumed that once certain processes of determination could be associated with community histories it would be possible to recommend new policies in terms of political reorganization, new laws, and new economic measures to strengthen the different urban community environments, (3) an investigation of the configuration of influential groups who are actively concerned with environmental land use decisions in the regions, (4) the development of a regional air quality model involving an extensive use of computer graphics, and (5) an examination of selected activities related to these studies to determine the legal implications of environmental research.

Inherent in the whole undertaking was the identification of a variety of factors that facilitate or inhibit the collaborative arrangement and the determination of the degree of synergism that would evolve. The concept is promising, however, the effectiveness and efficiency of the institutional arrangement being tested is yet to be determined.

The scale of the experiment is small in comparison to the kind of model Donald Canty suggests in his concept of "Metropolity." Canty's strategy calls for an elected body (a metropolitan development agency) which would be a federally supported instrument of national strategy. Its approach would be three-pronged:

(1) It would attempt to generate new jobs where the unemployed are now concentrated and to improve the housing and environment of those who stay there.

(2) It would work to create or open additional housing where centers of new jobs are to give those presently ghettoized (by either racial or economic discrimination) a new option.

(3) It would create centers of both new jobs and new housing in wholly new metropolitan communities, opening still another fresh option. These could vary in size from "minicommunities" of a few thousand population to full-scale satellite towns.[18]

Where the political and economic orientations are different from those in the United States, we see the signs of such developments already taking place——(Izcali, a planned urban center of over a million people just north of Mexico City or the classical example of Brasilia.)

Such schemes as the one advanced by the creation of the Urban Development Corporation in Jamaica provide still a different dimension to the way in which nations are attempting to cope with the drama of urbanization. The Urban Development Corporation, established by an act of Parliament in 1968, is a public corporation designed to promote the planned development of key areas in Jamaica. It is a quasi-governmental institution which shapes social policy pragmatically by providing the essential planning and infrastructure to arrest the forces of urban decay and to encourage orderly growth.

In summary, the major constraints of urbanization are on human development and social policy. The impact is characterized by social conflict, compromise, and commitment to conflict resolution. The measure of hope is to be found in the behavioral principle that the more substantial the social conflict (that is, the more central to the society's values or the more people are involved), the greater the pressures for its resolution.

In discussing some of the limitations of urbanization on such activities as human development and social policy, we recognize our own limitations to establish precise measures for determining the capacity of the environmental support system and for analyzing future urban trends. We recognize that the process of urbanization is situational, regional, national, and international and that it is imperative that we consider the holistic view of community in establishing our short and

---

[18]Donald Canty. "Metropolity," *City*, March-April, 1972, p. 40.

long range objectives. It is not a case of involving, *all at once,* the representatives from the myriad of disciplines, professional organizations, racial and ethnic groups, or public and private agencies who must contribute. Rather, it is a case of establishing *multiple beginning points* in which available resources are marshalled at appropriate stages through a management system for multiscale, multidisciplinary, planner-provider-consumer linkages.

Finally, we have suggested that the problems of environmental quality must include man as an integral part of that environment. We begin with man reexamining himself and his relationship with other men and other species and elements in the natural and man-made environment to create a desirable life quality.

In the words of Louis Wirth, "we must look for the symptoms which will indicate the probable future developments of urbanism as a mode of social life. The direction of the ongoing changes in urbanism will for good or ill transform not only the city but the world."[19]

In a similar manner, Lynton Caldwell relates the urban future and environmental quality to the prescription that "the further development and survival of a humane civilization depend upon the selective 'editing' of modern technoscientific culture in accordance with ecologically based criteria. This effort requires the analysis of existing behavior patterns and the sythesis of new cultural attitudes and institutions."[20]

I, too, suspect that the urbanization process characterized by human conflict, will continue with man at the epicenter. Man will resist change yet adapt because of his inclination for survival. He will continue to swing as the pendulum, half in darkness and half in light, trusting in the steadfastness of the fulcrum. In short, man will continue to urbanize the earth and seek preferable alternatives to environmental quality. He will create new relationships with the natural environment that sustains him and gain new insights about the humanism that enhances him.

---

[19]Louis Roth. "Urbanism as a Way of Life," in *Urban America, Conflict and Change.* J. John Palen and Karl H. Flaming, eds. (New York: Holt Rinehart and Winston, Inc., 1972), p. 182.

[20]Lynton Keith Caldwell, *Environment: A Challenge to Modern Society,* p. 136.

FURTHER REFERENCES

Hawley, Amos. *Urban Society: An Ecological Approach.* New York: The Ronald Press, Company, 1971.

Johnson, Elmer H. *Social Problems of Urban Man.* Homewood, Illinois: The Dorsey Press, 1973.

Michelson, William. *Man and His Urban Environment: A Sociological Approach.* Menlo Park, Calfornia: Addison-Wesley Publishing Company, 1970.

The Study of Urbanization. ed. Philip M. Hauser and Leo F. Schnore. New York: John Wiley and Sons, Inc., 1965.

APPENDIX

URBAN DEVELOPMENT GOALS FOR THE 1970's*

A. *NATIONAL LEVEL*

    1.   Urban development itself must be recognized as a major factor of economic growth in national development plans. Urban plans must also a) take account of the urban and environmental consequences of other national measures of economic growth; (b) allocate and schedule urban growth in terms of location requirements, environmental capacity, and the size and nature of cities and towns best suited to the nation in question; and c) estimate the land required for urbanization, the needed equipment and materials, and necessary investments. Regional capital budgets should be established as a primary means to implement both urbanization and housing plans.

    2.   Urban development and housing authorities or departments should be created and provided with sufficient power to purchase land for urban growth, check speculation, encourage and undertake research for the development of building materials and housing components and train people in the wide diversity of skills required for the effective development and management of cities. Such authorities would, when necessary, develop special programs to improve conditions in the shanty towns. They would also assist in developing and implementing regional planning. They should be represented at the highest level of development planning.

*United Nations, *Urbanization In the Second United Nations Development Decade, New York,* 1970, pp. 36-38.

3. A full-scale urban and regional development strategy should be adopted in which urban location and form would be used to stimulate the most productive and diversified use of the nation's resources and fulfill national housing goals. It should be clearly recognized that the housing sector is a key generator of employment and therefore of development in all countries. The building industry must be given at least the priority given to other major industries, with all necessary legislative, financial, and other measures to help it develop.

4. Direct public programs and publicly stimulated private action should allocate the equivalent of 5 percent of national income to finance housing and urban development. This would represent a substantial increase over current levels of investment in this sector for many developing countries, but it would still be far below the average level in advanced countries.

5. A full array of savings and credit institutions should be established to mobilize capital and to channel investment into housing and related services.

6. The construction and building materials industries should be strengthened for rapid expansion in all countries, reflecting their importance for all phases of national development. Long-term construction and housing programs are a basic requirement to strengthen these industries, stabilize employment and reduce building costs.

7. Urban studies and research centers should be established or expanded, to organize the interdisciplinary efforts needed for a genuine urban strategy at the national and regional level.

B. *INTERNATIONAL LEVEL*

1. Substantial additonal international resources should be provided in the form of financial aid and technical cooperation to achieve national goals for housing and urban development.

2. An international housing finance system should be developed to stimulate the creation and growth of national housing banks and savings institutions.

3. A network of internationally supported major research and training centers should be established in all developing regions and subregions. These should assist national Governments to train the required professionals and skilled cadres for programs of housing, building and planning. They should also undertake the necessary studies and maximize the interchange of international information

within the context of technical, economic and social development in each country. This information should be collected, organized and disseminated by a world-wide system of documentation.

4. The international organizational structure should be strengthened to deal with the full magnitude of the housing and urban crisis. This will involve intensified activity and more effective liaison between the United Nations and the regional economic commissions, specialized agencies and other bodies to assist Governments to formulate coherent urban policies, develop appropriate plans and programs, and implement them. Each major international agency concerned might well set us a liaison office to relate its work to the work of the agencies.

5. All international and national agencies concerned should undertake to campaign to arouse public concern over the problems of accelerating urbanization and the steps needed to reverse the trend towards deepening crisis. This is, after all, the crux. Without general awareness of the urgency of these problems it is unlikely that the proper action will be taken. What is lacking is the awareness of the general crisis gathering in the urban sector where more and more of the world's peoples will soon be living.

Colorado River Basin
Urbanization Workshops

QUESTION: To what extent does the population within the Colorardo River Basin influence decision making for the basin?

CONSENSUS: The general consensus was that most critical decisions, vis a vis the basic resource utilization of the basin, would be determined externally by three major sectors: the federal government, distant urbanization, and boundary urbanization.

The most important external sector affecting decisions within the basin is the federal government. Federal decisions on resource use are influenced by the demands of urbanization for those resources, especially energy and raw minerals.

The second most important sector is distant urbanization which, by its size, places demands upon, and makes decisions regarding the

Colorado River Basin itself. While the federal and state governments tend to act as intermediaries in these decisions, certain direct and overt demands do occur.

The third and most visible external force is the boundary urbanization such as Salt Lake City, Phoenix, Denver, Albuquerque, and Las Vegas.

QUESTION: How can the dilemma between the right to home rule and local self-determination by basin residents on the one hand, and the external need for the basin's resources on the other be resolved?

CONSENSUS: No consensus was reached on this issue; while there was a great deal of disagreement as to the morality of external sectors forcing decisions on the population of the basin, there was general acceptance of the reality. There was a feeling to continue recognition of local concerns when major decisions are made concerning the future of the basin and its resources.

CHAPTER XVIII

Resource Allocation and Management
in the Colorado River Basin

*John Baden, Herbert H. Fullerton and John Neuhold**

INTRODUCTION AND OVERVIEW

The states of the Colorado River Basin contain many natural resources of increasingly high value. We confront growing pressures for the extraction of these resources—primarily for use outside the region. It is clear that regardless of their location, i.e., on federal, state, or private lands, there will be a significant amount of extraction. The question we face is on what terms will these products be taken. The commonality shared by the Colorado River Basin states is an involvement in the above situation.

The vast majority of the resources taken from the Colorado River Basin will be utilized by people outside the region, but the utilization of the natural resources often entails serious social costs concentrated at the point of extraction. Many of the critical decisions affecting these resources are made in the political process. However, many of the politicians making decisions which impact on the region have constituencies outside the region. This is most obvious at the congressional level, but also it applies at the regional or state level of federal agencies and in those state bodies where corporations influence decisions.

Politicians have strong incentives to socialize the costs of and concentrate the benefits to their constituents. Thus, those politicians

*Respectively Assistant Professor of Political Science, Associate Professor of Economics, and Professor of Wildlife Science at Utah State University, Logan, Utah.

responding to constituents ouside the region are expected to prefer having the social costs of resource extraction born by those in the area from which the resouce is taken rather than by their constituents. Traditionally, politicians outside the region have been more sensitive to environmental quality considerations than have those from the region. When faced with high national demands for increasingly valuable resources however, we cannot assume this stance to be maintained. Thus, our fundamental objective is to arrive at a means of protecting the future environment of the Colorado River Basin in the face of these mounting pressures.

There are substantial factors which complicate this goal. First, the Basin states have a small percent of the U.S. population, making our political power relatively modest. Second, many officials from this Region favor economic development to such a degree that the social costs arising from development are substantially discounted or ignored. Third, because we are interested in the relationship of people's values to the quality of life available in the future, we are obligated to consider preferences of current residents and those of migrants to the region; i.e., preferences that may favor a high quality environment over development that significantly degrades that environment.

Many of the qualities that we are interested in preserving tend to have a common property or public feature. The various natural amenities fall into this category; i.e., clean air and water have a decidedly public attribute. Because of this common property feature, public actions are required for management. Thus, we plan to examine the public institutions in the regions, comparing their past and predicted performance for consistency with the stated goals of environmental quality. On the basis of our assessments we will recommend modifications in the institutional structure of the region.

In general it appears that if the environment of the region is to be protected and enhanced, institutions must be developed that have the capacity to: (1) identify trends and predict consequences of development, (2) gain the most beneficial terms of exchange with the balance of the country, (3) provide a mechanism by which individual concern can be aggregated into collective action consistent with goals for the basin.

To the social scientist, knowledge and capability to manipulate the elements of a system are of trivial concern unless such changes can be associated in some meaningful way to the aspirations and well being of people. Regional resource allocation or management within a hydrologic system does not appear to provide an exception to this rule. An ability to alter resource use rates or to reallocate important resources in the system become important only when they can affect the magnitude as well as the spatial and temporal patterns of important people-oriented output generated by the services of these resources captured within the basin. Quite obviously political and economic feasibility and ultimate success of technical alternatives which may be exercised as a part of management and possible reallocations of resources are heavily dependent upon people reactions to the real and anticipated impacts associated with them. It is within this context that the social scientist finds research interest in the question of resource allocation.

In enumerating resources which could be the focal point for management, water (quality and quantity) first comes to mind. However, concern for this heavily studied resource could easily be over shadowed by other not as well organized resources including clean air, open space, timber stands and fossil and nuclear energy resources. A major portion of these resources, including water, can be suitably classified as *quasi public* or as *common pool* resources, in the tradition of Garrett Hardin. As such, it is anticipated that complete reliance on market allocation of resources could lead to inefficient allocation and utilization since significant technical and ownership externalities (pecuniary and non-pecuniary) are typically present in the usage of such resources. Given these circumstances it is likely that the public sector will play a significant role in discharging resource allocation decisions either by direct intervention with traditional markets and/or by assignment of weights or pseudo prices through legislative councils or in the courts.

Resource allocation questions resolved by the public have most often favored equitable allocations of resources over equitable distribution of economic benefits generated from the efficient use of resources. For example, in the Colorado River Basin we have expressed a preference to depart from the doctrine of the prior appropriation in the division of Colorado River water by recognizing regional equity as prime concern in water allocation. This was done despite knowledge of differing marginal returns to water among sub-basins. Thus, we

allocation cannot be assessed on an *a priori* basis unless it is possible to predict decrements in total social product associated with any particular equity norm and the costs associated with redistribution of gains which would be forthcoming under an efficient allocation. If costs incurred in redistribution were greater than the reduction in total product obtained in a non-efficient allocative scheme then the latter would be the preferred choice. However the inverse situation could just as easily prevail and in either case the efficacy of a resource manager's judgement rests on the quality of information and data available to him and would be inversely related to the complexity of the problem faced. It is likely that this heavy information requirement and the somewhat arbitrary allocations which can and do occur in its absence which prompts us to opt for a market allocation of resources.

NATURE OF RESOURCES (GOODS) PRODUCED IN THE COLORADO RIVER BASIN

As noted in the introduction to this paper the most commonly recognized resource which has provided the focus for public allocative decisions in the Colorado River Basin is water. Almost without exception water has been treated as a "special" resource which "required" public intervention to assure maximum beneficial use, to prevent damage to third parties in exchanges and changes in time and place of diversion, and to prevent monopoly abuses, etc. It is expected that impetus for involvement of the public sector in the allocation and management for many other resources will be just as strong as was traditionally observed for water. The history of the basin is replete with examples of competition, conflict, planning and litigation in approximately that order. Although the objectives of public involvement were somewhat diffuse, it is not at all clear that public allocation decisions were marginally superior to those made by market. It could well be judged as a case in which beauty is in the eye of the beholder rather than any demonstrable advantage assignable to the public sector in dealing with "special" resources. This experience not withstanding, similar conflict in allocation can be expected to arise for other resources. Clean air, open space, fossil and nuclear fuels (energy production), all are characterized by high potential for significant externalities both in production and consumption activities. Extent of resource ownership is ill defined and concentrations of demand and supply are separated in space. These characteristics are accentuated in the basin because of obvious divergence in fiscal capacity and political sophistication as between resource supply areas and prime market or demand regions. Many of the resources (goods) of the basin attract inplace usage of the environmental resources (recreation, burning of coal) which tends to localize social cost in the resource supply area. Further new technologies tend to disperse benefits (energy) beyond traditional decision-making boundaries in which costs and gains are not effectively internalized. A commuter from Los Angeles has little "effective" concern with what effect the extraction of petroleum products has on the quality of air and water of Grand County, Utah or its residents. It appears that significant questions of resource allocation in the basin could be expected focus on the "mixed" cases between purely private resources (goods) in which extent of ownership is clearly defined and the opposite extreme in which exclusion and ownership are impossible, i.e., the purely public goods. Within this range between the polar cases we could expect to find the full set of resources (goods) which have served as the example for Pigou's classical definition of externalites (factory smoke and home laundry) and/or Hardin's "commons."

Thus, (1) based on historical precedents established in the allocation of water resource, (2) the similarity of many of the regions resources (significant externalities) to water, (3) the evolution of a sophisticated and articulate middle class who could benefit from regressive (in terms of income) allocative schemes perpetrated by the public sector we are predicting that compelling pressure will be generated on the public sector to assume a much more active role in resource allocation and management. This could be construed to imply a considerable diminution in existing credence placed on market allocations and greater dependence on "benevolent" public administrators. We are not prepared to render judgments concerning the relative merits of this predicted shift in mode, however, in the sections which follow we attempt to describe changing conditions in the socio-economic environment which leads us to this conclusion, to offer qualifications concerning potential difficulties which appear to be incipient with greater reliance on the public sector and to suggest possible insitutional forms or vehicles—which could be expected to evolve and possibly enhance the efficacy of the public sector in discharging its expanded (new) role.

PUBLIC INVOLVEMENT IN RESOURCE ALLOCATION DECISIONS

Many of the resources with which we are concerned have the characteristics of public goods or services. Often individuals and firms are given constrained property rights in such goods as water, grazing, a campground or a road through a national forest. Administrative actions change the rights to these goods and hence, shift costs and benefits. It is these shifts that generate public concern.

THE "PUBLICS"

It is clear that even among public goods not all of the public is equally affected or evenly concerned. Were the goods private, then differential interest could be expressed by varying purchases, i.e., coordination could be via the market. In the absences of this compelling advantage, coordination of diverse interests is of necessity via the political process.

It is important to note a disparity between the ease of political mobilization enjoyed by the large industrial consumers and the problems faced by the direct consumers of natural values such as beauty, solitude, and recreation. This difference is primarily the result of two factors: (1) the nature of the benefits sought and (2) the size of the groups.

Extractive industry seeks benefits (such as minerals or the right to use the airshed as a waste disposal system) which are in relatively fixed supply over the short run. This serves as an incentive for industry to organize and to encourage the administrative agencies to stress product factors rather than amenities. Each firm works through governmental decision-makers to gain the benefits.

In contrast with the above situation, benefits to "public" consumers contain far weaker incentives to organize. To the "public" consumers as a group the clean air and water provide "public goods." No citizen can be readily excluded from consuming the public goods.

This tendency toward independence is strengthened on the cost side by the size of the public consumption group. There is little likelihood that the benefits received by any one (or small group) of the individual users would be large enough to offset the costs of forming

an organization especially when exclusion of users who do not contribute to the organization is not feasible. From a political action viewpoint, there are many concerned citizens, but no one has a big enough
stake in the issue to warrant bearing the cost of acting. Thus, there
is a potential citizen base for a political lobby group, but it is only
a "latent group." Given this incentive structure, those who become
active in organizations devoted toward the production of public goods
tend to have very high emotional involvement and are sometimes described as zealots or eco-nuts. In brief, organizations and campaigns
that attempt to translate demands for collective goods into effective
demands encounter extremely difficult problems. There is virtually
no way to organize consumers of collective goods so they can, for example, directly "bribe" a copper smelter not to issue air pollution.
The effective demand created by one person's investment of either
time or money is likely to be very small indeed. The rationale of any
individual is as follows: I withhold my investment but the contribution of Lawrence Rockerfeller and others like him may save it. If the
effort is not successful, my money is down the drain; if it succeeds,
I will enjoy the benefits anyway. So I will opt for a free ride.

Thus, the nature of the benefits and the size of the group (especially as it affects each group member's share of the benefits) act as
incentives for organization of the extractive users and discourage
organization of the public consumers. Even if the public consumers
overcome these basic obstacles and try to organize, they face higher
costs in doing so than the private users. The costs of organizing within latent groups tend to be very high. Each individual sees the costs
of contributing to the group aims but no assurance that his individual
contribution will have any effect on the provision of the public good.
As a result of this failure to be able to compete for collective goods
in the market, the demands to minimize the negative impact of development are forced into the public sector.

In spite of the organizational problems discussed above, the environmental movement gained in numbers, oranizational effectiveness,
and intensity of feelings during the 1960's. Thus, the political environment also changed. This "environmental" change is explained by the
fact that the U.S. Congress is an excellent example of a controlled
population (535 members), where both special interest and geographic
territories are continually challenged and where only the politically

strong survive. Hence, the behavior of the successful politician is determined to a significant degree by his evaluation of the interests of the constituents. As the environmental question gained in public salience, senators and representatives at both the state and federal level were presented new opportunities to gain political credit by supporting environmental causes—especially when they affect economies in other states and other congressional districts.

Within this context various publics raise their opposition to disadvantaging sets of land management decisions. Now, however, with an increase in environmental awareness and an increasing demand for amenities, there is an incentive for the managers to listen. And we are back to the question, listen to whom, the loudest, the most politically powerful, the group who supports the bias of the professionals in the agency, or the more general, diffused sector of the public not sufficiently interested or adroit to provide an input?

THE "BUREAUCRACIES"

The first rule of any agency is survival—the second is budgetary expansion. Thus, while we can make normative statements couched in language sufficiently vague to generate consensus, (e.g., greatest good for the greatest number over the long run), we lack felicific calculus to defend our recommendation. Given the above rules and the political "market," the agencies will respond to those who can influence their destiny. The documentation of the latter point is exceedingly strong.

From the above perspective, one major problem is to design a public involvement apparatus that enables public bodies to accurately gage the preferences of those with a conjunction of interest in the decision and capacity to artilate that interest.

It is difficult to assess the degree to which it is the substance and implications of a decision rather than the procedure by which it is reached that is judged by the public. Given that those displeased with a decision have an incentive to depreciate the process by which it was generated, the evaluation of acceptability is made complex.

In addition to the above considerations, we have the risk of crediting the public with being excessively reasonable. Presumably one could arrive at standards for participation and achieve some agreement that if they are met, then the procedure for generating and processing public input is acceptable. If for example, everyone has an opportunity to advertise his position and the rationale thereof (neglect the impossibility of this scope of inclusion in many cases), if sufficient time provided for deliberation, and if additional qualifications are met, then one might judge the process to be acceptable. Acceptability, however, is in the eyes of the receiver. Members of the public may express the quite reasonable objection that the agency or the firm (or some composit alliance) has a natural advantage at mobilizing data. Since any non-random presentation of data biases decisions in some direction, the process of involvement may be unacceptable to segments of the public.

It appears then, that the only judgment of public acceptability is whether various sectors of the public feel that they have been screwed. Given that there are relatively few opportunities to press charges of political rape, we are forced to rely to an uncomfortable degree on the sensitivity of the political unit assigned responsibility for the area. This sensitivity can be expected to diminish as the responsible agency comes to occupy a monopoly position.

Information is expensive. Further, the cost of information is a function of its quality and the fineness of its grain. The majority of public involvement information correctly used by administrative agencies is of poor quality and large gain. This may be appropriate for most cases for there are tradeoffs, e.g., one gives up one square yard of public park for every two high quality interviews obtained.

The operation of prices in a market conveys condensed information and supplies to managers. As discussed above, public goods and services are not marketed, or carry only token prices. Hence, the managers of these resources lack the benefits of information provided by market prices. Even the most competent and conscientious administrators cannot, except by luck, provide the socially optimal supply of a good or service in the absence of knowledge of client preferences.

It has become compellingly obvious that administrators are generally unable to correctly define demands for public goods and services. Hence, they are advantaged if they can rely upon some sort of public involvement in the decision-making process. The process will be acceptable to those charged with administration to the degree that enables them to: (1) accurately age demands, and/or (2) correctly anticipate clients reactions to alternative plans of action. This is not, however, to suggest homogenous demands. Quite commonly various of the client groups (such as cross-country skiers and snow mobilers) will be in direct opposition. The larger area affected by the decision the more difficult it will be to arrive at a decision that does not generate severe opposition. Should the public involvement process function well, however, the opposition resulting from a decision should be anticipated and a rationale for the decision can be offered by the agency.

The agency will be tempted to structure or rig the participation in such a way as to justify the decision or sets of decisions preferred by the agency and to then define the action as one demanded by the public. The reality check of multiple political exposures and opportunities tends to reduce agencies' capacities to fix the game to their advantage.

In general, we expect that members of the public who benefit from a decision will feel that the method of public involvement employed, whatever it is, is acceptable. The agency will tend to find a method acceptable if (1) it is not "too" expensive, (2) if it is consistent with professional goals and (3) if it keeps them from being bit in the ass by a politically potent segment of the public.

As was discussed above, members of the public have little incentive to invest in contributing a public good. This generalization applies to the provision of information as well as the provision of other resources. Most people find sitting in meetings a costly bore and even loquacious people find it difficult to express a well reasoned position in public. In view of the above, the "workability" of any public involvement process must be judged in the context of budget constraints.

Within these constraints an involvement method is "workable to the degree that it generates data of the feasibility and grain preferred by the agency and does not strain the resources of the agency in the process. Among the relevant questions are: (1) Does the method employed tap the relevation political interests? (2) Do interested parties feel they have had an opportunity to make an input? (3) Can the program be administered with a "reasonable" amount of difficulty?

There are several reasons why an agency is involved in a public participation program. Several of these reasons may run concurrently. The more obvious reasons are discussed below.

A local office or division of an agency may run a public involvement program in compliance with some central directive. Although the local officials may learn that such efforts have direct payoffs, it is more likely that public involvement efforts conducted for these reasons will be rituals of compliance and produce a generalized waste. One might expect such efforts to be conducted with the primary goal of minimizing efforts of the bureaucrats involved, i.e., they will be conducted with maximized consistency with established patterns. It would be unrealistic to anticipate large payoffs in information from this process.

Similar to the above is the situation in which the office conducts a public involvement program as a ritual of pacification and compliance for a potentially cantankerous public or as a means of mustering support for an agency decision. This situation will deviate from the above in that the sponsoring office will make genuine efforts to involve and solicit information from the public. It is likely that at least some of the administrators will even believe that the process is conducted to guide agency decisions.

The final type considered is one in which the agency actually wishes to gage public preferences. The problems of evaluation in this situation are primarily technical and involve questions of effectiveness and efficiency.

When planners and other administrators state that "we must educate the public" they generally mean "we must convince the public that our way is the proper way." This position is neither as crass nor as self-serving as it may initially appear. Garrett Hardin's statement that "One of the most surprising things about science is the way it begins as common sense, and ends up with most uncommonsensical statements to which, nevertheless, common sense must give its assent once it has examined the evidence" offers a rationale for this position. In many cases the agency's policy, at first blush has the ring of "we must destroy the village in order to save it." And citizens have, with due cause, become skeptical of such lines. Burning brush on mountain meadows or killing game on national parks are both tactics employed to preserve the meadows and game. Both may be counter-intuitive to many people.

In each case the flow of information from the agency to the public is largely dependent upon the degree to which public policy preferences shift toward those consistent with scientific analysis. In nearly every use, the measurement of these shifts will have to rely primarily upon indirect indicators of time series changes in public attitudes.

Hopefully the above comments provide a framework from which to evaluate the success of public involvement programs bearing upon resource allocation. It is compellingly obvious that not all of the attributes can be maximized concurrently. In each case, however, we should remember that a bureaucrat, like any other person, is primarily self-interested. The task is to make his self-interest consistent with the public interest. This political fact must be included in the rationale for public involvement in the administrative process.

THE EFFICACY OF RESOURCE PLANNING (IMPETUS FOR INNOVATION IN INSTITUTIONAL FORMS)

PROBLEMS IN PLANNING

At the level of the individual and the firm planning is typically a continual process. The alternative to planning appears to be haphazard bouncing without the compass provided by an ordered set of goals. At this level, however, opportunistic shifts of plans are both expected and observed.

In the public sector we find that the demand for good planning regarding the allocation of resources seems to be exceeded only by the problems experienced with previous planning efforts. In addition to being expensive in terms of diverted, misdirected resources, and in terms of non-monetary social costs, these sets of failures may be presumed to be erosive to public confidence. Hence, it seems that there are several good reasons to minimize the potential for planning errors. We recognize, of course, that public decisions are public goods and the incentive to anticipate such errors are very much weaker in the public sector than in the private sector.[1]

It is clear that no amount of technically competent planning will successfully manage resource allocation problems if the error term, arising for example from random perturbations, swamps the variables taken into account in the planning process. This, of course, is especially severe if, as commonly occurs, the interdependent variable are

---

[1]G. Tullock, "Public Decisions as Public Goods" (1971).

also linked in a time series. In this case it is not surprising to find that the compounding of error makes planning success less than a randomly frequent event.

Planning for an unknown future then becomes a near impossibility for the process of planning, as the term "planning" is commonly understood (it is seldom defined, only "understood"), includes assumptions about future states. If these assumptions are incorrect the plans and current action made in reference to them are likely to be not only useless but actually counter-productive.

PLANNING THE HARVARD FOREST

Although the world contains many examples of the dangers discussed above, few are sufficiently simple and well documented to be instructive. At least one famous case, however, comes vividly to mind. In an article by Hugh M. Raup entitled "Some Problems in Ecological Theory and Their Relation to Conservation"[2] we are given an overview of the failure of planning for the Harvard Forest. The system while trivially simple as contrasted with the Colorado River Basin, was planned during the first third of this century. Although it can be argued that we have far better scientific understanding at this time than was available then, this argument would not discount the point of the example unless it was demonstrated that: (1) the best of our current talent were deployed on the sets of problems (as it probably was in the Harvard case), (2) that knowledge about interdependencies has grown faster than interdependencies, and (3) that the rate of change will not increase more rapidly than the rate of knowledge.

> The goal of the project was to bring the land to the highest possible point of sustained yield, profitable forest crop production and to maintain it.[3] The result was that:
>
> At any time during its first 50 years the Forest could have liquidated its wood capital and invested the proceeds with the Treasurer of the University. Had it done this in the early twenties, when stumpage prices were relatively high, its net return at the end of the 50 year period would have been nearly 10 times what it actually was, even calculating at simple interest, and its capital value would be 8 times greater than it now is.[4]

---

[2]*Journal of Ecology* 52:19-27, March, 1964. pp. 19-27.
[3]Tryon, in Raup, p. 19.
[4]Raup, pp. 25-26.

Since Harvard can afford the luxury of error, the study of its production should not prove offensive. First there were some biological errors but they are of little interest for our subject. We are in fact, willing to assume the ridiculous, i.e., that no such errors will occur in the basin.

In addition, the plans assumed certainty of demand (invariant prices) for forest products. The markets planned for have disappeared with replacement. Second, developments in wood technology have greatly modified demand structures. Hence, any assumption of certainty in long term planning is suspect. Raup notes that ". . . a better assumption would be that predictions beyond one or two decades were more likely to be wrong than right."[5] A similar situation is likely to exist in the CRB regarding projected demands for fossil fuel energy. Unless market forces are blocked and prices distorted, the commonly cited projections are likely to be overstated by several orders of magnitude. Related to the point, planners of Harvard Forest assumed operation in a closed economy. In fact, innovations occurred in the social economic environment of the forest in the forms of transportation, wood utilization, and institutional structures.

In this case then capability to predict, and thus plan successfully was limited by poor measurements, ignorance of the resource base, and rapidity of innovation. The general lesson is that long run uncertainties strongly suggest the utility of short run flexibility.

On the basis of his long association with this planning effort Raup suggests:

> . . . that we should plan ahead only so far as we can see with some degree of precision, and then readjust our plans at frequent intervals. We can be assured that there will never be enough facts available to give these plans any finality, and that we shall always be making judgments based upon probabilities. At every point of decision we will make use of whatever knowledge and measurement of value we can acquire, testing each for relevance to the point at issue as it relates to the frame of reference existing at the time. What we do with our capital or with our natural resources will rest upon these decisions.

In a problem area so complex as the CRB this advice seems especially appropriate.

---

[5]Raup., p. 25.

INSTITUTIONAL DESIGN FOR RESOURCE MANAGEMENT

INTERNALIZING ALLOCATIVE IMPACTS

We anticipate increased competition for resources in the basin. It is obvious that the marginal value of water will show a significant increase with an increase in the real price of agricultural products. Concurrently, however, the value of wild mountain streams will also increase as mountain recreation and residential developments are anticipated. An example of this conflict is found as a major issue in the Central Utah Project.

In the competitive context of the basin one would expect the rational individual to conceal or minimize information regarding the negative implications of his resource use and to discount the adverse affects that he generates. Further, if cooperative, voluntary arguments are suggested, there is an incentive to adopt hold-out tactics. It is clear then that if resources are to be rationally managed, willing consent must be replaced by the potential for coercion if collective decisions are to be enforceable on all parties. An alternative is to permit unregulated competition and wait for those generating the greatest sets of negative externalities to occupy a quasi monopoly position by driving out users whose resource requirements are for a higher quality resource base. This process can be conceptualized on a scale of impact in which each use having a heavy impact that is incompatible with lighter users displaces the light users. Thus, the benefits from the displaced uses are foregone. Clearly, there is a potential advantage to be derived from a shifting to a managed resource base. It is this benefit that attracts political entrepreneurs. In general, potential benefits from increased positive or reduced negative spillovers provide incentive to politicians to develop new institutions that will capture this benefit.

NEW PUBLIC ENTERPRISES AND DEPRIVATION COSTS

For the reasons indicated above, these institutions will have to operate on some decision rule other than willing consent, i.e, the potential for coercion must be present. Thus when the participants are considering the establishment of such an enterprise they must consider at least the following issues.

First, what are the optimal boundaries for the proposed enterprise? If, as some may suggest, the entire basin system, taken as a region, is reflected in a highly centralized bureaucratic organization, the jurisdiction would be too large for most purposes. When the jurisdiction is too large, people extraneous to the problem are drawn into the decision process. They provide support for the activity via some tax but fail to receive benefits. Thus, some form of side payment to this group is probably necessary if the coalition is to be sustained. This arrangement may be criticized on efficiency grounds as the forming and sustaining of coalitions tends to add substantially to the costs of political decision-making. Further, when this area is too large the level of information held by the average citizen is likely to be depressed.

In contrast with the above, when the area of inclusion is too small, all of the relevant externalities are not within the jurisdiction of the agency. Thus, we could find citizens paying to increase some spillover that largely benefits those outside the jurisdiction. Under this circumstance we anticipate a socially suboptimum level of production. In the CRB, this rule of effected interest was violated when Mexican interests were not weighted sufficiently heavily in regard to water quality.

The second consideration involves the costs that can be imposed upon citizens by the agency. One of the most important elements of a public collective decision is its potential for depriving people of their free choice. As Buchanan and Tullock have shown[6] the probability of a person being subjected to a high cost by the public decision is a function of the voting rules. In general these potential deprivation costs are a negative function of the proportion of individuals required to agree before a divsion becomes authoritative. Obviously the limiting case is the rule of unanimity which in effect states that each person holds a veto position over any decision. Under this rule deprivation costs would be zero but it is unlikely that anything would be accomplished due to the extremely high decision making costs.[7]

------

[6]See Tollock, G. "Public Choice: The New Science of Politics" and G. Tollock, "The Social Cost of Reducing Social Cost" in John A. Baden ed. "Managing the Commons." Unpublished collection, Utah State University, 1973. Additional discussion is found in Buchanan, J. and G. Tollock, *Calculus of Consent,* University of Michigan Press, 1962.

[7]Ostrom, V. "Collective Action and the Tragedy of the Commons" and V. Ostrom, "A Political Theory for Managing the Commons, in John A. Baden (ed.) "Managing the Commons." Unpublished Collection, Utah State University, 1973.

WHY MANAGEMENT INSTITUTIONS MUST EVOLVE

In an article entitled "The Cybernetics of Competition" one of the nations well known ecologists raises a critical issue regarding responsiveness of plans.

> Will any plan we adopt have adequate self-correcting mechanisms. It is one of the virtues of a market economy that any error in judgment as to what people want is soon corrected for. Price fluctuations communicate needs to managers. But in a planned economy, it has been often noted, planners who make errors are likely deliberately to interfere with the free flow of information in order to save their skins. Can a planned system include uncloggable channels of information?[8]

Given the magnitude and speed of changes that characterize modernized societies it is exceedingly unlikely that even if an optimal solution is reached at Time I the same solution will be optimal at Time II. Hence, we must confront the issue of adaptability to changing circumstances. Ideally, a feature similar to the homostatic adjustment mechanism of the market can be designed to foster the generation of benefits from adaptation to changing circumstances.

In arriving at such a design, one must recognize that the relevant boundaries are likely to change with changes in transport and communication technologies or in the amounts of resources employed. There are many activities that generate submarginal costs at low levels of production but, partially because of statistical interaction (between, for example, asbestos dust and auto exhaust), impose very high costs at even moderately higher levels of production. Hence, there should be provision for taking formerly non-relevant systems into account either by existing agencies or new agencies as their importance increases. Clearly the interactive effects which will be encountered in the potential development of oil shale is one example that would require new considerations.

Information is required when evaluating these physical systems and their social implications. But information is expensive. As noted above in the discussion of market allocation, those seeking solutions via the political process also operate with imperfect information. Parties in a common pool tend to distort or conceal information about their

---

[8]*Perspectives in Biology and Medicine* 7:58-84, 1963.

utilization of the resource. Further, if some common benefit is to be provided, an individual will tend to understate his share of the benefit in an attempt to reduce his share of the cost. This then is a version of the free rider problem. It is the task of the potential political entrepreneur to counter these tendencies and to minimize the potential depreviation costs which will be in the form of fines, assessments, and taxes.

CONCLUSION

Although it is only a necessary but non-sufficient condition for resource allocation, it would probably be difficult to overstate the importance of information if "optimum" solutions are to be obtained. We assume that institutional arrangements must continually readjust to changing circumstances. Given the "bargaining bias" we mentioned above, it seems that high quality information is most likely to be produced by a relatively disinterested third party. An example of such third parties are the various technology assessment efforts supported by RANN, of the NSF and to a limited extent by the Rockefeller and Ford Foundations. The off shore oil assessment group led by Kash and White at the University of Oklahoma may serve as a model for similar efforts in the CRB.

In those cases where the common problem is pecuniary, the establishment of appropriate pricing or taxing policies can also facilitate the achievement of optimum resource allocation. It is critical that any institutional design incorporating tax-price schemes recognize opportunity costs of uses excluded or foregone by other parties. These prices should provide the classic signals regarding resource supply-demand conditions and a source of revenue equal to the value of opportunties foregone by excluded users. In general, while we rule out permanent solutions (rigid), an overlapping set of institutions and jurisdictions that reflect the multitude of interests may foster continual modifications in the strategies necessary to produce socially optimum resource allocation Given the pervasive and recurrent difficulties that large, centralized bureaucracies have in taking time and place specific variables into account, in fostering or even tolerating innovations, in escaping capture from the stronger of its clientele, and of obtaining representation among various user groups, it appears obvious that such a "tidy" solution is radically inconsistent with the current and future possibilities in the Colorado River Basin.

CHAPTER XIX

Concepts of Carrying Capacity and Planning in Complex Ecological Systems

David M. Freeman and Perry J. Brown*

". . . The World of the year 2000 has already arrived, for in the decisions we make now, in the way we design our environment and thus sketch the lines of constraints, the future is committed. . . . The future is not an overarching leap into the distance; it begins in the present."

Daniel Bell[1]

The purpose of this paper is to examine the concept of carrying capacity for its utility in analyzing resource allocation problems in ecosystems as complex as the Colorado River Basin. Ninety percent of solving a problem has to do with formulating it usefully. Nothing is more wasteful and dangerous than analysis attached to the wrong questions. Therefore, historical carrying capacity approaches are reviewed, the limitations on the concept's utility are discussed, and a planning orientation which goes beyond traditional carrying capacity concepts is proposed in this paper.

USES AND LIMITS OF CARRYING CAPACITY CONCEPTS FOR RESOURCE ALLOCATION

Carrying capacity is not a new topic for either site or regional analysis. It has been considered in traditional natural resource man-

*Respectively Assistant Professor of Sociology and Associate Professor of Recreation, Colorado State University.
[1]Daniel Bell (ed.), *Toward the Year* 2000: *Work in Progress,* (Boston: Beacon Press, 1967), p. 1.

biological and physical limitations. Like the recreation writers, they consider social and psychological parameters as components of carrying capacity.

A brief discussion of the carrying capacity topic like we have presented does little justice to the vast amount of thought that has gone into its conceptualization. However, this presentation provides a base for critiquing the uses and limits of "carrying capacity" for resource allocation in the Colorado River Basin. Our concept of carrying capacity from a planning perspective is that it is a qualification of limits on a possible alternative future. We see carrying capacity determinations as an instrumental goal of environmental management. Our conceptualization goes something like this. A decision maker is charged with defining "quality." At his disposal he has information about natural resources, peoples' desires, institutions, and the current situation. This information is filtered through his own screening mechanisms and he articulates one or more alternative definitions of quality— or what is desired. Mixing these desired states with various management strategies, one can arrive at alternative futures. From that point, limits on the numbers of people or their distribution can be calculated for any future. Those limits are carrying capacities. For an area like the Colorado River Basin, one can forecast a future and indicate that resources of the system possess a capacity to support X number of inhabitants or Y population density. On one hand, carrying capacity has intuitive appeal to some people because it is a quantity which can be derived and utilized mathematically and because it is a single value which can be easily articulated and understood. On the other hand, these characteristics limit the utilization of the concept for resource allocation planning.

Uses

Before examining these limitations it is worthwhile to identify the uses of approaching planning problems with carrying capacity in mind. First, utilization of the carrying capacity concept demands a holistic approach to identifying and using information for planning. What must be accomplished is the writing of an operational objective (alternative future) for the goals expressed by the population. To prepare such an objective suggests a rather thorough examination of information dealing with the biological-physical-spatial base of a region, the social and psychological norms and characteristics of relevant populations and the institutionalized factors such as laws, governmental agency roles, and ownership patterns which occur within the region. All of these elements influence the way goals are objectified and since carrying capacity means an explicit and open statement of the objective function, all of these factors are open for review.

A second benefit accruing from the utilization of the carrying capacity concept is the potential for openness which the planning process provides. As we have said before, explicit objective functions must be stated under this system. This provides the potential opportunity for publics to examine the data base, assumptions, and conclusions of the planner. There is also the advantage to the planner of the system providing a focus for public involvement. That is, public involvement can be goal specific and geared to articulating alternative futures. The system presents opportunity for public involvement throughout its life. That is quite important for plan utilization if one assumes that if publics are involved in building plans, then the plans are theirs and reflect something they want.

Finally, from the perspective of organizing research and data collection for planning resource allocation, there are considerable benefits from utilization of the carrying capacity concept. The holistic nature of a carrying capacity based planning process with its systems analysis organization sets up a system for identifying researchable problems and of linking data and their interpretation generated from study of component problems. That is, the system provides for linkage of sub-systems into a more realistic whole. This occurs because the system demands that biological-physical-spatial base information, population preferences, and institutional elements be synthesized to arrive at explicit statements of alternative futures. That can only be accomplished through examining both the linkages between factors in these general components and between the general components. In essence, a framework for identifying researchable problems and data needs is set up.

LIMITATIONS

The problem posed by the idea of carrying capacity in a set of ecological systems as complex, heterogenous, and dynamic as the Colorado River Basin needs to be broken down into its constituent elements. Five ideas are central to the intelligible rendering of limits of the carrying capacity concept.

First, carrying capacity, when employed in forestry and range management, has been intimately connected to the second law of thermo-dynamics. Roughly stated, the second law holds that any closed system left to itself and unable to import additional energy over its boundaries will run down. Behavior in the social, biological and physical systems erodes the energy base. Therefore, it is the task of the analyst to discover the rates of energy flow; carrying capacity is equal to a system's ability to import energy at sustainable rates over time. This can be contrasted with the concept of carrying capacity, in the context of the complex social systems which are the dominant sub-systems in the ecology of the Colorado River Basin. These complex systems present conceptual difficulty with carrying capacity for a couple of reasons: 1) modern social systems are characterized by rapid advancement and diffusion of technology enabling new energy imports across system boundaries and more efficient uses of available energy thereby altering the capacity of such systems to support behavior; 2) social systems, while dependent upon physical energy flows are centrally organized around flows of symbolic information. Symbolic information, organized into complex language systems, does not "run down" through use. Carrying capacity in social systems is centrally determined by the organization of symbolic information, particularly into goals and objectives. The capacity of social organization to survive, expand, and to attain objectives is as centrally dependent on the organization of information as it is on physical energy flows. The first component of the carrying capacity problem is, therefore, the limiting reliance it has had on the second law of thermodynamics in some of its traditional conceptualizations.

The second component of the carrying capacity problem is that natural and social systems are enormously complex, and theory defying in their interdependencies. When a planner deals with a well defined region which has a fairly homogenous population (as defined by the goals to be achieved by planning) calculation of a carrying capacity to be used as the measure of the objective function seems realistic. For an area as large as the Colorado River Basin it is at best extremely difficult, and probably impossible, to apply the concept of human carrying capacity in planning. Within the geographical space of the basin there is a multiplicity of decision makers whose decisions will influence capacity and there are a multiplicity of goals which the residents want achieved. For instance, Hübner indicates that in 1967 the basin had 952 active local governments plus seven state governments and policy was made by 4,615 elected officials.[8] One might argue that these problems can be overcome by regionalization of governments and that a regional decision making body can be organized to set goals and carry out planning. It is our position that such a suggestion ignores political reality within the basin. Our view is one based upon the characteristics of local political jurisdiction and control which permit one jurisdiction to set its own goals and in achieving those goals to externalize as many costs as possible. It is a view of competition between political jurisdictions.

A third component of the carrying capacity problem involves difficulties in dealing with the public welfare. Carrying capacity based planning does not necessarily deal with public welfare questions. Diverse and conflicting social interests cannot be aggregated into operationally useful welfare functions via the carrying capacity concept. No yardstick exists which can prescribe that a quantity of human, capital, and natural resources directed to goal "A" (such as improvement of elementary education) will lead to more net human welfare than those same resources directed to goal "B" (such as curing cancer).[9] Yet, the whole point of planning is to make "better" choices and "better" means pursuing the "social" or "public" welfare in some sense. We do not see carrying capacity based planning necessarily contributing to the resolving of this dilemma.

A fourth limitation to utilization of carrying capacity in resource allocation is the possible perceptions publics may have of its implications. Establishment of a capacity suggests an eventual growth limitation which means a restriction on population movement and choice in residential and employment selection. Such restrictions like most environmental measures have the greatest effect on those politically

[8] C. W. Hibner, "Urbanization in the Colorado River Basin." Paper presented at the Conference on Environmental Management in the Colorado River Basin. Utah State University, 1973.

[9] On this point, see: Alice M. Rivlin, *Systematic Thinking for Social Action.* (Washington, D.C.: Brookings Institution, 1971.)

and economically less powerful.[10] Therefore, establishment of carrying capacities as quantified objectives of planning will likely lead to greater cleavages in society and their attendant problems. There is the possibility for inequitable effects to be resultant on publics as a consequence of implementing carrying capacity based planning. Almost all planning likely suffers from this same criticism. However, most planning does not make the situation so explicit and, therefore, planners so vulnerable.

Finally, the fifth component of the carrying capacity problem is the limited meaning of the capacity value. While the figure which is determined does provide a desirable target population or density to aim toward, it does not impart information about the desired spatial distribution of this population or the kinds of social systems it will utilize. Without its simultaneous presentation with an alternative future, carrying capacity only tells how many people the gatekeeper should let enter the system. It ignores the configuration of the domain within the fence.

BEYOND CARRYING CAPACITY BASED PLANNING IN THE COLORADO RIVER BASIN

The limitations of carrying capacity based planning are stimuli triggering a desire to find a different planning system for use in complex ecological systems like the Colorado River Basin. Essentially we suggest backing up, shedding the excess baggage or carrying capacity, and focusing on selection of alternative futures. The point of departure from current planning is how to deal with sub-optimization of welfare functions. The problem and a solution follow.

Insofar as social welfare has had meaning for policy, it has meant sub-optimization. Decision-making has been placed in competitive frameworks among individuals, private firms, public bureaucracies, and nations. Each actor has sought local advantage on the assumption that optimization of sub-system goals would somehow sum up to optimization of the total system's welfare. Yet, the experi-

---

[10]K. E. Boulding, "Environment and Economics," in W. W. Murdock (ed.), *Environment: Resources, Pollution, and Society.* Stamford, Connecticut, 1971. Sinauer Associates. Many other authors writing in the environmental realm have recognized this point.

ence of industrial and post-industrial societies has been that sub-optimizing strategies connected to powerful technologies which have substantial and often negative external impacts compels us to abandon the naive notion that social welfare is to be found by a decision system that rewards decision makers for finding ways to externalize their costs whenever possible.

What is the alternative to suboptimization? Simply put, since planning cannot learn about the nature of the public welfare in any prescriptive sense, learning systems for planners must be geared to expand welfare in a contextuating sense. Whereas planners cannot prescribe particular goal sets *A, B,* and *C,* as contributing more to net human welfare than alternative goals sets *X, Y,* and *Z,* it is possible to analyze the means by which the context of choice itself can be expanded. Irrespective of whether individuals or organizations choose to exploit a choice opportunity, welfare is served by enlarging the spectrum of choices. This supply assumption is founded on a demand perspective. There is considerable psychological evidence to suggest that maximization of both individual need satisfaction and societal satisfaction (welfare) only comes about when a wide variety of choices are offered or when individuals are so well socialized that they gain satisfaction from the same thing. This is additional evidence to suggest that people are quite imperfectly socialized and therefore current state satisfaction comes from a variety of opportunities to achieve satisfaction. In this context, planners cannot hope to specify the multitude of value judgments made daily by diverse and conflicting publics but it is their task to analyze the limited resources available to widen the context of choice—the planner's menu. The planners most central value is that of increasing options in complex systems which cannot be comprehensively mapped and in which prediction is only of a short range and tentative type. Social welfare cannot be usefully thought of as the achievement of any single goal or set of targets prescribed by any particular group, but must be viewed as a process of expanding the range of available options. Systems, and planners, without options go the way of Tyrannosaurus Rex and the Sabre Tooth Tiger. The planner who emerges from implementation of planning activity with fewer options than when he started is not long for the world of either private or public affairs because any solution for one set of clients is somebody else's problem. It is the competitive struggle over conflicting demands of publics that are triggered in the planning process.

Since solutions breed new problems, what the planner needs most is a steadily increasing flow of options to enable handling the constant series of problems that are generated in unchartable domains of complex ecosystems. Planners, sensitive to this view of the public welfare, must develop learning systems which allow them to differentiate between decisions which do not foreclose future options and those which shrink the context of choice. Planning for the social welfare means that each generation of decision makers must not be exploited by the option reducing mistakes of its predecssors, but it in turn must not be rapacious of future options of unborn generations.

The problem posed by planning in complex ecological systems is how to evolve a learning system for planning which will allow one to work interactively and in a framework that welds the specific intensive knowledge of narrow domains with concern for total systems effects. How can the planner construct a learning system which bridges the need to preserve decentralized decision-making in complex systems that defy centralized planning with the needs to insure that the context of options—the social smorgasboard of choice—is not shrunk by unanticipated repercussions of decentralized decisions in systems too complex for any single set of decision-makers to comprehend.

SHAPING A LEARNING SYSTEM

Because planning in social systems is a function of changing technologies and of patterns of information and physical energy flows, because complex ecosystems including their social system components defy prediction, because supply to increase social welfare can be usefully viewed, not prescriptively, but as the expansion of choice menus, and because planners must find ways to integrate specialized information with comprehensive concern for total systems effects, planning in complex ecosystems must have the capacity to sustain alternative futures—sets of options. Planners cannot predict the future in ways sufficiently subtle to usefully guide current decisions, but private and public decision-makers do continuously construct the future. Planners must have a learning system for guiding the iterative construction of futures. Alternative futures are alternative sets of contingencies—futures that appear as possible (and reasonably probable) descendants from present states of affairs.[11] Alternative futures are uncertain in a probalistic sense, but it is not essential to predict just which combinations of events are likely to emerge at particular times. What is essential is to: 1) recognize the open-endedness of the future, 2) define responsibility to future populations as expanding the array of options with which to confront the future, 3) pursue mixes of futures simultaneously retaining as many as possible as long as possible, 4) identify those critical points at which decisions promoting one alternative future jeopardize the viability of one or more other futures. Planning is not about one necessary future, but about sets of futures. Planners need make no necessary commitments to exploit any given potential future, they need only keep them viable so that future generations will not be unnecessarily chained by the irreversible shrinking of options by dead men. Sets of options—alternative futures—need to be defined for each ecosystem and each future should be kept open as long as possible, foreclosing a future only after the greatest possible study, analysis, and public input has been obtained. In essence then, for each ecological planning unit it is the planner's task to:

1) determine what futures could be realistically attained—such as water, recreational opportunity, timber, forage, wildlife, and energy production as well as mineral extraction and urban development;[12]

2) determine what specific actions must necessarily be taken if the future is to be realized;

---

[11]Bertrand de Jouvenel has employed the term "futurables" in this manner. See his: *The Art of Conjecture* (New York: Basic Books, 1967), esp. pp. 18-19. Another discussion of "future" to which the authors are indebted is Herman Kahn, "The Alternative World Futures Approach," in Morton A. Kaplan (ed.), *New Approaches to International Relations* (New York: St. Martin's Press, 1968), pp. 83-136.

[12]It might be desirable in some cases to use Delphi techniques for identifying alternative futures for any given ecosytems area. Such techniques draw upon "expert" perspectives, eliminate face-to-face confrontations of committees and meetings and avoid the persuasion, power plays, and bandwagon effects of particularly influential individuals or organizations. For materials on the Delphi method, see: Donald L. Pyke, "A Practical Approach to Delphi," *Futures* 2 (June, 1970), 143-152.

3) determine for each future what, if any, essential ordering of action exists—must some kinds of actions necessarily preceed others;

4) determine whether or not there is any ordering among the future themselves. For example, a future for grazing in the ecosystem does not preclude a future for urban development but urban development will preclude significant livestock grazing;

5) insofar as possible rank specific actions within futures according to their degree of reversibility, placing most reversible actions earlier on the agenda and the least reversible actions last;

6) examine those actions which are relatively irreversible, to determine whether or not there are negative externalities or spillovers which would jeopardize an alternative future;

7) determine whether or not a relatively irreversible impact also generate spillovers onto other futures constituting a critical action—a high cost decision;

8) postpone high cost critical decisions as long as possible, subject them to as much research as possible, and make them the focal point of as much public input as possible.

A simple decision matrix for the analysis of cross impacts of alternative futures might look as follows:[13]

Alternative Futures

Water production   .   .   .   .

Energy production   .   .   .   .

Timber production   .   .   .   .

Recreation opportunity production   .   .   .   .

Forage production   .   .   .   .

Wildlife production .   .   .   .

Minerals extraction .   .   .   .

Urban development .   .   .   .

---

[13]Cross-Impact analysis has received recent attention and some references are: Selwyn Enzer, "Cross-Impact Techniques in Technology Assessment," *Futures* 4, (1972), pp. 30-51. T. J. Gordon and H. Hayward, "Initial Experiment with the Cross Impact Matrix Method of Forecasting," *Futures* 1 (1969),

Specific Actions Required by Each Future Ordered according to any essential sequencing and according to the principle of reversibility of impact.

Examination of such a matrix reveals which specific actions for any particular alternative future will jeopardize options for another future. Critical high cost decision points are revealed in a way not possible by separate planners working within their own limited future frameworks.

DECISION RULES FOR THE LEARNING SYSTEM

What rules for decision-making can be formulated for analyzing the cross impacts of alternative futures? Four are tentatively suggested.

First, actions should be ranked within each future as to their reversibility. Reversible actions can be treated as low cost decisions and be taken without the benefits of great amounts of research, analysis, and public participation because of their flexibility.[14] The more the irreversibility, the more the decision should be postponed, the more scarce research resources should be expended, and the more public participation should be sought.

Second, impacts of scale should be examined. Power plant construction at level "X" may not jeopardize an alternative future but construction at level 5x, 10x, or 30x might well do so. The question is, at what level of scale will one type of impact become a threat to another future? The decision rule is that planners should not allow scale to grow so as to interfere with other futures in one subsystem unless such futures can be retained in another subsystem.

Third, because major uncertainties are inevitable in complex ecosystems, the burdens of uncertainty must be allocated to promote both innovation and preservation of options. In the past, it has been frequently assumed that any project or program which was profitable to its developers was a contribution to social welfare unless and until

---

[14]The rule of irreversibility and the subsequent ones regarding the cumulative impacts of scale and allocating burdens of uncertainty have been put forth in David M. Freeman, "Politics of Planning and the Problem of Public Confidence: A Sociology of Conflict Approach," in Society of American Foresters. 1972 Annual Meeting. Hot Springs, Arkansas, *Proceedings*. Washington, D.C., 1972. A more extensive discussion of these and other criteria for decision making is found in David M. Freeman, *Technology and Society: Issues in Assessment, Conflict, and Choice* [Chicago: Rand McNally (forthcoming).]

opposition emerged to definitively establish the harmfulness of the activity. The burdens of uncertainty have been placed on the oppositions. Yet, by the time such oppositions can identify a harm, get organized, and establish the casual connections, irreversible detrimental impacts may well have been established in patterns that nobody would have wanted. On the other hand, if innovators of programs must prove the harmlessness of their activity before they are allowed to begin, much socially desirable innovation may well be dampened. The question is, to what extent should the burdens of uncertainty be shifted to project proponents? The decision rule is that when the scale of activity is low and when there are no known spillovers which will eliminate alternative futures the planner should allow the burdens of uncertainty to be placed on opponents of any given activity. Before expansion of scale of operations, the burdens of uncertainty should be shifted increasingly to proponents so as to force them to demonstrate harmlessness.

Fourth, each alternative future represents benefits to some social groups and costs to others. Every decision to promote one future rather than another at any given time represents a transfer of social welfare from group to group and from time to time. Planners can expect that forces of political support and opposition will organize around alternative futures in the never ending struggle to obtain conflicting goals with scarce resources. Groups relevant to futures can be usefully broken down into five types:[15]

1) *Positive Core Groups*—those actors who perceive that they have a direct economic, legal, political or other material stake in that future and who expect to obtain such rewards directly from pursuit of that future. For example, commercial lumbering companies are core groups for timber futures; ranchers for grazing futures; suburban developers for urbanization futures.

2) *Positive Ideological Bias Groups*—those which have no direct stake in the future and who expect no material pay-

---

[15]This typology of political actors was inspired by the work of Warren F. Ilchman and Norman T. Uphoff who develop a somewhat different, but related typology, in their *Political Economy of Change* (Berkeley: University of California Press, 1971), pp. 42-47.

offs from exploiting that future, but which deem exploitation
of that future to be legitimate and proper.

3) *Neutral Groups*—those which do not consider a future to
be relevant to their interests.

4) *Negative Ideological Bias Groups*—those which do not expect to suffer in any material way from exploitation of a
future, but to whom such exploitation is improper or wrong.

5) *Negative Core Groups*—those which expect that exploitation of a future will directly materially jeopardize their
future(s).

The relevant question is to what extent will any given decision
within the framework of any given future generate intense conflict
cleavages between positive and negative core groups and their respective associates in the ideological bias categories? Conflict cleavages
which merge with each other on overlapping lines are associated with
propensities to commit violence, with non-negotiability of issues, and
with the flow of resources to cut down choices as polarized opponents
bitterly resist each other. On the other hand, conflict cleavages which
merge on cross-cutting lines of conflict allow room for negotiation
among actors who are allies on some issues while they are opponents
on other matters; in such cross-cutting conflict systems levels of
threat are low or moderate, and resources are not centrally directed
toward cutting down the options of opponents who are sometimes
allies.[16] The decision rule, then, consists of three parts:

1) Identify the patterns of cleavage emergent around the future
under scrutiny for decision—which groups fit as the positive and negative cores and ideological biases?

2) Examine other futures to identify lines of cleavage which
will cross-cut those of the original future.

3) Make decisions concerning multiple futures which will allocate advantage and disadvantage in such a manner that the
positive core groups on one future issue are allied with the
negative core groups on other future(s). Keeping cleavages

---

[16]For analysis of cleavages and planning, see: David M. Freeman,
"Social Conflict, Violence and Planned Change: Some Research Hypotheses,"
*Coexistence: A Journal for the Comparative Study of Economics, Sociology,
and Political Science* 9 (1972), pp. 89-100.

cross-cut serves to avoid polarization, keeps levels of threat lower, makes negotiation about trade-offs possible, and keeps options open. Polarization around overlapping cleavages creates high levels of threat as some actors see significant futures for themselves centrally threatened and all available resources become committed to reducing the opponents' options. Because opponents on all sides are threatened by any exercise of options by their enemies, resources in polarized systems flow to cut down choice—the social menu gets badly battered.

CONCLUSION

While carrying capacity based planning has some useful properties it does not lead to solving all conceptual problems within the planning process. It leads the planner down the desirable path of holistic analysis but comes up short when planning within complex ecological systems. It focuses too heavily on determination of a carrying capacity. What is needed is the development of a planning process which goes beyond carrying capacity analysis and incorporates an ability to maintain sets of options—alternative futures. That is, there is need for a *futures capacity* based planning process.

The answer to George Lunberg's twenty-five year old question "Can Science Save Us?" was a resounding "no" when articulated in terms of science exclusively in the physical and biological realms.[17] But in an emerging era of social sciences in systems frameworks, the answer might be a tentative "possibly." The answer must be cast in terms of a science contributing to learning systems which can: 1) allow for suboptimization and decentralized decision making required in complex modern societies, but with the discipline of preserving and expanding contexts of choice; 2) integrate knowledge of few variables in narrow domains with strategic considerations of future choice—without paralyzing analysis by the requirement that it be fully comprehensive; 3) allow the flexibility and advantage of incremental planning but with defense against the "tyranny of small decisions" which can unintentionally foreclose future options. In sum, then, in complex ecosystems planning must have capacity to carry

---

[17]George Lundberg, *Can Science Save Us?* (New York: Longsman, Green, second edition, 1961.)

alternative futures which is, in turn, a function of the reversibility of our decisions, the cumulative effects of scale, the allocation of uncertainties, and the patterns of conflict cleavage which emerge around resource allocations. Alternative futures are a precious resource in and of themselves. Planners must husband, conserve, and expand them with as much consideration and care as any material resource.

Research Needs Statement

CHAPTER XX

The Development and Environmental Protection of the Colorado River Basin

D. Wynne Thorne*

THE PRELIMINARY ASSESSMENT OF KNOWLEDGE GAPS AND RESEARCH NEEDS

INTRODUCTION

The Colorado River Basin is one of the major hinterlands of the United States. This vast area of more than 150 million acres with less than one-fifth of the population density of the country as a whole, contains the land that is most remote from railroad or highway within the contiguous states. The region holds great undeveloped mineral and energy resources, is of distinctive natural beauty, and will play an increasingly significant role in the development and stabilization of the U.S. economy and culture.

This fragile land limited by water and sparse-vegetation, requires careful management to prevent deterioration. Entrenched public reluctance to sacrifice environmental quality to encourage resource development provides one protection for a rational future. But simple opposition to environmental degradation is a negative and needs to be balanced and guided by adequate information and evaluations as

*Director, Agricultural Experiment Station, Utah State University

to the trade-offs between environmental limitations and economic and social gains. One point has been made clear in the Conference. Resource development and use, and the maintenance of environmental quality are based on conflicting values. Society must choose between alternatives and this should be done with full knowledge of the costs and benefits involved. This will require greater wisdom on the part of public officials and resource developers.

The Committee on Research Needs was assigned the task of assessing available data and knowledge concerning the basin and identifying new knowledge and pertinent research needed to undergrid the wise and efficient development of the basin while protecting the interests and rights of people in it and granting only such changes in the environment as are acceptable to an informed public.

We begin by examining the state of knowledge and research needs within the primary problem areas that were identified for the conference and arrange the research needs in their general order of priority among and within the primary areas.

This report consists of a few selected general recommendations for the region, with explanatory comments and, where appropriate, more detailed suggestions.

BACKGROUND GUIDELINES

Goals. General agreement on clearly stated goals for the basin should be the basis for all planning and action programs.

> *A commission should be established by the governors of the basin states to prepare and submit to the several concerned states, goals for the Colorado River Basin for the year 2,000 and general guidelines for their attainment. These goals should incorporate the development of natural resources while preserving the rights of individuals and the quality of the environment.*

Federal, state and local governments must be involved in mediating the great issues between local ambitions for development and environmental conservation, between the pressures acting on the land market and the wider public interests. With rapid technological development, increasing affluence and consumption levels, and a more mobile population, the Rocky Mountain region is facing the most rapid utilization of land and natural resources it has experienced since the coming of the railroad.

Any valid analysis of the problems and recommendations for study and action would require at least the development and agreement on definite goals by the states in the region. Such overall goals must protect the basic rights of individual citizens, be in harmony with national goals, and take into consideration the diverse interests and modes of action of private enterprise, communities, counties, states, and sub-parts of the entire region. The need for frequent review and modification of goals must also be recognized throughout the course of planning and action programs.

Proposed goals should be analyzed for compatibility, acceptability and feasibility. Toward this end, an interstate effort will be required to bring together those institutions that are responsible for the establishment and implementation of public policy. Concurrently, public involvement must be developed to insure general understanding and acceptability of goals before adoption.

Research can assist with evaluating goals and with measuring their achievement. A prime purpose of research would be to help determine where we are today and help anticipate the future in evaluating resources.

Among the significant topics to be considered in formulating goals are: Anticipated rates of population and economic growth; standard of living and per capita incomes of resident population; limitations to be placed on reductions in environmental quality; resources to be utilized primarily within the region and those available for export; and the impact of development on the quality of human life.

Inventory of Natural Resources. Reliable and well classified data about the Region serves as a base for planning and research.

> *All public agencies and political subdivisions should immediately direct coordinated efforts to completing the inventory, classification, and evaluation of data pertaining to the potential uses of the land, water, air, climate, mineral, plant, and animal resources of the basin.*

Volumes of data are now available on resources of the Colorado River Basin. Even though new techniques can provide additional valuable data, an even more pressing need is to evaluate, classify and interpret the data now available in ways that can be readily grasped by the public and particularly by decision makers. If the merits of these resources were put into an economic-environment system, the impacts of development on the environment could be assessed and the trade-offs between developing or not developing various resources and industries could be better understood. Such a model would greatly assist decision makers for the basin.

Past resource studies have not fully recognized that the region is a kaleidoscope of resource ownership, management, leasing overlays and multiple uses. Fifty-six percent of the land in the basin is under the management of six different federal agencies for some twenty land use purposes, singly and in combination. Other portions are state land; still others are being acquired or annexed by cities, schools, park districts, utilities and institutions. Finally, the private ownership pattern represents many partial and transitional land uses, from options for land development to leases for recreation, mining and grazing. All these jurisdictional combinations can change land use overnight, or seasonally. If the several states making up the basin have a serious interest in the future of the region they must assume a more realistic and responsible role in assessing its resources, their ownership and management and their possible development and utilization.

An inventory and evaluation of human resources are essential parts of a regional resource study. The ethnic and cultural groups present, the technical capabilities of the labor force present and potential labor supplies, and the needs for further training are types of information required if basin development programs are to be adequately planned to serve the welfare of the people of the area. Research can provide a basis for analyzing and evaluating human resources.

Priorities for Research Needs

Energy. Research to study the development of energy resources is first in order of major research topics because of the extensive basin resources and national urgency for their utilization.

> *The extensive hydrocarbon resources of the basin need thorough investigation to evaluate their potentials for development in*

light of foreseeable changes in technology, price structures, and national and international energy supplies. The impact of different levels and types of development on the total environment and on demands for other resources and facilities of the Region must also be critically weighed.

Extensive reserves of bituminous coal, oil shales, and tar sands make the Colorado Plateau Region one of the richest storehouses in the world of fossil fuels. In addition, much of the uranium being used in nuclear power plants has been derived from the basin. The bulk of these resources has been scarcely touched but our fuel crisis is making massive energy developments seem imminent. Warnings to proceed with such development with caution and with the best available knowledge must therefore be reiterated and backed with research. Such research should immediately evaluate the best technologies and strategies for the processing of the various energy resources of the basin. Other investigations should analyze the comparative costs and returns from alternative resources and technologies and the returns from exporting the crude resources as compared with electric power, gas or refined oils.

We recommend, in agreement with the National Academy Task Force on Rehabilitating Land Surface Mined for Coal in Western United States, that surface mining of hydrocarbon resources not be permitted on either public or private lands without prior commitment to rehabilitation plans designed to minimize long-range environmental impacts, that all fuel developments and processes meet on-and-off-site and water regulations, and that the time table for rehabilitation be concurrent with mining operations. Regional planning should be fully considered in the environmental impact analysis of the region, and the planners should clearly indicate the basis on which conditions at the proposed mine sites are to be evaluated.

Environmental impact studies represent an intelligent way of anticipating consequences of action. The final choice among alternative developments can only be made with wisdom when the consequences of the alternatives are clearly understood.

Our general order of priorities for research within the broad area of energy development is as follows:

1. Priority must be given to developing effective and efficient technologies for mining and processing the energy resources in the

Colorado River Basin while minimizing unfavorable environmental impacts. We encourage extensive technological investigations leading to utilization of all practical sources of energy, including such relatively unused sources as geothermal basins, solar energy and wind.

We note with commendation the establishment of the Electric Power Research Institute, financed by the electric power industries. The substantial financial support provided and the broad spectrum of research being undertaken should favorably affect the efficient and prudent development of the energy resources of the Colorado River Basin.

2. Research is needed to define the relative costs of producing electric power in this region versus its production in other areas. The marginal advantage or disadvantage imputed to the region in power production will determine the feasibility of investments for controlling environmental impacts and in fact whether electric power development should take place in the region.

3. Studies are needed to determine how development of the energy resource in the region would affect the social welfare of its inhabitants. Ways in which the people of the area can be assured a reasonable share of the benefits from the exploitation of its energy resources need careful investigation. The potential social and economic costs of eventual depletion of energy resources needs full evaluation. Possible means of covering ways in which the social cost of energy resource development must also be explored.

4. Investigations should be made to anticipate potential impacts of developing the fossil fuels of the region on urban development, recreational resources, agriculture, and transportation systems.

5. Since we Americans are the greatest per capita users of energy, detailed studies are needed as to the incremental values of energy in economy and in the enrichment of human lives. There appears to be substantial opportunities for the conservation of energy through modest changes in habits and life styles. Such opportunities should be identified and ways explored and evaluated for influencing behavior patterns that will prevent unnecessary waste of energy.

AGRICULTURE

As the applied science of land and associated water, plant and animal resources, agriculture is second in order of area research needs.

> *Agricultural research in the CRB must be intensified: to maxi-*
> *mize crop, livestock, forest, and wildlife productivity within the*
> *sustainable capacity of available resources; to provide an infor-*
> *mation base to heal the sores of agriculture, energy, mineral,*
> *recreation, transportation, and urban development; and to in-*
> *sure the continued contribution of the region toward the supply*
> *of food and fiber for the region, the nation, and the world.*

The Upper Colorado River Basin is the largest region in the United States without a comprehensive agricultural research center. Steps are being taken to assess these research needs and to determine how cooperation between present research agencies in the several states can be brought into better focus on problems of the basin. These planning efforts should be expanded and hastened.

For an expanded agricultural research endeavor beyond present efforts the following priorities are recommended:

1.   A much greater and more diversified effort should be made to evaluate the effects on soils, water and plants and animals of extensive developments of the mineral, energy, and recreational resources of the region. Simultaneous attention should be given to defining the associated impacts from transportation and urban developments that will accompany such resource exploitations.

2.   Research should be concentrated on procedures and materials for healing the sores of resource exploitation. Emphasis should also be placed on ways to minimize the impacts of mining, recreation and associated activities on the quality of the environment.

If for example, coal and shale resources are developed by surface explorations without substantially more information on how these disturbed lands are to be rehabilitated, plus a tested reserve of knowledge about plants that can be established and that will endure under such harsh conditions, disastrous destructive processes could be initiated that would threaten the future of much of the upper and lower parts of the basin.

3.   Expanding development of basin agriculture, oil shale, and other activities poses the threat of significant changes in the salt load of the Colorado River. Existing national and international agreements and standards relative to salt in the river may stringently limit regional development. Further research is needed to predict the

consequences of various possible activities on changes in salt load and to explore ways of avoiding increases in salt discharge.

4.   Range lands constitute the most extensive resource of the basin. Consequently, limited net returns per acre from improvement practices can result in large total benefits to the region. Much of the area falls into ecological zones where evidence indicates increased feed and possibly increased water yields may result from vegetation modification and other practices. Additional research and action programs are needed to capitalize on these potentials.

5.   Diverse and often irreversible patterns of land use have begun to engulf areas before reliable analysis and public consideration are given to the consequences. The present popular promotion and sale of land as an investment opportunity or as sites for second homes is but one example of trends in land use that may create planning, economic and environmental quality management difficulties. Such land use patterns and their consequences need study.

6.   Agriculture within the basin varies tremendously, including the intensive cropping and livestock feeding units of the Salt River and Imperial valleys, the less intensive general crop and livestock producing areas of the upper basin, and the vast expanses of extensively managed grazing lands. The potentials for intensification of agriculture in the region need to be explored, because of the significant quantity and diversity of agricultural products grown in the basin and because there are extensive opportunities for further intensification of agriculture, this industry deserves and needs an increased backup of research.

Recent studies of opportunities for agriculture development in the area have been conducted by scientist in state Agricultural Experiment Stations in cooperation with the Four Corners Commission. Thirteen feasible enterprises have been identified with much of the emphasis being in range improvement and in better utilization of forest resources. Steps for implementation should be taken.

7.   In the basin, hunting and fishing interests clash most vigorously with livestock interests. Present information supports the thesis that the productivity of native vegetation can be enhanced by improved management practices, and that a planned and controlled mix of livestock and big game can optimize benefits to the public. While studies to date have provided such tentative guidelines, an enlarged and more

intensive series of investigations is needed to resolve the many still problematical issues and sources of conflict.

8.   Intensive analysis is needed as to the comparative advantages and disadvantages of various agricultural subregions and commodities of the basin in relation to regional, national and world markets.

Public policies, market demands and alternative management systems must be evaluated as a way of providing guidelines to public and private investments in agriculture.

The Upper Colorado River Basin should be better served by agricultural research. Because of fragmentation by state boundaries and a degree of isolation from research centers, interstate cooperation is essential to undergrid research needs of the region.

RECREATION

Recreation is third in priority of the major areas of research needs because of its potential for development in the basin and the knowledge needed for its development and management.

A broader and more substantive information base is needed as to the future of recreation in the Colorado River Basin and how recreation resources can be managed to contribute to maximization of social welfare.

A region so rich in natural beauty and interest that 15 major areas have been designed as national parks or monuments must count recreation and tourist activities among its major opportunities and responsibilities. The development and conservation of these recreational resources must be a primary responsibility of planners as well as of management agencies. The unique qualities of these resources give the basin a comparative advantage in attracting visitors and permanent residents.

Before effective planning for recreation can be carried out, we must know more about the kinds of recreational experiences people desire and alternative ways in which these can be obtained. Planning and facility development should provide diverse recreational opportunities rather than merely recreational areas. Mr. Stankey helpfully pointed out the spectrum of recreational experiences, from appreciation types that are oriented to the environment, to social learning and interaction types that may be relatively independent of the natural environment. Greater understanding of the needs of people for recreation and of the therapeutic benefits to be gained from an intimate association with nature would give managers a better foundation for planning the development of recreational resources.

The following investigations are recommended as base for planning and managing recreation in the Colorado River Basin.

1. A more detailed inventory and analysis is needed of areas in the basin that have distinctive recreational potentials, and of recreational experiences that can be readily provided in each.

2. Guidelines are needed that will help us define the carrying capacity of recreational areas based on the types of recreational experience they provide. Freeman and Brown have provided helpful concepts and have outlined steps toward such a goal.

3. Kinds of recreational experience need definition with attention given to the environments or resources required for their realization. We need a way to measure the value of a recreational experience. Such measures as visitor days do not allow for variations in satisfaction caused by differences in natural sites or by variations in intensity of use throughout the year.

4. Costs of developing and maintaining recreational resources need analysis relative to user and public benefits or in terms of functions such as the public's willingness to pay. Development costs vary among recreation areas and least cost provision for various recreational experiences depends on knowledge of cost relationships.

5. Alternatives for financing the development of recreational opportunities need to be examined. The examination should consider relative benefits and costs.

6. Improved methods are needed for evaluating the social benefits generated by recreational opportunities, and for relating these social benefits to levels of public investment.

7. A more extensive and intensive market analysis is needed of recreation in the basin. How do recreation demands now and for the future compare with the calculated carrying capacity of present areas and of additional areas having potential for development?

8. There are opportunities for private development of recreational resources that need further attention. Improved development of fishing and wildlife resources and the offering of services in that area are in early stages of expansion.

9. Since it is almost inevitable that recreational use of the basin's resources will have to be limited in some way a study needs to be made of various ways of rationing such use. Some alternatives are: user fees, user licenses or permits, and limits on length of stay per trip and number of trips per individual.

URBANIZATION

Urbanization and transportation are related areas needing research because they are linked in the broad area of regional planning and development required to provide for people and services.

Since a continuing concentration of people in urban centers in the Colorado River Basin is anticipated, in line with national trends (despite currently light overall density), and since urbanization can be either a blessing or a curse in terms of the lives of the people involved, positive steps should be taken toward regional planning that evaluates urbanization in relation to resource development, land use patterns, natural beauty and recreation, and transportation systems.

Foreseeing the future can assure survival if man acts wisely in response to predictions. Urbanization is largely an irreversible process. Our conference position papers have dramatically pointed out that urbanization is proceeding with the same unrelenting vigor in the basin as elsewhere in the nation. Because of an abundance of space and of undeveloped resources, of necessity a number of new urban centers will evolve over the next few decades.

Unless the entire urbanization process is understood and accounted for in effective and extensive regional planning that is based upon reliable information and insights, a great opportunity for wise regional development will have been missed and the lives of future residents of the basin will be less rewarding than they should be. During the past ten years, great advancements have been made in planning techniques. Modeling systems have been developed that, when applied to the diverse conditions and resources of the basin, could materially aid regional planning by predicting the impacts and trade-offs possible among different segments of the economy.

Some specific areas of needed research relative to urbanization include:

1. In view of the unique space, physiography and resources conditions of the basin, special studies are needed to provide guidelines as to locations, and potential growth patterns of urban centers, how large each center should be permitted to become and how various urban activities should be planned and zoned so economic viability and quality of living can be attained.

2. Studies are needed as to how social services and public facilities can be provided and financed in the emerging urban and rural urban centers of the region.

3. Urbanization should be examined as a reflection of man's conflict with himself and with nature. If man is "psychologically unprepared for urbanization" in the sense that technological integration tends to force clashes between cultural groups, then we might profit from seeking improved patterns for social integration or more suitable environments within the urban setting. Since the projected development of the basin will generate new urban centers, a unique opportunity is before us for testing new principles.

4. Urbanization environmental studies must go beyond the physical qualities of homes, work space, air, noise, and population density and consider the roles of human behavior, social order and conflict, and man as a valuing, creative and adaptive being. Consideration as to how human value systems can accommodate to the urban environment is one approach worthy of investigation.

A close collaboration of universities and local governments within the region would facilitate studies of the social and economic problems of urbanizing areas, and could lead to economic and social policies that would benefit people by reducing social conflict, while assuring needed opportunities for all. One such pattern has been developed in San Diego.

TRANSPORTATION

Since the future development and welfare of the CRB depends so importantly on transportation, special investigations should be instituted to supplement and undergrid planning. Estimates of use and foreseeable changes in population and economic development could be useful in planning, including the development of systems models that will reveal the dynamic interrelationships among transportation, population distribution, eco-

nomic development of areas served or not served, utilization of recreation sites, and development of the full potential of agriculture, fossil fuel reserves and other resources.

Transportation objectives center on developing the most compatible network and a total system of transportation for the region, with plans based on both past and projected use as well as the impact of the system on other compounds of the economy and social welfare. Public investments in transportation systems should be based on extensive analysis and evaluation of all segments of the economy and of social welfare. The background investigations should take into consideration that improved transportation networks would facilitate marketing of timber, coal, oil, minerals and recreational resources, with accompanying impacts on the environment. Transportation networks obviously can be vital in facilitating trade-offs between various parts of the economy and among geographic subdivisions.

Recommended research endeavors to guide transportation development for the region include:

1. A central agency, not directly associated with any one component of our transportation systems, should study present and future transportation networks of the CRB and attempt to define how the greatest efficiency and maximum economic and social benefits can be obtained from public investments. One question needing an answer is the relative need for an overall transportation management agency and, if considered desirable, how this should be organized and operated.

2. Models of the economy, population, and potential resources, that incorporate social and economic goals, should be formulated in relation to transportation systems with adequate feed-backs so events in each part of the economy or sub-area of the region will be registered in the total system. Using these models, answers should be sought as to the alternative ways transportation networks can best serve public and private needs. Allowance must be made for new or foreseen technology in transportation in relation to the unique conditions and needs of the basin.

3. Improved technology and facilities are urgently needed to better interface air transport with urban and suburban areas.

4. Continuing research is needed to provide transportation with

more efficient ways to use energy resources while maintaining a quality environment.

5.   Studies are needed on how to achieve equitable financing of transportation systems, considering relative availabilities of federal, state, local and private funds and where each, or combinations should be directed.

PUBLIC UNDERSTANDING

While listed last in research priority the need for studies on how to better involve the public is real. The topic is, however, a general one that is pertinent to all public decision making programs where communications between decision makers and the public is vital.

There are needs for developing readily understood concepts for placing various aspects of environmental quality on a comparable scale. Research to develop and test such concepts should receive national and regional emphasis.

1.   People traditionally oppose issues they do not understand and consequently the success of environmental protection endeavors depends greatly on developing effective measures for expressing various aspects of environmental quality on a common base. Two concepts have been proposed that appear to have merit: environmental quality index values and measures of carrying capacity.

Index values should be applicable for summarizing and interpreting data and have flexibility for expressing related values for different aspects of environment such as air quality, water quality, land use and aesthetics.

2.   The concept of carrying capacity need further modification to express the broad spectrum of human uses and reactions to environmental change. The extent to which carrying concepts depend on physical data and the extent to which they are the product of value judgments may determine the validity with which the concepts can be used in trade-offs and bench mark standards.

These and other concepts and associated educational endeavors that can increase public understanding of environmental quality changes are in need of extensive study.

3. Investigations are particularly needed to find more effective ways of arousing public interest in such matters as environmental quality and public policy development. There is also need for finding improved communication channels to reflect public opinion back to policy and decision makers.

GENERAL STRATEGIES

The effective attainment of continuing programs that will administer the development of the resources of the basin while maintaining acceptable levels of environmental quality will plausibly require either the broad and strong support of people in the basin and in the involved states or criteria and programs will have to be imposed by a larger region or the Federal government. Most people of the region favor local autonomy. A reasonable alternative is a cooperating federal-state-local program in which local people have opportunities for participation in decision making.

If effective development-environment protection planning and execution are to be attained for the basin several issues will need study and resolution into effective programs.

Is the Colorado River Basin a viable planning or management unit? If not, what are the minimum or optimum areas that should be included? Need all parts of all involved states be included?

The region contains numerous political and geographic divisions with attendant special interests and biases. There is a complex pattern of land and resource ownership involving Federal and state agencies, Indian tribes and private companies and individuals. There are numerous institutions and organizations in or interested in the basin. These many components need to be identified and studied as to potential patterns of involvement in regional programs. Patterns of cooperation and coordination among these divergent groups should be sought toward the end of minimizing the administrative layers that are formed to carry out public goals and responsibilities.

One organizational pattern that merits study and possible adaptation to the region is that of the Federation of Rocky Mountain States. Such an organizational arrangement might undertake a broad initial task of developing and promoting general acceptance of goals for the region.

Certainly, unless concerned people and states act promptly, irreversible patterns of development and environmental change will be established. It seems likely that incentives will have to be provided by the Federal government before effective environmental protection programs will be initiated. Investigations that will likely be helpful in planning regional programs include the development of a regional model that will encompass the mineral, fosssil, fuel, land, water and people resources of the region; that will consider the possible economic activities and that will further evolve a time table and strategy for development within the region, based on markets, comparative advantages for each activity and institutional arrangements and attitudes and interests of people.

A perplexing question is how can such diverse and complex research be accomplished. There are considerable scientific capabilities in stated and Federal agencies, in institutions of higher education and in private organizations in and out of the region. Financial resources in state and regional planning organizations can draw on these many talents. Past experience has indicated the wisdom of utilizing a strong peer review system to decide on areas of research need and to review and evaluate each research proposal for quality and for the capability of personnel involved in its execution.